MODERN COLLEGE ALGEBRA

MODERN COLLEGE ALGEBRA
Second Edition

ELBRIDGE P. VANCE | *Oberlin College*

ADDISON-WESLEY PUBLISHING COMPANY, INC.
READING, MASSACHUSETTS · PALO ALTO · LONDON · DON MILLS, ONTARIO

This book is in the
Addison-Wesley Series in Introductory Mathematics

ACE – FIRST EDITION

t opportunities in elementary mathe-
tunately many of us have not taken
vored to do so in this book, and not
algebra as a logical subject, but also

is the education of the student in the
e must realize that precise definitions
es are necessary, and that any system
and hypotheses, together with results
ng. The second aim of this book is
algebra necessary for work in later
skill and ability to work efficiently in
shed in a manner so that the student's
d, but enlivened.

ced by the Committee on the Under-
athematical Association of America,
ollege Entrance Examination Board,
Although much of the material covered
the contents is mine.

e book in addition to the postulation
notion of sets is introduced at the
he order axioms along with a detailed
Limited but sufficient use is made of
equations has more significance. The
duced early, and are an integral part
r of the book. The theoretical rather
are emphasized, although computation
troduced carefully and used in several
ordered pairs, to the study of complex
atment of determinants are other dis-
made to present intuitively each new
ssion.

t the end of each article help to unify
epts and theorems to which later refer-

ence is made. Some problems necessary for the continuity of the discussions are marked with a triangle (▶), and should always be assigned. Included in the Appendix are tables of powers and roots, and a four-place table of logarithms.

I wish to express my appreciation to my colleagues who have given advice and suggestions. I am also indebted to the staff at Addison-Wesley Publishing Company for their valuable assistance in producing this book.

Oberlin, *Ohio*   E. P. V.

PREFACE – SECOND EDITION

When the first edition of this book was written, the influence of the Committee on the Undergraduate Mathematics Program of the Mathematical Association of America, the Commission of Mathematics of the College Entrance Examination Board, and the School Mathematics Study Group upon mathematics at this level was already seriously felt. Since that time certain other suggestions have been made by various influential groups. Some of these suggestions appear to be important, while others have not been so widely accepted. It is because of the changing mathematical world, and the suggested introduction of additional new topics both at the college and secondary school level, that a new edition of this book seemed appropriate.

This edition includes new material on matrices and a new approach to vectors. Both these topics are strongly recommended in any modern approach to mathematics at this level, and both are perfect preparation for later courses in linear algebra. Also, in this edition several references are made to computing machines and to methods used in that field.

One other feature of this second edition is that the problems have been augmented. In addition, there are included four new sets of review problems at appropriate places. Many of the review problems are similar to problems actually encountered in calculus. Some emphasize the important ability to manipulate, while others deal with more theoretical ideas.

A number of users of the first edition have suggested improvements. I shall continue to welcome such help in the future, and again wish to express my appreciation to all those who have helped in the formation of this book.

Oberlin, Ohio   E. P. V.

CONTENTS

CHAPTER 1

SETS AND NUMBERS

The basic quantitative procedures of science, both physical and social, involve counting and measurement. Counting characterizes a collection or set of objects by a number. Measurement assigns a number to some property of an object. Counting and measurement are far from simple concepts, as is the notion of a set, and each has been the subject of many studies in the field of scientific methodology. The important thing for us in the present study is the fact that both counting and measurement lead to numbers and sets, and through the use of numbers and sets it is possible to obtain much insight into the workings of nature. We shall begin with a brief discussion of sets, then classify various types of numbers and introduce and study some basic operations and notions of numbers and sets which are fundamental in all fields of mathematics and science.

1–1 SETS AND BASIC NOTATION

The basic notion of a set, whose importance in mathematics was first considered by Georg Cantor (1845–1918), is so fundamental to the different branches of the subject that it is impossible to give a precise definition in terms of more basic concepts. However, it is so deeply imbedded in our intuition that we shall rely on our experience to consider the notion of set. We may think of a set as a collection (or aggregate) of objects of any sort, restricting ourselves to those objects that are clearly enough described so that there is no question as to whether a certain object does or does not belong to the set. For example, we might consider as sets:

a) The set of students in the Oberlin College freshman class,
b) The set of students in this class whose last name begins with the letter V,
c) The set of positive integers (counting numbers) less than 5,
d) The set of the authors of this book,
e) The set of all states in the United States with a population under 10,000,
f) The set of all straight lines (in a plane) that pass through a given point,
g) The set of all points that lie on a given line,
h) The set of all fossils in the world,
i) The set of letters in the word "Mississippi."

If an object belongs to the set, it is called a member or *element* of the set, but, if the object does not belong to the set, it is not an element of the set. To indicate membership in a set we use the sympol $\in$. Capital letters are usually used as the names of sets, and small letters as names for the elements. Thus, if a is an object and A is a set, we write $a \in A$ as an abbreviation for "a is an element of A," or "a belongs to the set A." Similarly, if we wish to indicate that a is not an element of A, we write $a \notin A$.

Clearly, as we see from the examples, there are many different sets as well as different sized sets. Each of the examples listed above is different, although some may be of the same size. Examples (a), (b), (c), (d), (e), (h), and (i) are finite, while (f) and (g) are infinite. In general, we say that a set has a finite number of elements if one can enumerate the elements of the set in some order and then count* the elements until a last one is reached. A set is called *finite* if it has a finite number of elements; otherwise it is called *infinite*.

Note that the number of elements in example (i) is four, although there are eleven letters in the word, "Mississippi." Thus, the number of elements in this example and in (c) is the same. As in example (d), a set may have only one element, and in fact, as in example (e), may not have any elements. A set, such as that in (h), may be finite even though very large. The order of enumeration of the elements does not affect the set itself.

The use of sets in elementary mathematics is helpful in the clarification of certain ideas, in the simplification of certain rather complicated concepts, and also in the unification of the studies of different but related concepts. With this in mind, we introduce the two most common methods for describing a set, the *roster* or *tabulation method*, and the *rule* or *defining property method*.

The roster method. We may indicate a set by listing the elements and enclosing them in braces.

The rule method. We may indicate a set by enclosing in braces a descriptive phrase, and agreeing that those objects, and only those, which have the described property are elements of the set.

Illustration 1. The set $V = \{a, e, i, o, u\}$ defines the set V of vowels in the English alphabet. This set may also be written†

$$V = \{x, \text{ such that } x \text{ is a vowel in the English alphabet}\}.$$

A shorter and more efficient notation is

$$V = \{x | x \text{ is a vowel in the English alphabet}\},$$

where the vertical bar is read "such that."

Illustration 2. If we recall that an even integer is any integer which is divisible by two, the set $E = \{2, 4, 6, 8, 10\}$ may also be written

$$E = \{x | x \text{ is a positive even integer less than 12}\}.$$

---

* We assume the intuitive knowledge of the so-called counting numbers, 1, 2, 3, . . . , where the dots signify we do not stop at 3 but keep going indefinitely.
† Note that in these illustrations the "x" is used as a symbol for an arbitrary element of a set, not as a letter of the alphabet.

Illustration 3. It is very difficult to write the set

$$N = \{x | x \text{ is a positive fraction between 1 and 2}\}$$

by the roster method.

Illustration 4. It is also difficult to specify the set

$$Z = \{\text{your cat, my Saint Bernard, the earth, Peter, Emily}\}$$

by the rule method.

It is because of examples such as those given in Illustrations 3 and 4, that both methods of describing sets are used.

In any study of sets one of the basic requirements is the ability to compare the sizes of different collections of objects. This is accomplished by one of the great foundational concepts of mathematics, that of "one-to-one correspondence."

> **Definition 1–1.** A *one-to-one correspondence* exists between two sets A and B if it is possible to associate the elements of A with the elements of B in such a way that each element of each set is associated with exactly one element of the other.

For example, the normal human being can associate his fingers with his toes so that each finger is associated with just one toe. In any given group of married couples, there is an obvious correspondence of this type. In the previous illustrations, such a one-to-one correspondence exists between V and E, E and Z, or Z and V. If such is the case, we say the two sets are the same size, although it should be clear that they are not equal.

> **Definition 1–2.** Two sets A and B are *the same size* if there exists a one-to-one correspondence between their elements. Two such sets are said to be *equivalent*.

PROBLEMS

Use both the roster method and the rule method to specify the sets in Problems 1 through 5.

1. The members of your immediate family
2. The counting numbers less than 10
3. The fractions whose numerator is 1, and whose denominator is a counting number less than 10
4. The single digits used in our decimal system
5. The counting numbers which are multiples of 6 and less than 50

Use the rule method to specify the sets whose elements are tabulated in Problems 6 through 10.

6. $E = \{2, 4, 6, 8\}$
7. $S = \{1, 4, 9, 16, 25\}$
8. $N = \{1, \frac{1}{2}, \frac{1}{3}, \frac{1}{4}\}$
9. $P = \{1, 4, 7, 10, 13\}$
10. $T = \{10, 100, 1000, 10000\}$

Use the rule method to specify the sets described in Problems 11 through 15, and tell why the roster method is difficult or impossible.

11. The counting numbers greater than 100

12. The students in your school who have been abroad

13. The United States citizens who have read The Constitution

14. The books in the Oberlin College library

15. The set of all triangles whose area is less than 3

16. Give an example of a set which has just two elements; one element; no elements; an infinite number of elements.

▶ **17.** *Two sets A and B are said to be equal* if each element of *A* is an element of *B* and each element of *B* is an element of *A*, and we write *A* = *B*. Determine whether *A* and *B* are the same size (equivalent) and if so, whether *A* = *B*.*

a) $A = \{1, 3, 5\}$, $B = \{3, 5, 1\}$
b) $A = \{1, 3, 5\}$, $B = \{a, b, c\}$

Assume x is either -1 or 0 or 1.

c) $A = \{x | x^2 = 1\}$, $B = \{1, -1\}$
d) $A = \{1\}$, $B = \{x | x^2 = 1\}$
e) $A = \{1\}$, $B = \{x | (x - 1)^2 = 0\}$
f) $A = \{1\}$, $B = \{x | x^2 - x = 0\}$

18. For each of the sets listed below, tell which is finite and which is infinite. For the finite sets, tell which are equivalent and which are equal.

a) The set of the first two odd counting numbers
b) The set of all odd counting numbers less than 5
c) The set of all odd counting numbers
d) The set of letters in the word "Canadian"
e) The set of points on a given line exactly one unit from a given point on that line.
f) The set of points in a given plane exactly one unit from a given point in that plane.
g) The set whose elements are the numbers 1 and 3.

▶ **19.** For each of the sets listed, tell which are equivalent and which of these are equal.

a) The set of letters in the word "indian"
b) The set of letters in the word "naid"
c) The set of letters in the word "dain"
d) The set of letters in the word "naidin"
e) The set of letters in the word "tain"
f) The set of letters in the word "retain"

20. For each of the sets listed, tell which are equivalent and which are equal.

a) The set of letters in the word "anna"
b) The set $\{a, n, n, a\}$
c) The set $\{a, n\}$
d) The set of letters in the word "an"

---

* Problems preceded by a triangle (▶) are essential to an understanding of later parts of the book, and should be assigned to every student.

1–2 SUBSETS

Every vowel in the English alphabet is, of course, a letter in this alphabet. If we call A the set of all the letters in the English alphabet, the set V is included in the set A. Similarly, the set E in Illustration 2 of Article 1–1 is included in the set of all even counting numbers. We wish to define this notion in general.

Definition 1–3. The set A is a *subset* of the set B if every element of A is an element of B. If B has elements that are not elements of A, then A is a *proper subset* of B.

Since this concept is frequently used, it is convenient to denote this symbolically by $A \subset B$, which is read "A is a subset of B" or "A is included in B." Thus

$$A \subset B \text{ if and only if } x \in A \text{ implies } x \in B.*$$

It should be noted that every set may be regarded as a subset of itself; that is, for all A, $A \subset A$.

Let us return to the set $A = \{x \mid x$ is a letter in the English alphabet$\}$. We observed that V was a subset of A. If $C = \{x \mid x$ is a consonant in the English alphabet$\}$, C is also a subset of A. In this discussion the set A is an over-all set of elements, with which we are concerned throughout our discussion. Such a fixed set in any discussion is called the *universal set*, and is always denoted by U. Of course, different universal sets can be used for different considerations. In one discussion U may be the set of all real numbers, in another, the set of all points in the plane, and so on. In first-grade arithmetic, U was the set of counting numbers.

Definition 1–4. The *universal set* in any discussion is the totality of members under consideration as elements of any set.

No element in V was an element of C, and vice versa. Sets related in this way occur frequently, and we say two such sets are *disjoint*. The sets given in Illustrations 2 and 3, Article 1–1, form another example of two disjoint sets.

Definition 1–5. Two sets, A and B, are *disjoint* if and only if A and B have no elements in common.

There is one set of special importance. The *empty set*, or *null set*, denoted by $\emptyset$, is the set in any discussion that has no elements. For example, the set consisting of all elements in both V and C is $\emptyset$. Similarly, the set of counting numbers which are perfect squares and end in 7 is $\emptyset$. The statement that the set of elements satisfying a certain condition is empty is equivalent to the statement that no

---

* The "if and only if" statement in mathematics is an important one. In this case it means: (1) if $x \in A$ implies $x \in B$, then $A \subset B$, and (2) if $A \subset B$, then $x \in A$ implies $x \in B$. In general any such statement consists of two facts. These two can be considered as a theorem and its converse. A definition is always considered an "if and only if" statement.

elements satisfying that condition exist. By its very definition, the empty set is a subset of every set.

One further definition should be given.

Definition 1–6. Two sets A and B are *equal* ($A = B$) if and only if $A \subset B$ and $B \subset A$.

As a direct consequence of this definition, if one set has an element not in the other, the two are unequal, and we write $A \neq B$.

Illustrations. The set

$$X = \{x | x \text{ is a counting number between 0 and 10}\} = \{1, 2, 3, 4, 5, 6, 7, 8, 9\}.$$

The set

$$Y = \{y | y \text{ is an even counting number less than 7}\} = \{2, 4, 6\}.$$

The set

$$Z = \{z | z \text{ is a counting number and has a perfect square between 3 and 40}\}$$
$$= \{2, 3, 4, 5, 6\}.$$

Under these conditions, we may say $Y \subset Z$, $Y \subset X$, and $Z \subset X$. Z is a proper subset of X so that $Z \neq X$. Also, $\{3\} \subset X$, $\{3\} \subset Z$, and $3 \in X$, but we cannot say $3 \subset X$. (Why?).

In Definition 1–2 we defined the concept of "the same size" for two sets. It is this notion of a one-to-one correspondence which makes it possible to define the size of any set. First we say that two equivalent sets have the same *cardinal number*. We are now able to deal with the notion of size for any set, although we shall consider only finite cases.

All sets equivalent to the set $\{a\}$ have the same cardinal number. This cardinal number we call *one*, and write 1. Similarly, all sets equivalent to the set $\{a, b\}$ again have the same cardinal number, called *two* and denoted by the symbol 2. In general, we have the following definition.

Definition 1–7. The cardinal number of any finite set A is n, if the set A can be put into one-to-one correspondence with the set $\{1, 2, 3, \ldots, n\}$. The null set has zero for its cardinal number.

Illustrations. In referring to the previous illustrations, the cardinal number of X is 9, Y is 3, and Z is 5.

PROBLEMS

Specify each of the sets in Problems 1 through 4 by the roster method, and in each case give the universal set.

1. The set of subjects you are taking for credit

2. The ages in years of the members of your family

3. The counting numbers which are positive integral multiples of 7 and less than 100

4. The digits in your telephone number

5. If $A = \{1, 2, 3, 4, 5\}$, $B = \{2, 3, 4\}$, and $C = \{2, 4, 5\}$, which of the following are true?

a) $A \subset B$ b) $A \subset C$ c) $B \subset A$
d) $B \subset C$ e) $C \subset A$ f) $C \subset B$
g) $C \subset C$ h) $\emptyset \subset B$ i) $B = C$

6. For the sets in Problem 5,

a) What is the set with elements both in B and C?
b) What is the set with elements in B and $\{1, 5\}$?
c) What is the set with elements in C and $\{1, 5\}$?

7. If $X = \{1, 2, 3\}$, identify the set Y such that $\{1\} \subset Y$, $Y \subset X$, and $X \neq Y$.

8. a) List the subsets of the set $\{a, b\}$. Note that there are $2^2 = 2 \times 2$ subsets.
  b) List the subsets of the set $\{a, b, c\}$. Note that there are $2^3 = 2 \times 2 \times 2$ subsets.

9. For the set $\{a, b, c, d\}$, list the possible subsets containing

a) four elements b) three elements
c) two elements d) one element
e) no elements

10. What is the sum of the number of subsets in (a) through (e) in Problem 9? Is this consistent with the results in Problem 8?

11. If $D = \{0, 4, 7\}$, we say that $7 \in D$, or $\{7\} \subset D$, but cannot say $7 \subset D$, since 7 is not a set. Which of the following are true?

a) $4 \in D$ b) $4 \subset D$ c) $0 \in D$
d) $\emptyset \in D$ e) $\emptyset \subset D$ f) $0 \subset D$
g) $4 = \{4\}$ h) $4 \in \{4\}$ i) $0 = \emptyset$
j) $0 \in \emptyset$

12. If $A = \{a, b, c\}$ and $B = \{a, b, c, d\}$, which of the following are true?

a) $A \in B$ b) $A \subset B$ c) $a \in A$
d) $b \in B$ e) $b \subset B$ f) $\emptyset \in B$
g) $\emptyset \subset A$ h) $a \in B$ i) $B \subset A$

13. If $a \in X$, $b \in Y$, $X \subset Z$, and $Y \subset Z$,

a) is $a \in Z$? b) is $b \in Z$? c) is $a \in Y$?
d) Can there be an element in Z which is an element of both X and Y?
e) Can there be an element in Z which is an element of X but not Y?
f) Can there be an element in Z which is neither an element of X nor of Y?

14. Note that Definition 1–5 (the definition that A and B are disjoint) may be written

$$\text{If } a \in A, \text{ then } a \notin B, \text{ and if } b \in B, \text{ then } b \notin A.$$

Write in a similar notation (Definition 1–6) the definition that $A = B$.

▶ **15.** Show by using Definition 1–4 that set equality has the following properties.

a) Set equality is *reflexive:* For any set A, $A = A$.
b) Set equality is *symmetric:* For any two sets A and B, if $A = B$, then $B = A$.
c) Set equality is *transitive:* For any sets A, B, and C, if $A = B$ and $B = C$, then $A = C$.

1–3 OPERATIONS ON SETS

Once more let us return to our example, where the universal set U is the set of all letters in the English alphabet. If $V = \{a, e, i, o, u\}$ again denotes the set whose elements are the vowels, the remaining letters also form a set (in this case the set C, whose elements are all the consonants). In general, such a set is called the *complement* of the original set, so that C is the complement of V.

> **Definition 1–8.** The *complement* of any set A, with respect to any stated or understood universal set, is the set of elements of the universal set that do not belong to A.

This complement is denoted by A', and is written symbolically

$$A' = \{x \,|\, x \in U \text{ and } x \notin A\},$$

or more frequently, since it is understood that $x \in U$,

$$A' = \{x \,|\, x \notin A\}.$$

If $B = \{a, b, c, d, e\}$, where this is a subset of the set of all letters in the English alphabet, the set whose elements are either in this set B or in V, or in both, is the set $D = \{a, b, c, d, e, i, o, u\}$. Such a set is called the *union* of the sets B and V. The set whose elements are in both B and V is the set $E = \{a, e\}$. The set E is called the *intersection* of B and V.

> **Definition 1–9.** The *union* of two sets A and B is the set of elements that belong to at least one of the sets A and B, that is, to A or B.*

We symbolize this union as $A \cup B$ (read "A union B"), and write

$$A \cup B = \{x \,|\, x \in A \text{ or } x \in B\}.$$

> **Definition 1–10.** The *intersection* of two sets A and B is the set of elements that belong to both A and B.

We symbolize this intersection as $A \cap B$ (read "A intersection B"), and write

$$A \cap B = \{x \,|\, x \in A \text{ and } x \in B\}.$$

---

* In our everyday language the word "or" in the expression "p or q" sometimes means "p or q or both p and q" and other times "p or q, but not both p and q." In mathematics, it is always taken in the inclusive sense, synonymous with the legal use of "and/or," so that A *or* B means "A or B or both A and B."

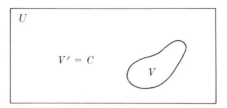

Figure 1–1

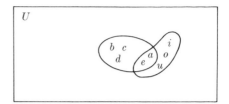

Figure 1–2

Relations among subsets may frequently be clarified by a pictorial representation. With a rectangle representing the universe, any subset A may be indicated by a closed region within the rectangle. Then A', the complement of A, is that closed region within the rectangle but outside A. Such pictures, called Venn diagrams after the English logician John Venn (1834–1883), can, of course, be used for problems with any finite number of sets. Figure 1–1 represents the universe of all letters in the English alphabet, V the set of vowels, and its complement $V' = C$ the set of consonants. Figure 1–2 illustrates the set V and the set B, with the elements a and e in common.

Illustration. Let $U = \{1, 2, 3, 4, 5, 6, 7, 8\}$ be the universe, and consider the subsets $X = \{1, 2, 3, 4, 5\}$, $Y = \{1, 2, 3\}$, and $Z = \{4, 6, 8\}$.

If we apply the definitions of this section, we have

$$X \cup Y = \{1, 2, 3, 4, 5\},$$
$$Y \cup Z = \{1, 2, 3, 4, 6, 8\},$$
$$Z \cup X = \{1, 2, 3, 4, 5, 6, 8\},$$
$$X \cap Y = \{1, 2, 3\}, \qquad Y \cap Z = \emptyset, \qquad Z \cap X = \{4\}.$$

We can, of course, form complements of these sets, unions and intersections of complements, and so on. For example,

$$X' = \{6, 7, 8\}, \qquad Y' = \{4, 5, 6, 7, 8\}, \qquad Z' = \{1, 2, 3, 5, 7\},$$
$$(X \cup Y)' = \{6, 7, 8\}, \qquad (Y \cap Z)' = \emptyset' = U,$$
$$X' \cup Y' = \{4, 5, 6, 7, 8\}, \qquad X' \cap Y' = \{6, 7, 8\}.$$

In Fig. 1–3, the sets X, Y, Z, taken in pairs, are illustrated by Venn diagrams.

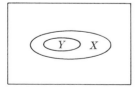

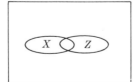

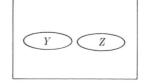

Figure 1–3

PROBLEMS

1. If $U = \{0, 1, 2, 3, 4, 5, 6, 7, 8, 9\}$, the set of digits in our decimal system, and

$$A = \{0, 1, 2, 3, 4, 5\}, \qquad C = \{4, 5, 6, 7\},$$
$$B = \{2, 3, 4, 5\}, \qquad D = \{6, 7, 8, 9\},$$

find and tabulate

a) $A \cup B$ b) $B \cup C$ c) $C \cap D$
d) $D \cup A$ e) $B \cap D$ f) $B \cap C$
g) $A \cup \emptyset$ h) $B \cap \emptyset$ i) $C \cup U$
j) $D \cap U$ k) B' l) C'
m) $(A \cup B)'$ n) $(B \cap D)'$ o) $(U \cup \emptyset)'$

2. If $U = \{x \mid x$ is a letter in the English alphabet$\}$,

$A = \{x \mid x$ is a or one of the next four letters in the English alphabet$\}$
$\quad = \{a, b, c, d, e\}$,

$E = \{x \mid x$ is e or one of the next four letters in the English alphabet$\}$,

$I = \{x \mid x$ is i or one of the next four letters in the English alphabet$\}$,

find

a) $A \cap E$ b) $E \cap I$ c) $I \cap \emptyset$
d) $\emptyset \cup A$ e) $A \cup \emptyset$ f) $E \cap U$

3. Complete the given statements, where X is any subset of the universe U.

a) $X \cup U$ b) $X \cap U$ c) $X \cup \emptyset$
d) $X \cap \emptyset$ e) $X \cap X$ f) $X \cup X$
g) $X \cup X'$ h) $X \cap X'$ i) $\emptyset \cap U$

▶ 4. For any set A, the set of subsets of A is said to be *exhaustive* if the union of these subsets is A, and is said to be disjoint (recall Definition 1–5) if no two of the subsets have any elements in common. If $A = \{a, b, c\}$, tell whether the following set of subsets is exhaustive; disjoint.

a) $\{a\}, \{b\}$ b) $\{a\}, \{b, c\}$ c) $\{a, b\}, \{b, c\}$
d) $\{a\}, \{a, b\}$ e) $\{a\}, \{b\}, \{c\}$

5. If in the diagram in Fig. 1–4, the area of the interior of the rectangle represents set A, the triangle set B, and the circle set C, indicate the area represented by

a) $A \cup B$ b) $A \cap B$
c) $A \cap C$ d) $B \cup C$
e) $(A \cup B) \cap C'$ f) $(A \cup B)' \cap C$

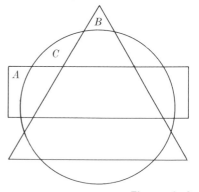

6. Show by using Venn diagrams that

a) $A \cup B = B \cup A$
b) $A \cup (B \cup C) = (A \cup B) \cup C$
c) $A \cap (B \cup C) = (A \cap B) \cup (A \cap C)$
d) $(A \cup B)' = A' \cap B'$

Figure 1–4

7. Show by using Venn diagrams that

a) $A \cap B = B \cap A$ b) $A \cap (B \cap C) = (A \cap B) \cap C$

c) $A \cup (B \cap C) = (A \cup B) \cap (A \cup C)$ d) $(A \cap B)' = A' \cup B'$

8. Show by using Venn diagrams that

a) $A \cup B = A$ if and only if $B \subset A$ b) $A \cap B = B$ if and only if $B \subset A$

c) $B \subset A$ if and only if $A' \subset B'$ d) $(A')' = A$

9. Tell under what conditions on the sets A and B we would have each of the following.

a) $A \cap B = \emptyset$ b) $A \cap B = U$ c) $A \cup B = U$

d) $A \cup B = \emptyset$ c) $A \cap B = A$ f) $A \cup B = A$

g) $A \cap \emptyset = \emptyset$ h) $A \cap U = A$ i) $A \cup U = U$

j) $A \cup U = A$ k) $A \cup \emptyset = U$ l) $A \cup \emptyset = \emptyset$

10. Tell whether each of the following statements is true or false for any two sets A and B.

a) A is always contained in $A \cup B$.   b) B always contains $A \cup B$.

c) A is always contained in $A \cap B$.   d) B always contains $A \cap B$.

If $A \supset B$, then

e) $A \cap B$ always is equal to A.   f) $A \cap B$ always is equal to B.

g) $A \cup B$ always is equal to A.   h) $A \cup B$ always is equal to B.

▶ 11. If $n(A)$ represents the number of elements in the set A, we note that $n(A) = 3$ for the set in Problem 4. Give an example of two finite sets A and B, where

a) $n(A \cup B) = n(A) + n(B)$ b) $n(A \cup B) \neq n(A) + n(B)$

What is the condition on A and B so that (a) will always hold?

▶ 12. Show by using a Venn diagram that for any finite sets A and B,

$$n(A \cup B) = n(A) + n(B) - n(A \cap B).$$

▶ 13. It is sometimes desirable to consider the order of the elements in a set as significant. A pair of elements in which we distinguish one of the elements as the first and the other, not necessarily different, as the second is called an *ordered pair*. We denote such an ordered pair by (x, y), where x is the first and y is the second element. This is quite different from $\{x, y\} = \{y, x\}$, since order is immaterial when we are merely listing the elements of a set. We wish to distinguish between (x, y) and (y, x), and do so by defining the equality of two ordered pairs. *Two ordered pairs, (x_1, y_1) and (x_2, y_2), are equal* if and only if $x_1 = x_2$ and $y_1 = y_2$.

If X and Y are sets, the set of all ordered pairs (x, y) such that $x \in X$ and $y \in Y$ is called the *product set*, or cartesian product,* of X and Y, and is denoted by $X \times Y$. In symbols,

$$X \times Y = \{(x, y) | x \in X \text{ and } y \in Y\}.$$

* The reason for this name will be clear as a result of the discussion in Chapter 4.

For example, if $X = \{a, b\}$ and $Y = \{1, 2\}$, then $X \times Y$ is the set of ordered pairs $(a, 1)$, $(a, 2)$, $(b, 1)$, $(b, 2)$. However, $Y \times X$ is the set of ordered pairs $(1, a)$, $(1, b)$, $(2, a)$, $(2, b)$, so that $X \times Y \neq Y \times X$.

Find all the sets of ordered pairs for the product spaces $X \times X$, $X \times Y$, $Y \times X$, and $Y \times Y$ if

a) $X = \{a\}$, $Y = \{b\}$ 　　　　　　　　 b) $X = \{a, b\}$, $Y = \{c\}$

c) $X = \{a, b, c\}$, $Y = \{1, 2, 3\}$

14. Find (describe) all the sets of ordered pairs for the product spaces $X \times I$ if

$$X = \{a, b\}$$

and

$$I = \{1, 2, 3, \ldots\},$$

the set of counting numbers.

15. What can be said about the set $A \times B$ if either A or B is the set of counting numbers?

16. We define the sum of two cardinal numbers a and b, denoted by $a + b$, to be the cardinal number of the set $A \cup B$ if

i) a is the cardinal number of A,
ii) b is the cardinal number of B,
iii) $A \cap B = \emptyset$.

a) What is the cardinal number of $\{$Peter, Douglas, Emily$\}$?
b) What is the cardinal number of $\{$Susan, Bob$\}$?
c) Find the sum of these two cardinal numbers by finding the cardinal number of their union.

17. We define the product of two cardinal numbers a and b, denoted by ab, to be the cardinal number of the set $A \times B$ if

i) a is the cardinal number of A,
ii) b is the cardinal number of B,
iii) $A \cap B = \emptyset$.

Show that the product of $(2)(3)$ is 6, by referring to the sets mentioned in Problem 16.

18. By referring to Problems 16 and 17, give an example to show that for cardinal numbers

a) $7 + 8 = 15$ 　　　　　　　　　　　　 b) $7(8) = 56$

1–4 INTEGERS

The first set of numbers encountered by everyone is the set of counting numbers, $1, 2, 3, \ldots$, to which we frequently referred in our discussion concerning sets. The mathematician calls this set of numbers *the set of positive integers,** counting*

---

* Note the distinction between *the* set of positive integers, and *a* set of positive integers. *The* set means the set of all positive integers, while *a* set of positive integers means merely that its elements are integers, but that it does not necessarily contain all the integers.

numbers, or *natural numbers*, and uses it as the foundation for our entire number system. It is denoted by $N = \{1, 2, 3, \ldots\}$. This set of numbers, together with the negative integers $-1, -2, -3, \ldots$ and the zero integer constitute the complete *set of integers*, which we shall denote by I.

In a study of any number system, such as the set of integers, in addition to the numbers themselves, we concern ourselves with certain basic operations on these numbers. The two most basic are addition and multiplication.

Definition 1–11. If A is a set of numbers, A is *closed* under the operation of addition if the sum of any two numbers, distinct or not, in A is also in A.

This is called the closure property of addition. A similar definition can be given for multiplication, or, in fact, any operation. A well-known property of the set of integers is that if any two integers are added or multiplied, the result is an integer. In line with the above definition, we say I *is closed under addition and multiplication*. There are, of course, many sets whose elements are integers which are not closed under either addition or multiplication. The set $\{1, 2, 3\}$ is one such set. Neither the number 5, the sum of 2 and 3, nor the number 6, their product, is in the set. The set $\{-1, 0, 1\}$ is not closed under addition, but is closed under multiplication.

PROBLEMS

1. We noticed that the set of integers I was closed under addition and multiplication. Is it closed under

   a) subtraction?   b) division?

2. Is the set of natural numbers N closed under

   a) addition?   b) multiplication?   c) subtraction?   d) division?

3. Examine the following sets with regard to closure under addition and multiplication.

   a) $\{1\}$ b) $\{1, 2, 3, 4, 5, 6\}$ c) $\{1, 0\}$

▶ 4. An *even natural number* is any natural number which may be expressed $2k$, where k is a natural number. Is *the* set of even natural numbers closed under

   a) addition?   b) multiplication?

▶ 5. Define an odd natural number. Is *the* set of odd natural numbers closed under

   a) addition?   b) multiplication?

Definition 1–12. If a, b, and c are integers such that $a \cdot b = c$, a and b are called *factors* or *divisors* of c, and c is a *multiple* of a or b.

Thus, 2, 3, and 5 are factors of 30, as are -6 or -15. We recall (Problem 4) that an *even integer* is any integer which has 2 as a factor (or is a multiple of 2). If we define an *odd integer* to be any integer which is not even, it is possible to express any odd integer as $2k + 1$, where k is some integer. The integer -8 is even since $-8 = 2 \cdot -4$, while 9 is odd since $9 = 2 \cdot 4 + 1$.

All positive integers except the number one may be classified as either *composite numbers* or *primes*. A positive integer is called *composite* if it is different from one and can be expressed as the product of two or more positive integers, different from itself, which are its factors. In certain cases some of these factors may be equal.

For example, 4, 6, 9, and 12 are composite, for $4 = 2 \cdot 2$, $6 = 3 \cdot 2$, $9 = 3 \cdot 3$, and $12 = 3 \cdot 2 \cdot 2$. In fact, every even integer greater than 2 is composite.

A positive integer is called *prime* if it is different from one and is not composite. In other words, it can be expressed as a product of two positive integers only in the trivial way in which one factor is itself and the other the integer one. Examples of prime numbers are 2, 3, 5, and 7.

The *decomposition* of any composite number, that is, the expression of such a number as a product of prime numbers, is most important. Such a decomposition is always possible, since each factor which is composite can be expressed as the product of smaller factors, and ultimately the factors will all be prime. Thus, $60 = 12 \cdot 5 = 4 \cdot 3 \cdot 5 = 2 \cdot 2 \cdot 3 \cdot 5$. Moreover, a decomposition is unique* although the proof of this fact does not concern us in this discussion. Specifically, a composite number can be expressed as a product of prime factors in one and only one way, except for the order of the factors. Thus 60 can also be expressed as $15 \cdot 4 = 5 \cdot 3 \cdot 4 = 5 \cdot 3 \cdot 2 \cdot 2$. Two integers are called *relatively prime* or *prime to each other* if they contain no common prime factors. We shall consider factors again in a more general way in Article 3–5.

PROBLEMS

1. List all the factors of 12; of 120.

2. List the common divisors of 30 and 50.

3. If E is the set of all even integers and O is the set of all odd integers, notice that $E \subset I$ and $O \subset I$. What can be said about

a) $E \cup O$?   b) $E \cap O$?

4. If E is the set of all even integers (integral multiples of 2) and T is the set of all integral multiples of 3, what can be said about $E \cap T$?

5. If S is the set of all integral multiples of 6 and T is the set of all integral multiples of 10, what can be said about $S \cap T$? With the result of this and Problem 4, can you state a generalization?

6. List the prime numbers between 1 and 100.

7. In the ninth book of his *Elements*, Euclid (3rd century B.C.) proved that the set $\{p \mid p$ is a prime number$\}$ is an infinite set. Is this set closed under

a) addition?   b) multiplication?

---

* For the proof of this statement as well as a general discussion of prime numbers, see R. Courant and H. Robbins, *What Is Mathematics?* New York: Oxford University Press, 1941; and W. J. LeVeque, *Elementary Theory of Numbers*. Reading, Mass.: Addison-Wesley Publishing Company, 1962.

8. Many primes occur in pairs separated by one integer. Such pairs are 3 and 5, 5 and 7, 11 and 13, 17 and 19. In fact, it has been conjectured, but never proved, that there is an infinite number of such pairs. List all such pairs less than 100.

9. Many mathematicians have unsuccessfully tried to discover an expression which will always result in a prime number. Consider the expression $p = n^2 - n + 41$.*

   a) What is the value of p for $n = 1, 2, 3, 4, 5$?
   b) What is its value for $n = 9, 10, 11$?
   c) Are the values of p in (a) and (b) prime numbers?
   d) What is the value of p when $n = 41$? Is this a prime number?

10. Recall that any even integer n can be expressed $n = 2k$ for some integer k. Use this definition to show that the set $E = \{x \mid x$ is an even integer$\}$ is closed under

   a) addition   b) multiplication

11. Show that the set $O = \{x \mid x$ is an odd integer$\}$ is closed under multiplication.

12. Show that the square of an even integer is even and that of an odd integer is odd.

▶ 13. Show that if the square of any integer is even, the integer itself is even. (Recall that any integer is even or odd, and use Problem 12.)

14. Show that if an integer is a multiple of the integer a, its square is also a multiple of a.

15. List the set consisting of composites less than 25 and express each composite as a product of primes.

16. a) If P represents the set of all prime numbers, what is $N \cap P$?
   b) What is $I \cap P$?

1–5 RATIONAL AND IRRATIONAL NUMBERS

The classification of numbers as *rational* involves the formation of the quotient† of an integer by an integer. If a is an integer and b is an integer different from zero, then a/b may be defined as the number c which, when multiplied by b, gives a. That is, c is the quotient and is defined by the equation $cb = a$. Fractions of the form $a/0$ are not defined. We therefore say that $a/0$ does not exist, and division by zero is not permitted.

    Definition 1–13. Any number which can be expressed as the quotient or ratio of two integers (excluding division by zero) is called a *rational number.*

    The entire set of all such numbers is called *the set of rational numbers*, and is denoted by F. The numbers $\frac{5}{3}$, $-\frac{13}{2}$, and 1.414 are rational numbers. Any integer n, say 3, is a rational number, since $n = (n/1)$. Consequently, $I \subset F$. The number 1.414, which is an approximation for $\sqrt{2}$,‡ is a rational number, since

$$1.414 = \tfrac{1414}{1000}.$$

---

* n^2 represents n times n.
† The word "quotient" is defined in Article 2–4.
‡ A number which, when multiplied by itself, results in 2.

Any rational number may be written as a decimal. For example, $\frac{7}{4} = 1.75$, or $\frac{2}{11} = 0.1818\ldots$. The decimal 1.75 is said to terminate, while the decimal $0.1818\ldots$ is called a *periodic** or *repeating decimal* since the two digits 18 repeat themselves. Indeed, a rational number may be identified by the fact that its decimal expansion either terminates or, if unending, is periodic. Numbers which are nonperiodic and unending, when expressed as decimals, are *not rational*. For example, the numbers $\sqrt{2}$, π (the ratio of the circumference of any circle to its diameter), and e (the base for logarithms used in calculus), which cannot be expressed as the quotient of two integers, cannot be written as terminating or unending periodic decimals.

The proofs that π and e are not rational are quite difficult and involve considerably more mathematics than we have at our disposal. However, a comparatively simple proof that $\sqrt{2}$ is not rational is possible. Our method of proof will be to assume that the statement of the theorem we wish to prove is false. On this assumption, we shall work logically with what we know and thus arrive at a contradiction. Because of this contradiction, we realize our assumption was incorrect, and consequently the statement of the theorem must be true. Such an argument is frequently called the method of *indirect proof* or *reductio ad absurdum*.

Theorem 1–1. The number $\sqrt{2}$ is not a rational number.

Proof. Since we wish to prove that no integers p and q exist such that $p/q = \sqrt{2}$, we shall assume two such integers exist. Moreover, if two such integers exist, we may reduce the fraction p/q to lowest terms by dividing out any common multiple. We therefore have

$$p/q = \sqrt{2}, \tag{1–1}$$

where p and q are relatively prime. If we multiply each member of this equation by q, and square, we get

$$p^2 = 2q^2. \tag{1–2}$$

Because of the closure property of I, p^2 and q^2 are integers, and in fact, p^2 is an even integer. Because of the result of Problem 13, p is an even integer, and we set it equal to $2r$, where r is an integer. Thus, $p = 2r$. If this value of p is substituted into Eq. (1–2), we have $4r^2 = 2q^2$, or

$$2r^2 = q^2,$$

and therefore q^2 is an even integer. It follows that q is an even integer. We have now arrived at a contradiction, namely, that the two relatively prime integers, p and q, both have 2 as a factor. Our original assumption is thus impossible, and there do *not* exist any integers p and q where $p/q = \sqrt{2}$; that is, $\sqrt{2}$ is not rational.

---

* By "periodic" decimal we mean that a digit or block of digits repeat either from the decimal $(0.161616\ldots)$ or after a certain stage $(3.2454545\ldots)$.

It is not difficult to prove that F is closed under the operations of addition or multiplication, provided we know the method of adding or multiplying fractions discussed in Articles 3–7 and 3–8. In fact, F is closed under all four of the elementary operations, including subtraction and division (except by zero), so that F is much more useful than I. It is not, however, a system which is completely satisfactory, for it does not permit numbers which, when written as decimals, may continue indefinitely without any period. For example, the number 0.1010010001 . . . is not permitted.

The entire set of numbers expressible as decimals (terminating or not) is called the *set of real numbers*, and those in this set which are not rational form the set of *irrational numbers*. If we let R denote the set of all real numbers, we have $N \subset I \subset F \subset R$. Moreover, with R as the universal set, F', the complement of F, can denote the set of all irrational numbers. Unfortunately, F' is not closed under addition since, for example,* the sum of $\sqrt{2}$ and $-\sqrt{2}$ (a number which is easily proved irrational, see Problem 12) is 0, a rational number. Neither is F' closed under multiplication, for $\sqrt{2} \cdot \sqrt{2} = 2$. However, any irrational number can be approximated by a rational number. For example, the rational number which approximates $\sqrt{2}$, correct to three decimal places, is 1.414. The rational number $\frac{22}{7}$ is a common approximation for π, while a more accurate one is 3.1416. The set of all real numbers may be classified as follows:

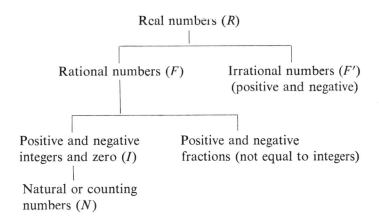

We shall deal primarily with real numbers in this book, but other types of numbers will arise from generalizations or extensions of real numbers. In Chapter 13, for example, we shall discuss the set of complex numbers, which includes imaginary numbers as well as real numbers. However, unless otherwise stated, all numbers will be regarded as belonging to the set of real numbers, and R will be our universal set.

---

* If a statement or theorem is proved, it must be proved for all possible cases. If, on the other hand, we are required to disprove a statement, one example for which the statement is false will suffice.

PROBLEMS

1. Show that the following numbers are rational by Definition 1–13.
   a) 0.6   b) $4\frac{3}{7}$ c) -14.73 d) 0

2. Show that the following are rational numbers.
   a) $-6 + \frac{3}{7}$ b) $(2/3)/(5/2)$
   c) $(2 + \sqrt{5}) + (7 - \sqrt{5})$

3. Show that the following numbers can be expressed as terminating or periodic decimals and are therefore rational.
   a) $\frac{2}{3}$ b) $\frac{4}{7}$ c) $\frac{1}{32}$ d) $\frac{1}{17}$

4. In expressing $\frac{1}{17}$ as a decimal:
   a) What is the periodic repeating block of numbers?
   b) How many digits are there in this block of numbers?
   c) What are the remainders at each stage of the division process used to obtain this block?
   d) Explain why the division of p and q, where the integer p is less than the integer q, will always result in a terminating or periodic decimal. This explanation outlines a proof of what theorem?

5. Show that the following numbers can be expressed as the quotient of two integers.
   a) $3.242424\ldots$ [If we let $x = 3.242424$, $100x = 324.242424\ldots$ If we subtract the corresponding members of these two equations, we obtain $99x = 321$, or $x = 107/33$.]
   b) $6.272727\ldots$ c) $5.818181\ldots$
   d) $0.555\ldots$ e) $0.142857142857\ldots$

6. a) Outline a method which will always result in a solution for Problem 5.
   b) Such a method outlines a proof of what theorem?

7. Prove that the set F is closed under
   a) addition   *Hint:* If $a = (p/q)$ and $b = (r/s)$, can $a + b$ be expressed as the quotient of two integers?
   b) multiplication   c) subtraction   d) division

8. Construct a Venn diagram with R for the universe indicating the subsets F, F', and I.

9. If we are given that
$$A = \{.001, \sqrt{3}, \sqrt[3]{-1}, 3.14159, 2.3737\ldots, 5, 3\tfrac{2}{3}\},$$
   find
   a) $A \cap N$ b) $A \cap I$ c) $A \cap F$ d) $A \cap F'$

10. If $S = \{.0237, \frac{22}{7}, \sqrt[3]{2}, \sqrt[3]{8}, .6666\ldots, .6667\}$, find
   a) $N \cap S$ b) $I \cap S$ c) $F \cap S$ d) $F' \cap S$

11. If we assume $\sqrt{3}$ is not rational, prove that $5 + \sqrt{3}$ is not rational.

12. Prove that $-\sqrt{2}$ is not rational.

13. Prove that $(a + b\sqrt{2})/c$, where a, b, and c are integers and c is not 0, is not rational.

14. Prove that no rational number exists whose cube is 2.

15. Prove that the sum of a rational and irrational number must be irrational.

16. Prove that the product of a rational number (other than zero) and an irrational number is irrational.

17. Show by example that the product of two irrational numbers may be rational.

18. If a and b are any two rational numbers,

    a) show that $(a + b)/2$ must be rational,
    b) show that $\sqrt{ab}$ may not be rational.

1–6 EQUALITY

We recall the definition which concerned the equality of two sets. The equality relation in general, we shall assume, is reflexive, symmetric, and transitive (see Problem 15, Article 1–2). Specifically, for all elements a, b, and c of R:

Axiom E1. *Reflexive* property for equality: $a = a$.

Axiom E2. *Symmetric* property for equality: If $a = b$, $b = a$.

Axiom E3. *Transitive* property for equality: If $a = b$ and $b = c$, then $a = c$.

Furthermore, we shall assume the addition and multiplication properties.

Axiom E4. *Addition* property for equality: If $a = b$ and $c = d$, then $a + c = b + d$.

Axiom E5. *Multiplication* property for equality: If $a = b$, and $c = d$, then $a \cdot c = b \cdot d$.

Finally, we shall assume that any quantity may be substituted in any expression for an equal quantity.

We do not intend to belabor what is basic to the idea of equality, but rather wish to point out precisely what assumptions we do make, and we shall ordinarily use them henceforth without specific comment.

There are two main types of equations in mathematics, the *identity* and the *conditional* equation. These two have many of the same properties but differ in meaning. Let us distinguish between them.

Definition 1–14. An *identity* is a statement of equality which holds true for all permissible values* of the letters involved.

Each such identity will be denoted by the symbol $\equiv$, in order to emphasize its nature. The following simple examples will help to clarify the concept.

---

* The *permissible values* are all those values for which both sides of the equation are defined.

Illustration 1. $x + 2 + 5 - 4 - x \equiv 3$ holds for all values of x.

Illustration 2. $x^2 - 4 \equiv (x + 2)(x - 2)$, where x^2 represents x times x, holds for all values of x. This statement may be checked by substituting any value for x in both sides of the identity, and it is proved in Article 3–4.

The conditional equation is more commonly used.

Definition 1–15. The *conditional equation* is a statement of equality which holds true for some, but not all, permissible values of the letters involved.

One is usually required to solve such an equation, that is, to find all possible values (the solution) for which the equation is true. Later we shall discuss the solving of equations, but now let us consider the following examples.

Illustration 3. $x + 2 = 4$ is a conditional equation, since it is true only for $x = 2$.

Illustration 4. $x^2 - 7x + 12 = 0$ is a conditional equation, since it is true only for $x = 3$ or 4. Any other value substituted for x in this equation will not satisfy it.

The use of the symbol $\equiv$ for an identity and of $=$ for a conditional equation emphasizes the distinction between the two types of equalities.

CHAPTER 2

THE ALGEBRA OF
NUMBERS AS A LOGICAL SYSTEM

We have discussed rather briefly different sets of numbers. In this chapter it is our intention to present the real number system as a *deductive logical system*, and thus give some idea of not only the nature of the numbers themselves, but also the operations on these numbers and the properties they possess. As in any deductive system, we shall state our assumptions and definitions, and outline proofs for the most important theorems, leaving others for the reader to work out. Still others, similar to the theorems we discuss, we shall assume can be established and, as a result, accept without proof. In this way, we hope to convey the idea that any mathematical system involves a certain type of reasoning and that the methods of mathematicians are similar, whether the material be elementary algebra or some much more advanced field of mathematics.

2–1 THE DEDUCTIVE SYSTEM

If we recall the method of proof used in secondary-school geometry or any of the theorems proved in the last chapter, one thing is clear. Each proof involved some hypothesis and conclusion, where the conclusion came as a result of a logical process of reasoning from the hypothesis. But for us to be convinced of the truth of our conclusion, either we must assume the hypothesis true or we must have previously proved it. This hypothesis, in turn, must have been established by the use of facts still earlier established. Such a chain cannot back up indefinitely. There must, at some stage, have been a start. It is at this beginning, then, in a deductive system or argument that we say "We assume that certain facts are true." This beginning must consist of a number of words not defined and a set of statements not proved. Then, as we proceed from statement to statement, precise rules are used. Such basic laws of reasoning, intuitively used by all of us, are rarely stated. One such law states that a proposition is either true or false. Another states that if proposition A follows from proposition B, and B from C, then A follows from C.

A deductive method of reasoning, then, is the process of reasoning which starts with certain *undefined terms*, and certain assumed statements, called *axioms* or *postulates*, uses these to define additional concepts, and applies to these statements and definitions the *rules of deductive logic* to arrive at desired conclusions.

Although from the point of view of mathematical elegance, an irreducible minimum number of axioms is desired for any system, we shall not concern ourselves with a minimum number, but may list some axioms which can be proved from the others in order to present our system more clearly. Certain of these dependent axioms will be mentioned in the problems.

2–2 THE REAL NUMBERS

We are now in a position to present a set of axioms that are by no means unique, but which define or characterize the set of real numbers. It will be clear in considering these axioms that many of them are satisfied individually by other systems as well as the real numbers, and by this type of observation, their true meaning may be all the clearer. We shall separate the axioms into three groups. The first group (Axioms 1 through 6), which we shall consider in this chapter, are called the *axioms of a field*. The other two groups, the *order axioms* and the *completeness property*, will be presented in Chapter 4 and discussed at that time.

We therefore assume that the real-number system is a set of elements R (and form a field). These elements, the undefined terms, are called real numbers. There are also two operations, "$+$" and "$\cdot$", called addition and multiplication,* which are defined such that the following axioms hold.

Axiom 1. *The closure axioms.* For any a and $b \in R$, $a + b$ and $a \cdot b \in R$.

We recall that the sum or product of two integers is an integer, and that the sum or product of two rational numbers is a rational number. Axiom 1 is an equivalent statement for any two real numbers.

Axiom 2. *The associative axioms.* For any a, b, and $c \in R$,

$$(a + b) + c \equiv a + (b + c),$$
$$(a \cdot b) \cdot c \equiv a \cdot (b \cdot c).$$

The first part of Axiom 2 states that the result is not affected by the way in which we group real numbers for addition. The second part states the same for multiplication. Since addition is associative, we may write $a + b + c$ without parentheses, defining this to mean either $(a + b) + c$ or $a + (b + c)$. In fact, because of closure and the associative property, the sum of any number of real numbers is well defined, and again, a similar statement can be made for the product of any number of real numbers.

Axiom 3. *The commutative axioms.* For any a and $b \in R$,

$$a + b \equiv b + a,$$
$$a \cdot b \equiv b \cdot a.$$

Axiom 3 states that the order in which we either add or multiply real numbers does not affect the result.

---

* We shall use the usual symbols for grouping two or more numbers as a single quantity, namely parentheses ( ), brackets [ ], or braces { }, when it is clear that they are not used for defining sets. We shall also write ab or $a(b)$, or $(a)b$ or $(a)(b)$, for $a \cdot b$.

Axiom 4. *The distributive axioms.* For any a, b, and $c \in R$,

$$a \cdot (b + c) \equiv (a \cdot b) + (a \cdot c),$$
$$(b + c) \cdot a \equiv (b \cdot a) + (c \cdot a).$$

Axiom 4 states that the result is the same whether we multiply a certain real number by the sum of two real numbers or multiply a number by each of two numbers and then add. The first part of Axiom 4 is called the left-hand distributive law. Neither part of Axiom 4 is independent, but both may be proved by use of the other and the previous axioms. (See Problem 10 below.)

These four axioms may be considered together, for they concern the methods of combining the real numbers by means of the basic operations. They are so simple that you have probably always used them without realizing exactly what properties you were employing. Nevertheless, they are basic. The problems below will provide a better understanding of them and point out where they are used in our ordinary arithmetic and elementary algebra.

PROBLEMS

1. What is meant by the statement that sets are closed under the operation of "$\cup$"? of "$\cap$"?

2. If the operation "$\cup$" for sets A, B, C, ... is interpreted as "sum," analogous statements for Axioms 2 and 3, with regard to addition, would be

$$A \cup (B \cup C) \equiv (A \cup B) \cup C \qquad \text{and} \qquad A \cup B \equiv B \cup A.$$

By using Venn diagrams, show that these relations are true.

3. If the operation "$\cap$" for sets A, B, C, ... is interpreted as "product," analogous statements for Axioms 2 and 3, with regard to multiplication, would be

$$A \cap (B \cap C) \equiv (A \cap B) \cap C \qquad \text{and} \qquad A \cap B \equiv B \cap A.$$

By using Venn diagrams, show that these relations are true.

4. With the same interpretations as in Problems 2 and 3, Axiom 4 would state that for any three sets A, B, and C, $A \cap (B \cup C) \equiv (A \cap B) \cup (A \cap C)$. Show whether this relation is true by using a Venn diagram.

5. If the $\cap$ and $\cup$ are interchanged in Problem 4, we would have

$$A \cup (B \cap C) \equiv (A \cup B) \cap (A \cup C).$$

Show whether this relation is true by using a Venn diagram. Is the analogous statement true for real numbers?

6. All operations on real numbers are not associative.
   a) What can be said about the equality of $2 - (3 - 4)$ and $(2 - 3) - 4$?
   b) What can be said about $2 \div (3 \div 4)$ and $(2 \div 3) \div 4$?

   Give other examples of operations which are not associative.

7. Are the operations "$-$" and "$\div$" commutative for the set R? Give other examples of operations which are not commutative.

8. What real number should appear in the blank spaces below in order that the statements be true? State what axioms are used.

a) $5 \cdot (4 + \underline{\hspace{1cm}}) = 5 \cdot 4 + 5 \cdot 6$

b) $3 \cdot (\underline{\hspace{1cm}} + 4) = 3 \cdot 7 + \underline{\hspace{1cm}} \cdot 4$

c) $4 \cdot 8 + 3 \cdot \underline{\hspace{1cm}} = (\underline{\hspace{1cm}} + \underline{\hspace{1cm}}) \cdot 8$

d) $\underline{\hspace{1cm}} \cdot (3 + 7) = 8 \cdot \underline{\hspace{1cm}} + 8 \cdot \underline{\hspace{1cm}}$

9. In each of the following, several of the axioms are used to make the assertion of equality. Tell which ones are used and where.

a) $(x + 2) + a \equiv 2 + (a + x)$

$\quad$ *Hint:* $(x + 2) + a \equiv (2 + x) + a \quad$ (by Axiom 3)

$\qquad\qquad\qquad\quad \equiv 2 + (x + a) \quad$ (by Axiom 2)

$\qquad\qquad\qquad\quad \equiv 2 + (a + x)* \quad$ (by Axiom 3)

b) $(ab)c \equiv (cb)a$

c) $a(x + 2) + a(x + 3) \equiv a(2x + 5) \quad$ [We must assume we know $1 + 1 = 2$ and $2 + 3 = 5$.]

d) $(x + 1)6 + (x + 1)y \equiv (y + 6)(x + 1)$

e) $(b + c + d)a \equiv ab + ac + ad$

▶ f) $(x + y)(a + b) \equiv xa + ay + xb + by$

g) $(x + 2)(x + 3) \equiv x^2 + 5x + 6 \quad$ [We must assume we know $2 + 3 = 5$ and $2 \cdot 3 = 6$.]

▶ **10.** Prove the right-hand distributive axiom, $(b + c)a \equiv ba + ca$, by using the left-hand distributive axiom and any others that are needed. State the axioms used.

11. Axioms 1 through 4 have been used so frequently in common practice that we may not always realize when they are used. If we assume addition tables for numbers 1 through 9, and a knowledge of place value of the digits, we can add any two integers, and have the result completely justified. Let us add 37 and 45. Give the reasons for each step. Since $37 = 3 \cdot 10 + 7$, and $45 = 4 \cdot 10 + 5$, we have

$$
\begin{aligned}
37 + 45 &= (3 \cdot 10 + 7) + (4 \cdot 10 + 5) &&\text{Place value of digits} \\
&= [(3 \cdot 10 + 7) + 4 \cdot 10] + 5 \\
&= [3 \cdot 10 + (7 + 4 \cdot 10)] + 5 \\
&= [3 \cdot 10 + (4 \cdot 10 + 7)] + 5 \\
&= [(3 \cdot 10 + 4 \cdot 10) + 7] + 5 \\
&= (3 \cdot 10 + 4 \cdot 10) + (7 + 5) \\
&= (3 + 4) \cdot 10 + (7 + 5) \\
&= 7 \cdot 10 + 12 &&\text{Addition tables} \\
&= 7 \cdot 10 + (1 \cdot 10 + 2) \\
&= (7 \cdot 10 + 1 \cdot 10) + 2 \\
&= (7 + 1) \cdot 10 + 2 \\
&= 8 \cdot 10 + 2 \\
&= 82.
\end{aligned}
$$

---

* Note that Axiom E3, the third axiom for equality (Article 1–6), is used several times

12. Do the same for

    a) $21 + 36$ b) $78 + 45$ c) 12×16 d) 23×36

    (Assume the multiplication tables for integers 1 through 9 and that $10 \cdot 10 = 100$.)

13. Simplify the sum by combining similar terms. Tell what axioms are used. Assume the ordinary addition and multiplication of the integers.

    a) $(x^2 + 2x + 5) + (3x^2 + 5x + 2)$

    b) $3(x^2 + 5x + 6) + 4(2x^2 + 7x + 1)$

14. Express the following products as sums by using Axiom 4, and simplify as in Problem 13. Tell what axioms are used at every step.

    a) $(x + 2y)(x + 3y)$ b) $(2x + 3y)(x + 5y)$

    c) $(x + 1)(x + 2)(x + 3)$ d) $(x^2 + 5x + 10)(2x + 3)$

▶ **15.** One interpretation of Axiom E4 (Article 1–6) for equality states: If $a \equiv b$ and $c \equiv c$, then $a + c \equiv b + c$. Another might be, if $a \equiv a$ and $c \equiv d$, then $a + c \equiv a + d$. If the first of these properties is always true, we say addition on the right is permitted, while if the second is true, we say addition on the left is permitted. Fortunately, both of these are true for real numbers

    In any system, if addition on the right is permitted, what axiom allows us the further advantage of addition on the left?

16. Show why both multiplication on the right and on the left are permitted for real numbers.

In addition to the four axioms we have just studied, there are more complex axioms involving the properties of the numbers themselves and certain special numbers. Two of these are concerned with identity elements, one for each operation, and, as before, we state them under one number in Axiom 5.

Axiom 5. The identity axioms. There exist two unequal numbers (read "zero" and "one," respectively) such that for every $a \in R$:

$$a + 0 \equiv a,$$
$$a \cdot 1 \equiv a.$$

Since 0 and 1 are elements of R, and, by Axiom 3, these operations in R are commutative, we immediately know that $a + 0 = 0 + a = a$, and $a \cdot 1 = 1 \cdot a = a$. The real number *zero* is called the *identity* or *identity element* for the operation addition, while the number *one* is the *identity element* for multiplication.

There are two other axioms, which again we shall list together, that also imply the existence of certain elements or numbers in our set of real numbers. Since these two axioms are frequently used in proofs that also involve Axiom 5, we shall state them here.

Axiom 6. The inverse axioms. For each $a \in R$, there exists exactly one element of R, denoted by $-a$ (read "minus a" or "the negative of a"), such that

$$a + (-a) \equiv 0.$$

Also, for every $a \in R$ $(a \neq 0)$, there exists exactly one element of R, denoted by $1/a$ (read "the reciprocal of a") such that

$$a \cdot 1/a \equiv 1.$$

In each case, the result of combining (by either operation) any element with its *inverse* is the identity element for that operation. Therefore, by Axiom 6 we are stating that any number has an *inverse* with respect to each of the two operations. Since both addition and multiplication are commutative operations in R, we also have immediately $-a + a \equiv 0$ and $(1/a) \cdot a \equiv 1$. We noted in Article 1–5 that division by zero is undefined. It is for this reason that $a = 0$ is excluded in the second part of Axiom 6.

Example 1. Show that $-b + (a + b) \equiv a$.

Solution. By using the commutative and associative axioms, we have

$$-b + (a + b) \equiv -b + (b + a) \equiv (-b + b) + a.$$

Since $-b + b \equiv 0$ and $0 + a \equiv a$, we obtain the required result.

Example 2. When there is one and only one element with a given property, we say the element is *unique*. Show that zero, the identity element for addition, is unique.

Solution. If we assume zero is not unique, there is another element $0'$, such that $a + 0' \equiv a$ for all a. Thus, we would have $a + 0' \equiv a$ and $a + 0 \equiv a$ for all a, so that $a + 0' \equiv a + 0$. If we add $-a$ to each member of this equation, by Axiom E4, we have

$$-a + (a + 0') \equiv -a + (a + 0),$$

and by the associative axiom,

$$(-a + a) + 0' \equiv (-a + a) + 0.$$

Since $-a + a \equiv 0$ by Axiom 6, $0 + 0' \equiv 0 + 0$, and therefore, $0' \equiv 0$ (why?). Explain why this completes the proof.

It is also possible to prove that the identity element for multiplication is unique (see Problem 21 below).

PROBLEMS

One or more of the axioms for the set of real numbers R is used to make the statement in each of Problems 1 through 20. Tell precisely which of the six axioms are used and where they are used in each problem.

1. $3 + 0 = 3$ 2. $0 + 2 = 2$

3. $-a + 0 = -a$ 4. $1 \cdot 6 = 6$

5. $1 \cdot 1 = 1$ 6. $0 + 0 = 0$

7. $-1 \cdot 1 = -1$ 8. $\pi + (-\pi) = 0$

9. $-\sqrt{2} + \sqrt{2} = 0$ 10. $(-5) + [-(-5)] = 0$

11. $3 \cdot \dfrac{1}{3} = 1$ 12. $\dfrac{1}{-4}(-4) = 1$

13. $\dfrac{1}{5} \cdot \dfrac{1}{1/5} = 1$ 14. $1 \cdot \dfrac{1}{1} = 1$

15. $x + y \equiv x \cdot 1 + y \cdot 1$ 16. $0 + 1 \cdot (x + y) \equiv x + y$

17. $-(xy) + xy \equiv 0$ 18. $3\sqrt{2x} \cdot \dfrac{1}{3\sqrt{2x}} \equiv 1, \quad (x \neq 0)$

19. $-(a + 0 + b) + (b + a) \equiv 0$

20. $\dfrac{1}{2x + 3y}(2x + 3y) \equiv 1, \quad 2x + 3y \neq 0$

21. Show that the identity element for multiplication, namely one, is unique.

22. Show that for any real number $a \in R$,

     a) its inverse for addition is unique,
     b) its inverse for multiplication is unique.

23. If we consider the sets A, B, C, ... as elements and consider the set $\emptyset$ as the identity element for the operation "$\cup$" and the set U as the identity element for the operation "$\cap$," to what axioms are the following analogous:

$$A \cup \emptyset \equiv A? \qquad A \cap U \equiv A?$$

2–3 CERTAIN BASIC THEOREMS

Let us now prove several theorems that are direct results of the axioms in the last article. Not only are these results important in themselves; the general approach and methods of proof should also be studied and understood, because this material will be useful in the problems and for understanding later work.

In all the theorems and definitions in this article we shall consider the several letters a, b, c, ... as real numbers, elements of the set R. Moreover, unless there are specifically stated restrictions on these numbers, we shall assume the numbers to be any real numbers that make sense. Many of the theorems involving the operation of addition have a corresponding theorem which involves the operation of multiplication. We shall indicate this by adding an "A" or "M" to the number of the theorem.

Axiom E4, Article 1–6, has been used several times. We are now able to prove the converse of this statement, the so-called *additive cancellation property*.

Theorem 2–1A. If $a + c \equiv b + c$, then $a \equiv b$.

Proof. Since c is a real number, $-c$ is a real number by Axiom 6, and, using Axiom E4, we have $(a + c) + (-c) \equiv (b + c) + (-c)$. Applying the associative axiom, Axiom 2, we get $a + [c + (-c)] \equiv b + [c + (-c)]$, and since $c + (-c) \equiv 0$ (Axiom 6), this becomes $a + 0 \equiv b + 0$. Then, because of Axiom 5, $a \equiv b$, our desired result.

A similar theorem for multiplication is possible.

Theorem 2–1M. If $ac \equiv bc$, and $c \neq 0$, then $a \equiv b$.

Proof. (Give the reasons for each step.) Since $ac \equiv bc$,

$$(ac)\frac{1}{c} \equiv (bc)\frac{1}{c} \cdot$$

Thus

$$a\left(c \cdot \frac{1}{c}\right) \equiv b\left(c \cdot \frac{1}{c}\right)$$

or, $a \cdot 1 \equiv b \cdot 1$. Thus $a \equiv b$.

A second theorem, similar to that considered in Problem 22(a) of the last article, should be emphasized.

Theorem 2–2A. If $a + b \equiv 0$, then $b \equiv -a$.

Proof. If we add $-a$ on the left (recall Problem 15 in the first set of problems in Article 2–2) to both members of this equation, we have

$$-a + (a + b) \equiv -a + 0.$$

If we use the associative axiom, this becomes

$$(-a + a) + b \equiv -a + 0;$$

and since $-a + a \equiv 0$ on the left, and $-a + 0 \equiv -a$ on the right, we get $0 + b \equiv -a$, so that

$$b \equiv -a.$$

Since b represents any number which, when added to a, results in zero, and since we have proved $b \equiv -a$, we have in fact proved that the inverse for addition is unique. Again, there is an analogous theorem for multiplication.

Theorem 2–2M. If $ab \equiv 1$ and $a \neq 0$, then $b \equiv (1/a)$.

There are several theorems, similar in nature (and proof), which show important properties of our number system. We shall prove some of these, and list some other ones as problems. Note that for each such statement which involves addition, there is an analogous statement involving multiplication.

Theorem 2–3A. If $a \equiv b$, then $-a \equiv -b$.

Proof. Since $a \equiv b$, we may add $-a$ to both members of the equation, so that

$$a + (-a) \equiv b + (-a),$$

which gives $0 \equiv b + (-a)$, since $a + (-a) \equiv 0$. If we now look at what we wish to prove and notice the $-b$ on one side of our expected result, our next step is clear. We must add $-b$ to both members of our equation $0 \equiv b + (-a)$. We add $-b$ on the left of each member of the equation (why?) and get

$$-b + 0 \equiv -b + [b + (-a)],$$

which reduces to

$$-b \equiv -a \quad (\text{why?}).$$

This may be written $-a \equiv -b$, our desired result.

We now wish to prove one of the fundamental properties of the number zero, which, of course, we have used intuitively since we first began arithmetic. The proof may seem somewhat artificial, but ideas of how to start such proofs and methods for carrying them out come from experience and practice. Therefore the student should not be discouraged when he first encounters them.

Theorem 2–4. For all $a \in R$, $a \cdot 0 \equiv 0$.

Proof. Since $0 + 0 = 0$, we know that $a \cdot (0 + 0) \equiv a \cdot 0$. The left member of this equation may be expanded by the distributive axiom. Since the right member of this equation is the product of two real numbers, and thus a real number, it can be written $a \cdot 0 + 0$, by the identity axiom. Consequently,

$$a \cdot 0 + a \cdot 0 \equiv a \cdot 0 + 0.$$

Application of the left cancellation law for addition (see Problem 1 below), gives us our result.

This theorem might have been stated another way, if we recall that the word "or" in mathematics means "and/or" (see the footnote in Article 1–3).

Theorem 2–4. If $a = 0$ or $b = 0$, then $ab = 0$.

The converse of Theorem 2–4 is one of the most basic theorems in algebra. It is useful in the solutions of quadratic or higher-degree equations when they are solved by the method of factoring. Although we shall refer to it again when we come to that topic, we now state and prove it.

Theorem 2–5. If $ab \equiv 0$, then $a \equiv 0$ or $b \equiv 0$.

Proof. If $a \equiv 0$, the theorem is proved. If not, the number a has an inverse with respect to multiplication, namely $1/a$. If we multiply both members of the equation $ab \equiv 0$ by $1/a$, we get

$$(1/a) \cdot (ab) \equiv (1/a) \cdot 0.$$

With the use of the associative law, and the facts that $(1/a) \cdot a \equiv 1$, $1 \cdot b \equiv b$ on the left, and $(1/a) \cdot 0 \equiv 0$ on the right, we have our result.

In addition to studying the theorems we have proved, the student should do all the problems. Then most of the basic ideas in algebra and arithmetic should be clear, and the logical reasons behind the ideas should be apparent.

PROBLEMS

▶ **1.** If $c + a \equiv c + b$, show that $a \equiv b$. This is called the left cancellation property for addition. (Recall Theorem 2–1A.)

▶ **2.** If $ca \equiv cb$, and $c \neq 0$, show that $a \equiv b$.

  3. Prove Theorem 2–2A, by writing $a + b \equiv 0$ as $a + b \equiv a + (-a)$, using the commutative axiom and Theorem 2–1A.

  4. Show that if $a + b \equiv 0$, $a \equiv -b$.

  5. Prove Theorem 2–2M.

  6. If $a \equiv b$ and neither a nor $b \equiv 0$, show that $(1/a) \equiv (1/b)$.

  7. If $a \equiv -b$, show that $-a \equiv b$.

  8. If $a \equiv (1/b)$ $(a, b \neq 0)$, show that $b \equiv (1/a)$.

▶ **9.** Show that for all a, $-(-a) \equiv a$. *Hint:* $-(-a) + (-a) \equiv 0$.

  10. State and prove a theorem analogous to that in Problem 9, where the operation is multiplication.

▶ **11.** Show that $-0 = 0$. *Hint:* $0 + 0 = 0$ and $0 + (-0) = 0$. Give reasons for each of these statements.

  12. State and prove a theorem analogous to that in Problem 11, where the operation is multiplication.

  13. If $abc \equiv 0$, show that a or b or $c \equiv 0$.

▶ **14.** Show that $-(ab) \equiv (-a)b$, giving reasons for each step. We are now able to write $-ab$ for either of these two expressions. *Hint:*

$$-(ab) + (ab) \equiv 0 \equiv (-a + a)$$
$$\equiv (-a + a)b$$
$$\equiv (-a)b + ab.$$

As a result of this problem, we have, for example, $-6 = (-2)(3)$.

▶ **15.** Show that $(-1)a \equiv -(1 \cdot a) \equiv -a$. *Hint:* See Problem 14.

▶ **16.** Show that $(-a)(-b) \equiv ab$. As a result of this problem, we have, for example, $(-2)(-3) = 2 \cdot 3 = 6$.

  17. Explain why

  a) $(-1)(-1) = 1$ b) $(-1)(-1)(-1) = -1$

2–4   FURTHER THEOREMS

In this chapter we have used the sign "$-$" in only one way, namely, as with a letter such as $-a$, to denote the inverse of a number with respect to addition. We are now able to define subtraction, or the difference of two real numbers, in terms of addition and this inverse element.

  Definition 2–1. The expression $a - b$ is equivalent to $a + (-b)$ and is called "the difference of a and b" or "b subtracted from a."*

---

* Some mathematicians prefer to use an equivalent, but different, definition. See Problems 5 and 6 below.

As a result of this definition, the sign "$-$" will be used in two different senses, each of which should be clearly understood.

Illustration 1. Because of the definition of subtraction (and the associative and commutative axioms), we have

$$a + b - c \equiv a + b + (-c) \equiv a + (-c) + b \equiv a - c + b$$
$$\equiv (-c) + a + b \equiv -c + a + b.$$

As a consequence of this definition and of the results from Article 2–3, we have all the usual properties of subtraction.

    Theorem 2–6. $a(b - c) \equiv ab - ac.$

Proof. Since by definition, $b - c \equiv b + (-c)$, we have

$$a(b - c) \equiv a[b + (-c)],$$

and because of the distributive axiom, this is equal to $ab + a(-c)$. But

$$a(-c) \equiv -ac$$

by Problem 14 of Article 2–3, so that

$$a(b - c) \equiv ab + (-ac),$$

which, as a result of the above definition, may be written

$$a(b - c) \equiv ab - ac.$$

    Two additional frequently encountered properties which involve the "$-$" sign appear in Problem 4 below. Special attention should be given to them.

    Division of two real numbers is defined in terms of the operation of multiplication.

    Definition 2–2. The expression a/b, where $b \neq 0$, is equivalent to $a \cdot (1/b)$ and is called "the quotient of a by b."*

Illustration 2.

a) Since $(a/b) \equiv a \cdot (1/b)$ if $b \neq 0$, $b(a/b) \equiv a$;
b) Since $(a/1) \equiv a \cdot (1/1) \equiv a \cdot 1$, $(a/1) \equiv a$;
c) $(0/a) \equiv 0 \cdot (1/a) \equiv 0$ if $a \neq 0$.

Many of the properties of division and/or fractions are results of this definition and can be proved directly. Since there is rarely a unique method of proof, the student is encouraged not only to understand any proofs presented, but also to consider other and possibly simpler approaches. We shall give two basic theorems

---

* In the discussion of rational numbers in Article 1–5 we said a/b might be defined as that number c such that $a = bc$. This, in fact, may be done, but in the above logical treatment we prefer the definition in terms of a and the inverse of b as stated. (See Problem 14 of this article.)

in this article (in addition to those in the problems), and others will appear when the need arises.

Theorem 2–7.

$$\frac{a}{b} \cdot \frac{c}{d} \equiv \frac{ac}{bd} \qquad (b, d \neq 0).$$

Proof. By definition,

$$\frac{ac}{bd} \equiv ac \cdot \frac{1}{bd}.$$

But

$$ac \cdot \frac{1}{bd} \equiv ac \cdot \frac{1}{bd} \cdot \left(b \cdot \frac{1}{b}\right) \cdot \left(d \cdot \frac{1}{d}\right) \qquad \text{(Why?)}$$

$$\equiv a \cdot c \cdot \left(bd \cdot \frac{1}{bd}\right) \cdot \frac{1}{b} \cdot \frac{1}{d} \qquad \text{(Why?)}$$

$$\equiv \left(a \cdot \frac{1}{b}\right) \cdot \left(c \cdot \frac{1}{d}\right) = \frac{a}{b} \cdot \frac{c}{d}. \qquad \text{(Why?)}$$

The proofs of the next two theorems follow immediately from this theorem. Recall how frequently their results have been assumed in past experience.

Theorem 2–8.

$$\frac{a}{b} \equiv \frac{ax}{bx} \qquad (b, x \neq 0).$$

Proof. Since, by Theorem 2–7,

$$\frac{ax}{bx} \equiv \frac{a}{b} \cdot \frac{x}{x},$$

we have

$$\frac{ax}{bx} \equiv \frac{a}{b} \cdot 1 \equiv \frac{a}{b}.$$

Theorem 2–9. $(a/b) \equiv (c/d)$ if and only if $ad \equiv bc$ $(b, d \neq 0)$.

Proof. We recall that such a statement requires two proofs.

a) We must show that if $(a/b) \equiv (c/d)$, then $ad \equiv bc$. By Axiom E5, and the given condition $(a/b) \equiv (c/d)$, we know

$$\frac{a}{b} \cdot b \cdot d \equiv \frac{c}{d} \cdot b \cdot d,$$

so that

$$a \cdot \left(\frac{1}{b} \cdot b\right) \cdot d \equiv c \cdot \left(\frac{1}{d} \cdot d\right) \cdot b, \qquad \text{or} \qquad ad \equiv bc.$$

b) Also, we must show that if $ad \equiv bc$, then $(a/b) \equiv (c/d)$. Again, by Axiom E5, and the condition $ad \equiv bc$, we have

$$a \cdot d \cdot \left(\frac{1}{d} \cdot \frac{1}{b}\right) \equiv b \cdot c \cdot \left(\frac{1}{d} \cdot \frac{1}{b}\right),$$

so that

$$a \cdot \frac{1}{b} \cdot \left(d \cdot \frac{1}{d} \right) \equiv c \cdot \frac{1}{d} \cdot \left(b \cdot \frac{1}{b} \right),$$

or

$$\frac{a}{b} \equiv \frac{c}{d}.$$

The reasons for each step should be furnished by the student.

PROBLEMS

1. Explain why $a - a \equiv 0$.

2. Explain why $(a/a) \equiv 1$.

3. Show that $(a - b)c \equiv ac - bc$.

▶ 4. We learned in elementary algebra that the removal of parentheses (or any symbol of grouping) preceded by a minus sign requires a change of each sign within the parentheses. Specifically,

a) $-(a + b) \equiv -a - b$. *Hint:* See Problem 15, Article 2–3.

b) $-(a - b) \equiv -a + b$.

Show that these statements are true.

5. Show that $b + (a - b) \equiv a$.

6. Show that if $a - b \equiv c$, $b + c \equiv a$. Note that this is the property used in elementary school to check subtraction problems.

7. If $x + a = b$, show that $x \equiv b - a$. This is one of the properties frequently used in solving simple equations. Another is stated in Problem 11.

8. If $a \neq 0$, show that $a(b/a) \equiv b$.

9. If $(a/b) \equiv 1$, show that $a \equiv b$.

▶ 10. Show that

$$-\frac{a}{b} \equiv \frac{-a}{b} \equiv \frac{a}{-b}.$$

Hint: Recall $-(a/b) = -[a \cdot (1/b)]$.

▶ 11. If $ax \equiv b$ $(a \neq 0)$, show that $x \equiv (b/a)$.

12. If $(a/b) \equiv (c/b)(b \neq 0)$, show that $a \equiv c$.

▶ 13. If $c \neq 0$, show that

$$\frac{a + b}{c} \equiv \frac{a}{c} + \frac{b}{c}.$$

▶ 14. Assuming that $b \neq 0$, prove that $(a/b) \equiv c$ if and only if $a \equiv bc$.

▶ 15. Assuming that $b \neq 0$, prove that $(a/b) \equiv c + (d/b)$ if and only if $a \equiv bc + d$.

CHAPTER 3

EXTENSIONS OF THE LOGIC OF ALGEBRA

In this chapter we shall continue our discussion of fundamental notions and processes. Many of the theorems from the last chapter will be used as we construct the algebraic framework for most mathematics. The ideas considered here will appear throughout this book, and they must be thoroughly understood.

3-1 ADDITION OF ALGEBRAIC EXPRESSIONS

Any combination of symbols and numbers related by the fundamental operations of algebra is called an *algebraic expression*.

Illustration 1. $5a + 6b$, $2ax^2$, and $(6x + 5y)2x$ are algebraic expressions.

Any algebraic expression consisting of distinct parts connected by plus or minus signs is called an *algebraic sum*. Each distinct part, together with its sign, is called a *term* of the expression.

Illustration 2. In the algebraic sum $2x^2 - 3y^2 - 5$, $2x^2$ is one term, $-3y^2$ another, and -5 is a third term.

In a particular term consisting of two or more factors, any one of the factors or the product of any set of the factors may be called the *coefficient* of the product of the other factors. For example, in the term $2x^2y$, 2 is the coefficient of x^2y, $2x^2$ is the coefficient of y, and $2y$ is the coefficient of x^2. Frequently it is convenient to distinguish between numerical coefficients and letter-symbol coefficients. In determining the sum or difference of two algebraic expressions by combining similar terms, we use coefficients and continue to apply the associative axioms.

Illustration 3. The sum of $2x - 3y + 5$ and $x + 2y - 1$ is

$$(2x - 3y + 5) + (x + 2y - 1) \equiv 2x + x - 3y + 2y + 5 - 1$$
$$\equiv 3x - y + 4.$$

Illustration 4. The difference between $2x - 3y + 5$ and $x + 2y - 1$ is

$$(2x - 3y + 5) - (x + 2y - 1) \equiv 2x - 3y + 5 - x - 2y + 1$$
$$\equiv x - 5y + 6.$$

Both here and in Example 1, below, we use the result established in Problem 4, Article 2–4.

We have stated that algebraic expressions are called algebraic sums when either addition or subtraction is involved. If the expression consists of just one term, it is called a *monomial*. The algebraic sum or difference of two terms is called a *binomial;* and, in general, an algebraic expression consisting of a sum of any number of terms is called a *multinomial*. The expression $2x/3y^2$ is a monomial, while $3x^2 - 2y$ is a binomial.

Example 1. Simplify the expression $4x - [2x - 3y - (x + 4y)] + (x - 8)$ by removing parentheses or brackets. Then combine similar terms.

Solution. This is done by repeated application of the result from Problem 4, Article 2–4, and the associative axiom.

$$4x - [2x - 3y - (x + 4y)] + (x - 8) \equiv 4x - [2x - 3y - x - 4y] + x - 8$$
$$\equiv 4x - 2x + 3y + x + 4y + x - 8$$
$$\equiv 4x + 7y - 8.$$

The removal of parentheses (or any symbol of grouping) preceded by a minus sign requires changing the sign of each term within the parentheses, but parentheses preceded by a plus sign may be removed without changing the expression in the parentheses.

Example 2. Find the value of $-2xy + 3x - 4y$ when $x = 3$ and $y = -2$.

Solution. Substitute 3 for x and -2 for y:

$$-2(3)(-2) + 3(3) - 4(-2) = 12 + 9 + 8 = 29.$$

PROBLEMS

In each of the following, (a) find the sum of the expressions, and (b) subtract the second expression from the first.

1. $2a + 3b - 4$ and $a - 2b + 3$ 2. $a - 2b + 3c$ and $2a + 4b - c$

3. $4x + 3y + z$ and $2x + 3y - 2z$ 4. $2x + y + 5$ and $3y - 2z - 4$

5. $2(x - 3y)$ and $-5(2x + y)$ 6. $-(x + 2y - z)$ and $3(x - y + 2z)$

In each of the following, remove all symbols of grouping and combine like terms.

7. $x - (2y + 3x) - 2y$

8. $3x - (2y - 4x) + 6y$

9. $(2x - 3y) - (8x + 6y + 4)$

10. $(2x - 3y) + (y - 4z) - (z - 3x)$

11. $8x + [(3x - 2y) + (6x - 9) - (x + y)]$

12. $3y - [2y + 3x - (2x - 3y)] + 4x$

13. $2x - \{3y - [5x - (7y \quad 6x)]\}$

14. $9x - (2y - 3x) - \{y - (2y - x)\} - [2y + (4x - 3y)]$

In each of the following expressions, enclose the last three terms in parentheses preceded by a minus sign.

15. $a^2 - b^2 + 2bc - c^2$

16. $16 - x^2 + 2xy - y^2$

17. $4x^2 - 4y^2 - 4y - 1$

18. $9x^2 - 9y^2 - 6xy - x^2$

In each of the following expressions, enclose the coefficients of x within parentheses preceded by (a) a plus sign, (b) a minus sign.

19. $cx + dy - ax - by$

20. $5x - ax + 3 - 4x$

21. $ax - by + bx - ay$

22. $6x^2 - 8x + 3y - 7y^2 + 6x - 4$

Find the value of each of the following expressions for the given values of the letters.

23. $3x + 4$ when $x = 1$

24. $x^2 - 7x + 10$ when $x = 2$

25. $3x^2 - 2x + 1$ when $x = -2$

26. $-3x^2 - 4x + 3$ when $x = -4$

27. $2x + 3y$ when $x = -2$, $y = 3$

28. $4x - 3y$ when $x = -1$, $y = 3$

29. $2x^2 - 3xy + y^2$ when $x = 2$, $y = -3$

30. $3x^2 + 2xy - 4y^2$ when $x = -3$, $y = 1$

Let any expression in x followed by the symbol

$$\Big|_a^b$$

mean the value of the expression where b is substituted for x minus the value where a is substituted. For example,

$$2x^2 - 5x \Big|_2^3 = 2(3^2) - 5(3) - [2(2^2) - 5(2)]$$

$$= 18 - 15 - (8 - 10)$$

$$= 5.$$

Find the value of each of the following expressions.

31. $2x + 5 \Big|_1^2$

32. $4x - 7 \Big|_0^1$

33. $x^2 - 6x + 9 \Big|_1^3$

34. $5x^2 - 4x + 6 \Big|_{-2}^1$

35. $x^2 - a^2 \Big|_0^a$

36. $3x^2 - 4a \Big|_0^a$

37. $a^2x - 2ax^2 + 3a^3 \Big|_0^a$

38. $x^4 + x^2 \Big|_{-a}^a$

39. $x^3 - x \Big|_{-a}^a$

40. $2(x^3 - x) \Big|_0^a$

3–2 MULTIPLICATION OF ALGEBRAIC EXPRESSIONS

When the factors of a product are equal, the product is called a *power* of the repeated factor. We shall introduce a symbol to stand for such a product. The symbol a^2 represents the product $a \cdot a$. Similarly, $a \cdot a \cdot a$ may be represented by a^3, and, in general, we have the following definition.

Definition 3–1. If n is a positive integer, the symbol a^n, the nth power of a, is the product of n factors each equal to a. Thus

$$a^n \equiv \underbrace{a \cdot a \cdot a \cdots a.}_{n \text{ factors of } a} \tag{3–1}$$

In the symbol a^n, a is called the *base* and n the *exponent* of the power.

Illustration 1. $2^5 = 2 \cdot 2 \cdot 2 \cdot 2 \cdot 2 = 32$.

From this definition certain theorems on exponents follow.

Theorem 3–1. If n and m are positive integers, and $a \in R$,

$$\boxed{a^n a^m \equiv a^{n+m}.} \tag{3–2}$$

Proof

$$a^n \cdot a^m = \underbrace{a \cdot a \cdot a \cdots u}_{n \text{ factors } a} \cdot \underbrace{u \cdot a \cdot a \cdots a}_{m \text{ factors } a} = \underbrace{a \cdot a \cdot a \cdots a}_{n + m \text{ factors } a} = a^{n+m}.$$

The reader should also prove the following two theorems.

Theorem 3–2. If n and m are positive integers, and $a \in R$,

$$\boxed{(a^n)^m \equiv a^{nm}.} \tag{3–3}$$

Theorem 3–3. If n is a positive integer, and a and $b \in R$,

$$\boxed{(ab)^n \equiv a^n b^n.} \tag{3–4}$$

Illustration 2. $3^2 \cdot 3^4 = 3^6 = 729,$
$$a^4 \cdot a^7 = a^{11}.$$

Illustration 3. $(2^3)^2 = 2^6 = 64,$
$$(a^5)^3 = a^{15}.$$

Illustration 4. $(2 \cdot 3)^3 = 2^3 \cdot 3^3 = 8 \cdot 27 = 216.$

When no exponent is written, the exponent is understood to be 1.

Using these theorems and recalling the distributive axiom, we are now able to perform the multiplication of two algebraic expressions.

Example 1. Multiply $2x - 3y$ by $3x + 4y$.

Solution. Each term of the second binomial must be multiplied by the first binomial. [Recall Problem 9(f), Article 2–2.]

$$(2x - 3y)(3x + 4y) \equiv [(2x - 3y) \cdot 3x] + [(2x - 3y) \cdot 4y].$$

Each of these products on the right is expanded again by the right-hand distributive axiom, so that the result is $6x^2 - 9xy + 8xy - 12y^2$. If we combine similar terms, we have $(2x - 3y)(3x + 4y) \equiv 6x^2 - xy - 12y^2$.

In such problems it is sometimes convenient to arrange both multinomials in ascending (or descending) powers of one letter by the associative axiom, write one below the other, carry out the multiplication, and add the products. Consider the following example.

Example 2. Multiply $x^2 - 2y^2 + xy$ by $2x - y$.

Solution

$$
\begin{array}{l}
x^2 + xy \quad\; - 2y^2 \\
\underline{2x - y} \\
2x^3 + 2x^2y - 4xy^2 \\
\underline{\quad\; - x^2y - \;\; xy^2 + 2y^3} \\
2x^3 + \;\; x^2y - 5xy^2 + 2y^3
\end{array}
$$

PROBLEMS

Perform the indicated operations by using the theorems involving exponents.

1. $a^2 \cdot a^7$ 2. $3x^4 \cdot 2x^3$ 3. $3x^3 \cdot x^4 \cdot x^5$

4. $(-3)^4 \cdot (-3)^5$ 5. $y^{13} \cdot y^{11}$ 6. $(2^3)^4$

7. $(a^5)^4$ 8. $(3b)^5$ 9. $(5c)^3$

10. $(3a)^4$ 11. $(2a^3)^5$ 12. $(x^4)^n$

13. $(a^r \cdot a^s)^t$ 14. $(x^{2m} \cdot x^{3n})^4$ 15. $(2x^n)^n$

Perform the indicated multiplications and collect similar terms. Note that each of Axioms 1 through 4 is used in most of these problems.

16. $(4x - 3)(3x + 6)$ 17. $(x + 3)(2x - 5)$

18. $(5a + 2b)(5a - 2b)$ 19. $(4x + 2y)(4x - 2y)$

20. $(3x - 2)(2x + 5)$ 21. $(r^2 - s^2)(r - s)$

22. $(x - 2y)^2$ 23. $(x^2 - xy + y^2)(x + y)$

24. $(a + b - c)^2$ 25. $(x - 2y + 3)^2$

26. $(x - 2y + z)^2$ 27. $(a + b)^3$

28. $(a - 2b)^3$ 29. $(a^2 - b)^3$

30. $(2x + 3x^2 - 1)(3x - 2)$ 31. $(x^2 - 2x - 2)(x + 2x^2 - 4)$

32. $(-xy + 2x^2 - 3y^2)(x^2 - 4y^2 + xy)$

33. $(x - 1)(x + 2)(x - 3)$ 34. $(x - 2)(x + 3)(x + 2)$

35. $(x^4 + 2x^2y^2 + 4y^4)(x^2 - 2y^2)$ 36. $(a^{2n} - 7a^n + 10)(a^n - 1)$

37. $(a^{2n} - 7a^n + 10)(a - 1)$ 38. $(x - 2x^2 + 5 - x^3)(3x - 4 + x^2)$

39. $(x^{2n} + 2x^ny^n + y^{2n})(x^{2n} - 2x^ny^n + y^{2n})$

40. $(x^n - y^n)^3$ 41. $(x - y)^4$

42. $(a + b)^4$ 43. $(a^3 + 3a^2 + 3a + 1)(a + 1)$

44. $(a^2 - 2ab + b^2)(a^2 + 2ab + b^2)$ 45. $(x - 2)^4$

3-3 DIVISION OF ALGEBRAIC EXPRESSIONS

Before we are able to divide one algebraic expression by another, we must establish an additional theorem on exponents.

Theorem 3-4. If $a \in R$ ($a \neq 0$) and n and m are positive integers,

$$\frac{a^n}{a^m} \equiv \begin{cases} a^{n-m} & \text{if } n \text{ is larger than } m, \\[2mm] \dfrac{1}{a^{m-n}} & \text{if } m \text{ is larger than } n, \\[2mm] 1 & \text{if } m = n. \end{cases}$$

$$(3\text{-}5)$$
$$(3\text{-}6)$$
$$(3\text{-}7)$$

Proof. This result is established by writing

$$\frac{a^n}{a^m} \equiv \frac{\overbrace{a \cdot a \cdot a \cdots a}^{n \text{ factors } a}}{\underbrace{a \cdot a \cdot a \cdots a}_{m \text{ factors } a}},$$

and recalling Theorem 2-7.

Illustration 1. $\dfrac{x^8}{x^3} \equiv x^5$; $\dfrac{x^4}{x^{11}} \equiv \dfrac{1}{x^7}$; $\dfrac{x^6}{x^6} \equiv 1$.

We are now prepared to divide any multinomial by a monomial. This is done by dividing each term of the multinomial by the monomial and finding the algebraic sum of the resulting quotients. (Recall Problem 13, Article 2-4.)

Example 1. Divide $12x^3y^4 + 18x^4y^2 - 36xy^3$ by $3x^2y^2$.

Solution. It we use the property stated in Problem 13, Article 2-4, we have

$$\frac{12x^3y^4 + 18x^4y^2 - 36xy^3}{3x^2y^2} \equiv \frac{12x^3y^4}{3x^2y^2} + \frac{18x^4y^2}{3x^2y^2} - \frac{36xy^3}{3x^2y^2}$$

$$\equiv 4xy^2 + 6x^2 - \frac{12y}{x}.$$

We have defined an algebraic expression as the sum of algebraic terms (Article 3-1). Any algebraic term is an *integral rational* term in certain letters representing numbers if it consists of the product of positive integral powers of these numbers and a factor not containing them. For example, ax^2y and $3x^4y^{3/4}$ are integral rational terms in x, and ax^2y and $3x^4y^3$ are integral rational terms in y. The term $by^{1/2}$ is also integral rational in x, since it satisfies the definition. Any multinomial in which each term is integral rational is called an *integral rational expression* or *polynomial*.

Illustration 2. The multinomial $3 - 5x^3 + \frac{3}{5}xy^2$ is a polynomial in x and y. However, $-5/x^3$ is not integral in x, and $5\sqrt{x}$ is neither integral nor rational in x.

The degree of a term which is *integral rational* in some letter is defined to be the *exponent* of that letter. Thus ax^2y and $3x^4y^3$ are terms of the second and fourth degree in x, but first and third degree in y. *The degree of an integral rational term in two or more letters* is defined to be the sum of the exponents of those letters. Thus the degree of ax^2y in x and y is $2 + 1 = 3$, while the degree of $3x^4y^3$ in x and y is 7. *The degree of a polynomial* in certain letters is that of its term (or terms) of highest degree in those letters.

Illustration 3

a) $2x + 1$, $x^2 - 7x + 10$, and $3x^3 + 5x^2 - 6$ are polynomials of the first, second, and third degree in x, respectively.

b) $3x^2y^5 + 4xy^3 - 7x^3y^2$ is a polynomial of the third degree in x, fifth degree in y, and seventh degree in x and y.

Now let us consider the division of one polynomial by another. Our method will follow that used in arithmetic. The properties we shall use are stated in Problems 14 and 15 of Article 2–4. If we divide 28 by 9, the quotient is 3 and the remainder 1, and we write $\frac{28}{9} = 3 + \frac{1}{9}$.

To divide one polynomial by another:

1. Arrange each polynomial in descending powers of some common letter.

2. Divide the first term of the dividend (the polynomial to be divided) by the first term of the divisor. This step gives the first term of the quotient.

3. Multiply the divisor by the first term of the quotient, and subtract the product from the dividend.

4. Using the remainder thus obtained as a new dividend, repeat this process, thus finding the second term of the quotient.

5. Continue the process until a remainder is obtained which either is zero or is of lower degree in the common letter than the divisor. If the remainder is zero, the division is exact, and the division is an application of Problem 14, Article 2–4. If the remainder is not zero, the division is not exact, but is an application of Problem 15, Article 2–4.

The work should be arranged as shown in the example.

Example 2. Divide $3x^3 - 4x^2y + 5xy^2 + 6y^3$ by $x^2 - 2xy + 3y^2$.

Solution

$$
\begin{array}{r|l}
\text{(Dividend)}\quad 3x^3 - 4x^2y + 5xy^2 + 6y^3 & \ x^2 - 2xy + 3y^2 \quad \text{(Divisor)} \\
3x^3 - 6x^2y + 9xy^2 & \ \overline{3x + 2y} \qquad\qquad \text{(Quotient)} \\
\hline
\ 2x^2y - 4xy^2 + 6y^3 & \\
\ 2x^2y - 4xy^2 + 6y^3 & \\
\hline
\ 0 & \quad \text{(Remainder)}
\end{array}
$$

This result may be expressed in the form

$$\frac{3x^3 - 4x^2y + 5xy^2 + 6y^3}{x^2 - 2xy + 3y^2} \equiv 3x + 2y.$$

Example 3. Divide $5x^3 - 14x + 3$ by $x - 2$.

Solution. Since no x^2 term appears in the given dividend, the coefficient of that term is zero, and we have

$$
\begin{array}{r|l}
5x^3 + 0x^2 - 14x + 3 & \underline{\;x - 2\;} \\
\underline{5x^3 - 10x^2} & 5x^2 + 10x + 6 \\
\;10x^2 - 14x + 3 & \\
\;\underline{10x^2 - 20x} & \\
6x + 3 & \\
\underline{6x - 12} & \\
15 &
\end{array}
$$

This results in

$$\frac{5x^3 - 14x + 3}{x - 2} \equiv 5x^2 + 10x + 6 + \frac{15}{x - 2},$$

if x is not equal to 2.

A notation frequently used for a polynomial in x is the expression $P(x)$, read "P of x" (this expression does not mean P times x); likewise, a polynomial in x and y might be denoted $Q(x, y)$. In this notation, if $P(x)$ denotes the dividend, $D(x)$ the divisor, $Q(x)$ the quotient, and $R(x)$ the remainder of a division of two polynomials in x, our result could be stated

$$\frac{P(x)}{D(x)} \equiv Q(x) + \frac{R(x)}{D(x)}, \tag{3–8}$$

if $D(x)$ is not equal to zero, or

$$\boxed{P(x) \equiv Q(x) \cdot D(x) + R(x).} \tag{3–9}$$

(Note the similarity of this equation and the statement in Problem 15, Article 2–4.) Similarly, for division of two polynomials in x and y,

$$P(x, y) \equiv Q(x, y) \cdot D(x, y) + R(x, y). \tag{3–10}$$

Illustration 4. In Example 2 of this article,

$$
\begin{aligned}
P(x, y) &= 3x^3 - 4x^2y + 5xy^2 + 6y^3, & D(x, y) &= x^2 - 2xy + 3y^2, \\
Q(x, y) &= 3x + 2y, & R(x, y) &= 0.
\end{aligned}
$$

In Example 3,

$$
\begin{aligned}
P(x) &= 5x^3 - 14x + 3, & D(x) &= x - 2, \\
Q(x) &= 5x^2 + 10x + 6, & R(x) &= 15.
\end{aligned}
$$

PROBLEMS

Divide the following.

1. $9xy^2 - 6x^3$ by $3x$ 2. $4x^2y^3 - 24xy^4$ by $2xy^2$

3. $6x^3 - 9x^4y$ by $3xy$ 4. $-15x^2y^3 + 20x^3y^2$ by $-5x^2y^2$

5. $3x^2y - 4xy^2 + 6x^3y^3$ by xy

6. $7x^3y^2 - 14x^5y^3 + 28x^8y^5 - 21x^7y^6$ by $7x^3y^2$

Divide, finding the quotient and remainder, and write out the result of each problem in the form of Eq. (3–9) or (3–10).

7. $x^2 - 7x + 10$ by $x - 5$ 8. $2y^2 - 5y - 6$ by $2y - 1$

9. $3x^2 - 13x + 4$ by $x - 4$ 10. $2x^2 - 5x - 12$ by $2x + 3$

11. $2x^3 - 7x^2 + 11x - 4$ by $2x - 1$ 12. $y^3 - 4y^2 - 2 + 5y$ by $y - 1$

13. $x^2y - 6x^3 - 12xy^2 - 6y^3$ by $2x - 3y$

14. $2x^3 - 11x^2y + 13xy^2 - 4y^3$ by $x - 4y$

15. $4x^3 + 5 + 4x^2 - 13x$ by $2x + 5$

16. $4x^3 + 5x - 6$ by $2x - 3$

17. $5x^3 - 2x^2 + 3x - 4$ by $x^2 - 2x + 1$

18. $4x^2 + x - 6x^3 + 3$ by $3x^2 + 5$

19. $x^6 - y^6$ by $x - y$ 20. $x^7 - y^7$ by $x - y$

The process of division for polynomials in x (or any one letter) may be greatly simplified when the divisor is in the form $x - a$. This process, known as *synthetic division*, will be illustrated by using the problem of Example 3. Writing only the coefficients, we have

$$
\begin{array}{rr|rr}
5 + 0 - 14 & 3 & 1 - & 2 \\
5 - 10 & & 5 & 10 \qquad 6 \\
\cline{1-1}
10 - 14 & & \\
10 - 20 & & \\
\cline{1-1}
6 & 3 & \\
6 - 12 & & \\
\cline{2-2}
15 & & \\
\end{array}
$$

We next omit those coefficients that are definite repetitions: the first term in the 2nd, 4th, 6th, . . . lines and the second term in the 3rd, 5th, 7th, . . . lines. If we compress the remaining terms, write the first coefficient, 5, in the third line, and note that the 1 of the divisor can be omitted, we have

$$
\begin{array}{rrrr|r}
5 & +0 & -14 & 3 & -2 \\
& -10 & -20 & -12 & \\
\hline
5 & 10 & 6 & 15 & \\
\end{array}
$$

The coefficients of the quotient are also omitted, for they appear as the first three coefficients on the third line, while the remainder, 15, appears as the last number.

The final step of simplification is to replace the subtractions by additions, that is, to change the signs in the divisor (-2 to 2) and in the second line. Thus

$$
\begin{array}{rrrr|r}
5 & +0 & -14 & 3 & \ 2 \\
  & 10 & 20 & 12 & \\
\hline
5 & 10 & 6 & 15 &
\end{array}
$$

This arrangement represents the synthetic division of $5x^3 - 14x + 3$ by $x - 2$. It yields the quotient $5x^2 + 10x + 6$ and the remainder 15.

Let us summarize the process of synthetic division. To divide a polynomial $P(x)$ by a binomial $x - a$, arrange on a line (in order of descending power) the coefficients of $P(x)$, inserting zero for the coefficient of any missing power of x, and write a on the right. Bring down the first coefficient of $P(x)$ to the first position on the third line. Multiply this first coefficient by a, writing the product in the second line under the second coefficient of $P(x)$. The sum of this product and second coefficient is placed in the third line. Multiply this sum by a, add the product to the next coefficient of $P(x)$, again writing the new sum on the third line, and so on, until a product has been added to the final coefficient of $P(x)$.

The last sum in the third line represents the remainder. The preceding numbers represent the coefficients of the powers of x in the quotient, arranged in descending order. The quotient is a polynomial of degree one less than the degree of $P(x)$. The process of synthetic division will be very useful in later work.

Example 4. By synthetic division, find the quotient and the remainder of $2x^4 + 3x^3 - 4x^2 + 5x + 6$ divided by $x + 3$.

Solution. In this example $x - a = x - (-3)$, so that $a = -3$.

$$
\begin{array}{rrrrr|r}
2 & +3 & -4 & +5 & +6 & \ -3 \\
  & -6 & +9 & -15 & +30 & \\
\hline
2 & -3 & 5 & -10 & 36 &
\end{array}
$$

Thus the quotient is $2x^3 - 3x^2 + 5x - 10$, and the remainder is 36.

PROBLEMS

By synthetic division, find the quotient and the remainder in each of the following divisions.

1. $3x^2 - 2x - 4$ by $x - 3$
2. $2x^3 + 3x^2 - 7$ by $x + 1$
3. $x^3 - 2x^2 + 9$ by $x + 2$
4. $x^3 + 4x - 7$ by $x - 3$
5. $x^4 - 2x^3 - 3x^2 - 4x - 8$ by (a) $x - 2$, (b) $x + 1$
6. $2x^4 - x^3 - 18x^2 - 7$ by (a) $x + 3$, (b) $x - 3$
7. $3x^4 - 7x - 20$ by (a) $x - 2$, (b) $x + 2$
8. $2x^4 - 3x^3 - 20x^2 - 6$ by (a) $x - 4$, (b) $x + 3$

Use synthetic division to find the quotient and remainder in the following divisions and express the answer in the form of Eq. (3–9).

9. $x^3 - 2x^2 + 3x - 4$ by $x - 3$

10. $2x^3 + x^2 - x + 4$ by $x + 1$

11. $x^4 - 5x^3 + x^2 - 6$ by $x - 1$

12. $x^3 + 3x^2 - 2x - 5$ by $x + 2$

13. Find the value of $x^3 - 2x^2 + 3x - 4$ at $x = 3$.

14. Find the value of $2x^3 + x^2 - x + 4$ at $x = -1$.

15. Find the value of $x^4 - 5x^3 + x^2 - 6$ at $x = 1$.

16. Find the value of $x^3 + 3x^2 - 2x - 5$ at $x = -2$.

17. Compare the values obtained in Problems 13 through 16 with the remainders in Problems 9 through 12.

18. a) Evaluate $ax^2 + bx + c$ at $x = p$.

b) Divide $ax^2 + bx + c$ by $x - p$.

c) Compare the remainder found in (b) with the value obtained in (a).

d) Would you expect the same type of result for any degree polynomial?

3–4 SPECIAL PRODUCTS

There are certain special products which occur so frequently in algebra that they have been classified. These are given below. *The letters in the formulas may stand for any algebraic expression.* Each is a direct result of the axioms in Chapter 2. The reader should not only verify each by actually carrying out the steps and giving the reasons, but also memorize them, so that he can recognize both the product from the factors and the factors from the product.

$$a(x + y) \equiv ax + ay. \tag{3–11}$$

$$(x + y)(x - y) \equiv x^2 - y^2. \tag{3–12}$$

$$(x \pm y)^2 \equiv x^2 \pm 2xy + y^2. \tag{3–13}*$$

$$(x + a)(x + b) \equiv x^2 + (a + b)x + ab. \tag{3–14}$$

$$(ax + b)(cx + d) \equiv acx^2 + (ad + bc)x + bd. \tag{3–15}$$

$$(x \pm y)^3 \equiv x^3 \pm 3x^2y + 3xy^2 \pm y^3. \tag{3–16}$$

$$(x \pm y)(x^2 \mp xy + y^2) \equiv x^3 \pm y^3. \tag{3–17}$$

The reader should determine which of the above formulas is used in the following illustrations.

---

* The sign $\pm$ is read "plus or minus." If the upper (lower) sign is used in the left member, it is also used in the right, so that $(x \pm y)^2 \equiv x^2 \pm 2xy + y^2$ means $(x + y)^2 \equiv x^2 + 2xy + y^2$ and $(x - y)^2 \equiv x^2 - 2xy + y^2$.

Illustration 1. $(2x^2 - 3y)(2x^2 + 3y) \equiv (2x^2)^2 - (3y)^2$
$$\equiv 4x^4 - 9y^2.$$

Illustration 2. $(x + 2)(x + 5) \equiv x^2 + (2 + 5)x + 10$
$$\equiv x^2 + 7x + 10.$$

Illustration 3. $(3x + 4y)(2x - 3y) \equiv 6x^2 + (-9 + 8)xy - 12y^2$
$$\equiv 6x^2 - xy - 12y^2.$$

Illustration 4

$(x + y - 1)^3 \equiv [(x + y) - 1]^3$
$$\equiv (x + y)^3 - 3(x + y)^2 + 3(x + y) - 1$$
$$\equiv x^3 + 3x^2y + 3xy^2 + y^3 - 3x^2 - 6xy - 3y^2 + 3x + 3y - 1.$$

Here $(x + y)$ is considered first as one term.

Illustration 5

$(3x + 2y)(9x^2 - 6xy + 4y^2) \equiv (3x + 2y)[(3x)^2 - (3x)(2y) + (2y)^2]$
$$\equiv (3x)^3 + (2y)^3$$
$$\equiv 27x^3 + 8y^3.$$

PROBLEMS

Find the following products.

1. $2a(3x - 4y)$
2. $-3x(2x + 7y)$
3. $-7xy(3x^2 + 4y)$
4. $4x^2yz(z^2 + xy + yz)$
5. $(2x - 3y)(2x + 3y)$
6. $(7x + 5y^2)(7x - 5y^2)$
7. $(x + 2y)(x - 2y)(x^2 + 4y^2)$
8. $(x - 3)^2$
9. $(2x + 7y)^2$
10. $(3x^2y - 5z^2)^2$
11. $(x - 2)(x - 5)$
12. $(2x + 3)(x - 5)$
13. $(xy^2 - z^2w)^2$
14. $(\frac{1}{2}x + \frac{2}{3}y)^2$
15. $(4x - 3y)(7x + 3y)$
16. $[(x + 1) - z][(x + 1) + z]$
17. $(2x + 3y + 3)(2x + 3y - 3)$
18. $(2x + 3y + 4z)^2$
19. $(x - 2y - z)^2$
20. $(2a + b)^3$
21. $(x + 2)(x^2 - 2x + 4)$
22. $(x - 3)(x^2 + 3x + 9)$
23. $(x + 3y + 2z - 4w)(x + 3y - 2z + 4w)$
24. $(4x - 2y - 3z + 3w)(4x + 2y + 3z + 3w)$
25. $(a - b + c - d)^2$
26. $(2a + 3b - c - 4d)^2$
27. $[2(x + 2y) - 3][2(x + 2y) + 4]$
28. $[2(x - 3y) + 5][3(x - 3y) - 2]$
29. $(2x + 3y)^3$
30. $(5x - 3y)^3$

3–5 FACTORS AND FACTORING

The process of factoring an algebraic expression is similar to that of finding the factors of a composite number. Recall the discussion of prime and composite integers in Article 1–4. This process, which is usually restricted at this elementary stage to factoring polynomials with rational coefficients and to factors completely free from irrational numbers, is frequently performed by reversing the processes considered in Article 3–4. Such a factorization is considered complete when each algebraic factor is a *prime factor;* that is, an algebraic expression that cannot be factored without violating the above restrictions.

The more common types of factoring are illustrated below. Note the importance and application of the distributive axioms in this discussion.

Example 1. Factor $2ax^2 - 4ay^2 + 8a^2x$.

Solution. The polynomial in this problem has $2a$ as a common factor.

$$2ax^2 - 4ay^2 + 8a^2x \equiv 2a(x^2 - 2y^2 + 4ax).$$

Example 2. Factor $x(a + 2b) - 3y(a + 2b)$.

Solution. Each of the two expressions has the common term $(a + 2b)$. Therefore,

$$x(a + 2b) - 3y(a + 2b) \equiv (x - 3y)(a + 2b).$$

Example 3. Factor $(4x^2/y^2) - (9a - b)^2$.

Solution. This expression is the difference between two perfect squares.

$$\frac{4x^2}{y^2} - (9a - b)^2 \equiv \left(\frac{2x}{y}\right)^2 - (9a - b)^2$$

$$\equiv \left[\frac{2x}{y} + (9a - b)\right]\left[\frac{2x}{y} - (9a - b)\right]$$

$$\equiv \left(\frac{2x}{y} + 9a - b\right)\left(\frac{2x}{y} - 9a + b\right).$$

Example 4. Factor $9x^2 - 30xy + 25y^2$.

Solution. This algebraic expression is a perfect square.

$$9x^2 - 30xy + 25y^2 \equiv (3x - 5y)^2.$$

Example 5. Factor $27x^3 + (8/y^3)$.

Solution. The algebraic expression is the sum of two cubes. Accordingly,

$$27x^3 + \frac{8}{y^3} \equiv \left(3x + \frac{2}{y}\right)\left(9x^2 - \frac{6x}{y} + \frac{4}{y^2}\right).$$

Example 6. Factor $12x^2 + 7xy - 10y^2$.

Solution. This trinomial in the form of Eq. (3–15) is factored by trial and error. The result will be in the form $(ax + by)(cx + dy)$, where $ac = 12$, $bd = -10$, and $ad + bc = 7$. Here a and c are both plus, and b and d are different in sign. The correct combination, we find, is $12x^2 + 7xy - 10y^2 \equiv (4x + 5y)(3x - 2y)$.

Example 7. Factor $6x^4 + 7x^2y^2 - 3y^4$.

Solution. This is the same type as Example 6.

$$6x^4 + 7x^2y^2 - 3y^4 \equiv (3x^2 - y^2)(2x^2 + 3y^2).$$

Although the first term on the right is the difference of two squares, it cannot be factored further, for such factorization would introduce irrational quantities.

PROBLEMS

Factor the following completely.

1. $4x - 20$
2. $10x + 15yz$
3. $3y^2 - 9y$
4. $4x^3y^2 + 6x^2y^3$
5. $xy^2z^3 - 3x^2yz^2 + 5xy^3z^2$
6. $a^2b^3c^4 - a^3b^4c^5 + 2a^2b^4c^4$
7. $3y(2x + 5) - 4x(2x + 5)$
8. $3y(4 - y) + 6x^2(4 - y)$
9. $2z^2(x + 3y) - 6xz(x + 3y)$
10. $3x(3 - 2y) - 2xy(3 - 2y)$
11. $9 - a^2$
12. $16x^2 - 9y^2$
13. $225a^8 - 64b^2$
14. $(c^6/d^8) - 121$
15. $x^3y^4 - 25xd^6$
16. $0.01x^4 - 196y^8$
17. $(x + 2y)^2 - z^2$
18. $(3x - 2y)^2 - 25z^2$
19. $(a + b)^2 - (c + d)^2$
20. $9(2x - y)^2 - 4(2a + b)^2$
21. $81(4x - 3y)^2 - 25(3z + w)^2$
22. $x^2 + 6x + 9 - (y^2 + 4y + 4)$
23. $x^2 - 8x + 16$
24. $4a^2 - 12ab + 9b^2$
25. $66xy + 9x^2y^2 + 121$
26. $2x^3 - 28x^2 + 98x$
27. $5z^2 - 30wz + 45w^2$
28. $x^{2n} + 2x^ny^n + y^{2n}$
29. $(3 - x)^2 + 8(3 - x) + 16$
30. $25 - 30(2x - 3y) + 9(2x - 3y)^2$
31. $a^3 - 8$
32. $1 + (8/x^9)$
33. $8x^{6n} + 27y^{3m}$
34. $x^3 - (y^3/64)$
35. $27(x - y)^3 - 8(x + y)^3$
36. $5(a - 2b)^3 - 625(a - 2b)^3$
37. $x^2 - 7x + 12$
38. $y^2 - 2y - 8$
39. $a^2b^2 - ab - 20$
40. $2x^2 + 8x + 6$
41. $35x^2 - 24x + 4$
42. $3y^2 - y - 10$
43. $6a^2 + 7a - 20$
44. $2x^2 - 23xy - 39y^2$
45. $(x + y)^2 - 7(x + y) + 10$
46. $(y + z)^2 + (y + z) - 42$
47. $2(2x + y)^2 - (2x + y) - 10$
48. $6(x + y)^2 + 5(x + y)(y + z) - 6(y + z)^2$
49. $12(a + b)^2 - 14(a + b)(c + d) - 10(c + d)^2$
50. $4(x - 2)^2 + 5(x - 2)(y + 4) - 21(y + 4)^2$

There are many algebraic expressions which, by proper grouping, can be put into one of the forms in the previous examples and then factored.

Example 8. Factor $ax - ay - bx + by$.

Solution. If, by the associative axiom, we group the first two terms together, and the last two together, and (use the distributive axiom) factor out the common term, we transform the expression into the form of Example 2.

$$ax - ay - bx + by \equiv a(x - y) - b(x - y)$$
$$\equiv (x - y)(a - b).$$

Example 9. Factor $4x^3 - 12x^2 - x + 3$.

Solution. Again we group the first two terms and the last two terms.

$$4x^3 - 12x^2 - x + 3 \equiv 4x^2(x - 3) - (x - 3)$$
$$\equiv (x - 3)(4x^2 - 1)$$
$$\equiv (x - 3)(2x + 1)(2x - 1).$$

In both these examples we could have grouped the first and third, and the second and fourth terms, and obtained the same result.

Example 10. Factor $4x^2 - 12xy + 9y^2 + 4x - 6y - 3$.

Solution. If we group the first three terms, the solution becomes clear.

$$4x^2 - 12xy + 9y^2 + 4x - 6y - 3 \equiv (2x - 3y)^2 + 2(2x - 3y) - 3$$
$$\equiv [(2x - 3y) + 3][(2x - 3y) - 1]$$
$$\equiv (2x - 3y + 3)(2x - 3y - 1).$$

Example 11. Factor $x^4 + 2x^2y^2 + 9y^4$.

Solution. If the coefficient of the second term were 6, the expression would be a perfect square. Therefore, if we add (and subtract) $4x^2y^2$, our solution becomes evident.

$$x^4 + 2x^2y^2 + 9y^4 \equiv x^4 + 6x^2y^2 + 9y^4 - 4x^2y^2$$
$$\equiv (x^2 + 3y^2)^2 - (2xy)^2$$
$$\equiv (x^2 + 3y^2 + 2xy)(x^2 + 3y^2 - 2xy).$$

PROBLEMS

Factor the following expressions.

1. $ax - ay - by + bx$

2. $ax - 2ay - 6by + 3bx$

3. $x^3 - 2x^2 + 4x - 8$

4. $y^3 - 2y^2 + 5y - 10$

5. $2a - 6 - ab^2 + 3b^2$

6. $x^3 + 3x^2 - 9x - 27$

7. $x^2 - 2x + 1 - y^2$

8. $xy^3 + 2y^2 - xy - 2$

9. $4x^2 - y^2 + 4y - 4$ **10.** $x^6 - 7x^3 - 8$

11. $x^2 + 2xy + y^2 - z^2 + 2zw - w^2$

12. $4a^2 - x^2 + b^2 - y^2 - 4ab - 2xy$

13. $x^2 + 4xy + 4y^2 - x - 2y - 6$

14. $x^3 - 5x^2 - x + 5$ **15.** $x^4 - 7x^2y^2 + 9y^4$

16. $y^4 + y^2 + 25$ **17.** $a^4 + 2a^2b^2 + 9b^4$

18. $x^4 + 5x^2 + 9$ **19.** $b^4 + 6b^2c^2 + 25c^2$

20. $25x^2 + 30xy + 9y^2 + 15x + 9y + 2$

21. $3ax - 6ay + 4bx - 8by + cx - 2cy$

22. $20xy + 7zw - 5yz - 28xw$ **23.** $z^4 + 4z^3 - 2z - 8$

24. $x^4 + 4y^4$ **25.** $a^8 - b^8$

26. $x^6 + 1$ **27.** $x^2 + 2xy - z^2 - 2yz$

28. $(x^2 + 2x - 3)^2 - 4$ **29.** $(x - y - 2z)^2 - (2x + y - z)^2$

30. $2(x + 2)^2(x - 3) + 3(x + 2)(x - 3)^2$

3–6 SIMPLIFICATION OF FRACTIONS

A basic principle for fractions, algebraic as well as arithmetic, states that the value of a fraction is not changed if its numerator and denominator are both multiplied or both divided by the same quantity (not zero). This principle was stated in Theorem 2–8. Hence, the simplification or reduction of a fraction to lowest terms is always possible. Factor both the numerator and denominator into their prime factors and, by using the basic principle, divide the numerator and denominator by the product of all their common factors.

Example 1. Reduce $(8x^4y^7)/(12x^6y^3)$ to lowest terms.

Solution
$$\frac{8x^4y^7}{12x^6y^3} = \frac{2^3x^4y^7}{2^2 \cdot 3x^6y^3} = \frac{2^2x^4y^3 \cdot 2y^4}{2^2x^4y^3 \cdot 3x^2}.$$

By dividing both numerator and denominator by $2^2x^4y^3$, we have

$$\frac{8x^4y^7}{12x^6y^3} = \frac{2y^4}{3x^2}.$$

Example 2. Reduce $(x^2 - 7x + 10)/(2x^2 - x - 6)$ to lowest terms.

Solution. If we factor both numerator and denominator, we have

$$\frac{x^2 - 7x + 10}{2x^2 - x - 6} = \frac{(x - 5)(x - 2)}{(2x + 3)(x - 2)},$$

and dividing both numerator and denominator by $x - 2$, that is, applying Theorem 2–8, we get

$$\frac{x^2 - 7x + 10}{2x^2 - x - 6} = \frac{x - 5}{2x + 3}.$$

The elimination of a common factor by dividing the numerator and denominator of a fraction by this factor is called *multiplicative cancellation*. Such a process should be done with care, for Theorem 2–8 is true only when $x \neq 0$. In this case the identity is true for all values of x except $x = 2$ or $x = -\frac{3}{2}$, which are not permissible values.

Example 3. Reduce $(12x^2 + 30x - 72)/(52x - 8x^2 - 60)$ to lowest terms.

Solution. $\dfrac{12x^2 + 30x - 72}{52x - 8x^2 - 60} \equiv \dfrac{6(2x - 3)(x + 4)}{4(3 - 2x)(x - 5)} \equiv \dfrac{3(x + 4)}{2(5 - x)}$.

This identity follows from the fact that $2x - 3 = -(3 - 2x)$. (Recall Problem 4, Article 2–4.)

PROBLEMS

Reduce the following to lowest terms.

1. $\dfrac{28}{63}$

2. $\dfrac{27x^3}{225x^5}$

3. $\dfrac{a^4x^3y}{a^2xy^3}$

4. $\dfrac{a^2 + ab}{3a + 2a^3}$

5. $\dfrac{a^2x - a^2y}{ax^2 - ay^2}$

6. $\dfrac{24a^2}{6a^2 - 9a}$

7. $\dfrac{x^2 - 1}{x^2 - x}$

8. $\dfrac{x^2 - 4x + 4}{x^2 - 4}$

9. $\dfrac{x^2 - 16}{x^2 - 8x + 16}$

10. $\dfrac{a^2 - 3a - 4}{a^2 - a - 12}$

11. $\dfrac{y^2 - y - 6}{y^2 + 2y - 15}$

12. $\dfrac{2x^2 + 5x - 12}{4x^2 - 4x - 3}$

13. $\dfrac{6a^2 - 7a - 3}{4a^2 - 8a + 3}$

14. $\dfrac{ax + ay - bx - by}{am - bm - an + bn}$

15. $\dfrac{14x - 24 - 2x^2}{x^2 + x - 20}$

16. $\dfrac{(4x^2 - 9y^2)(18x - 12)}{(2x - 3y)(12x - 8)}$

17. $\dfrac{x^2 - 36}{x^3 - 216}$

18. $\dfrac{2x^2 - 14x + 20}{7x - 2x^2 - 6}$

19. $\dfrac{2(x^2 - y^2)xy + x^4 - y^4}{x^4 - y^4}$

20. $\dfrac{y^6 + 64}{y^4 - 4y^2 + 16}$

21. $\dfrac{4a^2 - 1}{12a^2 + a - 4a^3 - 3}$

22. $\dfrac{a^2 - 2ab + 3b^2}{a^4 + 2a^2b^2 + 9b^4}$

23. $\dfrac{(x^2 - 16)(x^2 - 4x + 16)}{x^3 + 64}$

24. $\dfrac{15ab - 20a - 21b + 28}{21 - a - 10a^2}$

3–7 ADDITION OF FRACTIONS

The algebraic sum of two or more fractions having the same denominator is a fraction with the common denominator and a numerator which is the algebraic sum of the numerators of the fractions considered. This was proved in Problem 13, Article 2–4.

Illustration. $\dfrac{2x^2}{x-4} - \dfrac{3x}{x-4} + \dfrac{5}{x-4} \equiv \dfrac{2x^2 - 3x + 5}{x-4}.$

To find the algebraic sum of two or more fractions with different denominators, we must replace the fractions with equivalent fractions having the same denominators. It is preferable to use the *least common denominator* (LCD). The LCD of two or more fractions consists of the product of all the unique prime factors in the denominators, each with an exponent equal to the largest exponent with which the factor appears, and is really a result of the following important theorem.

Theorem 3–5. $\dfrac{a}{b} + \dfrac{c}{d} \equiv \dfrac{ad + bc}{bd}$ $(b, d \neq 0)$

Proof. We have

$$\frac{a}{b} + \frac{c}{d} \equiv \frac{ad}{bd} + \frac{bc}{bd},$$

by Theorem 2–8. If we now use Problem 13, Article 2–4, we have

$$\frac{ad}{bd} + \frac{bc}{bd} \equiv \frac{ad + bc}{bd},$$

which is our required result.

Example 1. Find the LCD of the fractions

$$\frac{3x}{x^2 - 4x + 4}, \quad \frac{5x^2}{3(x^2 - 4)}, \quad \frac{2}{2x^2 - x - 6}.$$

Solution. Factoring each denominator, we have

$$x^2 - 4x + 4 \equiv (x - 2)^2,$$
$$3(x^2 - 4) \equiv 3(x + 2)(x - 2),$$
$$2x^2 - x - 6 \equiv (2x + 3)(x - 2).$$

The LCD is $3(x + 2)(x - 2)^2(2x + 3)$.

After the LCD has been determined, equivalent fractions may be formed. Divide the LCD of a given fraction by the denominator of that fraction, and then multiply both numerator and denominator of the given fraction by the result. The equivalent fractions may now be added, as in the illustration above.

Example 2. Change the following fractions to equivalent ones, with their LCD as denominator, and find their sum.

$$\frac{4}{x + 2}, \quad \frac{x + 3}{x^2 - 4}, \quad \frac{2x + 1}{x - 2}.$$

Solution. The LCD is $(x + 2)(x - 2)$. Therefore,

$$\frac{4}{x + 2} \equiv \frac{4(x - 2)}{(x + 2)(x - 2)}, \quad \frac{x + 3}{x^2 - 4} \equiv \frac{x + 3}{(x + 2)(x - 2)},$$

$$\frac{2x + 1}{x - 2} \equiv \frac{(2x + 1)(x + 2)}{(x + 2)(x - 2)},$$

and

$$\frac{4}{x + 2} + \frac{x + 3}{x^2 - 4} + \frac{2x + 1}{x - 2}$$

$$\equiv \frac{4(x - 2)}{(x + 2)(x - 2)} + \frac{x + 3}{(x + 2)(x - 2)} + \frac{(2x + 1)(x + 2)}{(x + 2)(x - 2)}$$

$$\equiv \frac{(4x - 8) + (x + 3) + (2x^2 + 5x + 2)}{x^2 - 4}$$

$$\equiv \frac{2x^2 + 10x - 3}{x^2 - 4}.$$

PROBLEMS

Reduce the following to single fractions and simplify.

1. $\frac{2}{3} + \frac{5}{6} - \frac{3}{10}$

2. $5 - \frac{4}{9} - \frac{7}{15}$

3. $\frac{3x}{4y} - \frac{4y}{3x}$

4. $\frac{a^2}{b} - \frac{b^2}{a}$

5. $\frac{2x + 3}{6} - \frac{4x - 7}{9}$

6. $\frac{3x - 1}{5} + \frac{4 - 5x}{6}$

7. $x + y + \frac{x^2}{x - y}$

8. $\frac{x + 1}{x + 2} - \frac{x + 3}{x}$

9. $\frac{3x - 2y}{5x - 3} + \frac{2x - y}{3 - 5x}$

10. $\frac{2}{12x^2 - 3} + \frac{3}{2x - 4x^2}$

11. $\frac{5}{x} - \frac{4}{y} + \frac{3}{z}$

12. $\frac{4}{x^2 - 4x - 5} + \frac{2}{x^2 - 1}$

13. $\frac{2x - 1}{4 - x} + \frac{x + 2}{3x - 12}$

14. $\frac{x + 5}{x^2 + 7x + 10} - \frac{x - 1}{x^2 + 5x + 6}$

15. $\frac{x - 1}{2x^2 - 13x + 15} + \frac{x + 3}{2x^2 - 15x + 18}$

16. $\frac{2x + 3}{3x^2 + x - 2} - \frac{3x - 4}{2x^2 - 3x - 5}$

17. $\frac{3}{a - 3} + \frac{a^2 + 2}{a^3 - 27}$

18. $\frac{2xy}{x^3 + y^3} - \frac{x}{x^2 - xy + y^2}$

19. $\dfrac{2}{x^2 + 3x + 2} - \dfrac{3}{x^2 + 5x + 6} - \dfrac{4}{x^2 + 4x + 3}$

20. $x + 6 + \dfrac{5x + 1}{12x^2 + 5x - 2} - \dfrac{x}{3x + 2}$

21. $2y - 3 + \dfrac{y - 2}{4y^2 - 12y + 9} + \dfrac{y + 2}{2y^2 - y - 3}$

22. $\dfrac{1}{(x - y)(y - z)} + \dfrac{1}{(y - z)(z - x)} + \dfrac{1}{(z - x)(x - y)}$

23. $\dfrac{x}{(x - y)(y - z)} + \dfrac{y}{(y - z)(z - x)} + \dfrac{z}{(z - x)(x - y)}$

24. $\dfrac{2x - 1}{2x^2 - x - 6} + \dfrac{x + 3}{6x^2 + x - 12} - \dfrac{2x - 3}{3x^2 - 10x + 8}$

3–8 MULTIPLICATION AND DIVISION OF FRACTIONS

In algebra, as in arithmetic, the product of two or more fractions is a fraction whose numerator is the product of all numerators and whose denominator is the product of all denominators. In obtaining these products, the process of dividing out factors common to the numerator and denominator may be used. Results should be reduced to their simplest form. Note in Illustration 1 that this method is a direct application of Theorem 2–7, followed by an application of Theorem 2–8.

Illustration 1.
$$\frac{x - 4}{2x + 8} \cdot \frac{4x + 8}{x^2 - 16} = \frac{(x - 4) \cdot 2^2 \cdot (x + 2)}{2(x + 4)(x + 4)(x - 4)}$$
$$= \frac{2(x + 2)}{(x + 4)^2}.$$

We now have need for a theorem which will establish an expression for the division of two fractions.

Theorem 3–6. $\dfrac{a}{b} \div \dfrac{c}{d} \equiv \dfrac{a/b}{c/d} \equiv \dfrac{a}{b} \cdot \dfrac{d}{c}$ $\quad (b, c, d \neq 0).$

Proof. (Give the reasons for each step.)

$$\frac{a/b}{c/d} \equiv \frac{(a/b) \cdot (d/c)}{(c/d) \cdot (d/c)} \equiv \frac{(a/b) \cdot (d/c)}{(cd)/(cd)} \equiv \frac{(a/b) \cdot (d/c)}{1} \equiv \frac{a}{b} \cdot \frac{d}{c}.$$

As a result of this theorem, we are able to state a rule. The quotient of two fractions is the fraction formed by multiplying the dividend by the divisor inverted.

Illustration 2.
$$\frac{3x - 15}{x + 3} \div \frac{12x + 18}{4x + 12} = \frac{3x - 15}{x + 3} \cdot \frac{4x + 12}{12x + 18}$$
$$= \frac{3(x - 5)}{x + 3} \cdot \frac{4(x + 3)}{6(2x + 3)}$$
$$= \frac{2(x - 5)}{2x + 3}.$$

PROBLEMS

Perform the indicated operations on the following simple fractions, and reduce the results to simplest form.

1. $\frac{4}{3} \cdot \frac{5}{7}$

2. $\frac{3}{7} \div \frac{13}{11}$

3. $\frac{5}{8} \cdot \frac{4}{15}$

4. $\frac{4}{7} \div \frac{16}{21}$

5. $\frac{7}{22} \cdot \frac{33}{35}$

6. $\frac{6}{7} \div \frac{8}{9}$

7. $\dfrac{3x^3}{4y^2} \cdot \dfrac{5y}{x^2}$

8. $\dfrac{7a}{12b^3} \cdot \dfrac{20b^5}{35a^3}$

9. $\dfrac{40x^3y^2}{24xy^4} \div \dfrac{27xy}{8x^2y^3}$

10. $\dfrac{xy^3}{yz} \div x^2z$

11. $\dfrac{x^2 - y^2}{x^3 - y^3} \div \dfrac{x + y}{x}$

12. $\dfrac{x^2 - 2x + y^2}{x^3 - y^3} \cdot \dfrac{x^2 + xy + y^2}{x - y}$

13. $\dfrac{x^2 - 6x + 9}{x^2 - 7x + 12} \cdot \dfrac{x^3 - 4x^2 + 9x - 36}{x^4 - 81}$

14. $\dfrac{y^2 - 2y - 15}{y^2 - 9} \div \dfrac{12 - 4y}{y^2 - 6y + 9}$

15. $\dfrac{x^2 + 2x - 3}{x^2 + 7x + 12} \cdot \dfrac{x + 1}{x^2 + 4x - 5}$

16. $\dfrac{2x^2 - 3x - 14}{2x^2 - 3x - 5} \cdot \dfrac{2x^2 - x - 10}{2x^2 - 5x - 7}$

17. $\dfrac{y + 1}{x - 2} \cdot \dfrac{x^2 + 2x}{6} \cdot \dfrac{y - 1}{xy^2 - x}$

18. $\dfrac{ab + ac}{ab - ac} \cdot \dfrac{b}{b + c} \div \dfrac{b}{b - c}$

19. $\dfrac{x^4 - y^4}{(x - y)^2} \cdot \dfrac{y^2}{x^2 + y^2} \cdot \dfrac{x - y}{xy + y^2}$

20. $(a^2 - b^2) \div \left[\dfrac{a^2 + ab}{b^2 + ab} \div \dfrac{a^2 - ab}{b^2 - ab} \right]$

21. $\dfrac{9x^2 + 6x - 8}{6x^2 + 5x - 4} \cdot \dfrac{2x^2 - 7x - 4}{2x^2 - 5x - 12} \cdot \dfrac{4x^2 + 4x - 3}{6x^2 - x - 2}$

22. $\left[\dfrac{y^3 + 4y^2 - 5y}{y^2 - 2y + 1} \div \dfrac{y^2 + y - 2}{y^4 + 8y} \right] \cdot \dfrac{y - 4}{y^2 - 2y + 4}$

23. $\left[\dfrac{2x}{x - 1} + \dfrac{x^2}{x^2 - 1} \right] \div \dfrac{x^3}{1 - x}$

24. $\left[\dfrac{3x}{x - 3} - \dfrac{3x + 2}{x^2 - 6x + 9} \right] \cdot \left[\dfrac{x + 2}{x + 3} - \dfrac{x}{x^2 + 6x + 9} \right]$

Most of the fractions considered have been simple fractions. Any fraction which contains one or more other fractions in either numerator or denominator, or in both, is called a *complex* fraction. It may be simplified by reducing the numerator and denominator to single fractions and then dividing.

Example. Simplify

$$\dfrac{a - \dfrac{1}{a}}{a - \dfrac{1}{a^2}}.$$

Solution

$$\frac{a - \dfrac{1}{a}}{a - \dfrac{1}{a^2}} \equiv \frac{a^2 - 1}{a} \div \frac{a^3 - 1}{a^2}$$

$$\equiv \frac{(a + 1)(a - 1)}{a} \cdot \frac{a^2}{(a - 1)(a^2 + a + 1)}$$

$$\equiv \frac{a(a + 1)}{a^2 + a + 1} \cdot$$

PROBLEMS

1. $\dfrac{3 + \dfrac{4}{5}}{\dfrac{2}{3} - 1}$

2. $\dfrac{\dfrac{a}{b} + \dfrac{a}{c}}{ab + ac}$

3. $\dfrac{x - \dfrac{x}{y}}{z - \dfrac{z}{y}}$

4. $\dfrac{\dfrac{4x}{5} + \dfrac{2y}{3}}{\dfrac{3x}{5} - \dfrac{3y}{4}}$

5. $\dfrac{\dfrac{2}{x} + \dfrac{5}{y}}{\dfrac{2}{x} - \dfrac{5}{y}}$

6. $\dfrac{\dfrac{1}{x} + \dfrac{1}{y}}{\dfrac{1}{x^2} - \dfrac{1}{y^2}}$

7. $\dfrac{x^2 - \dfrac{1}{x}}{x + 1 + \dfrac{1}{x}}$

8. $\dfrac{\dfrac{1}{2} - \dfrac{4}{x^3}}{\dfrac{1}{x^2} + \dfrac{1}{4} + \dfrac{1}{2x}}$

9. $\dfrac{\dfrac{9x^2 - 4y^2}{x - y}}{\dfrac{y - 2x}{} - 1}$ $\dfrac{9x^2 - 4y^2}{x - y}\Big/\left(\dfrac{}{y - 2x} - 1\right)$

10. $\dfrac{\dfrac{x}{y} + \dfrac{y^2}{x^2}}{\dfrac{y}{x^2} - \dfrac{1}{x} + \dfrac{1}{y}}$

11. $\dfrac{x + \dfrac{y}{x + y}}{x + y - \dfrac{x}{x + y}}$

12. $\dfrac{a}{1 - \dfrac{1}{1 + \dfrac{1}{a - 1}}}$

3-9 INTEGRAL AND ZERO EXPONENTS

In Article 3–2 we discussed the meaning of a^n $(a \neq 0)$ where n was any positive integer. To define a^n where n is any integer, positive, negative, or zero $(n \in I)$, we may use the theorems on exponents [Eqs. (3–2) through (3–7)]. We recall from Eq. (3–7) that $a^n/a^n = 1$. If Eq. (3–5) were permissible, we would have $a^{n-n} = a^0 = 1$. This is not permissible because m must not equal n, but we can now use this relationship and Eq. (3–6) to justify the following definitions.

Definition 3–2. For any $a \in R$ $(a \neq 0)$,

$$\boxed{a^0 \equiv 1.}$$ (3–18)

·*Definition 3–3.* For any $a \in R$ $(a \neq 0)$ and any positive integer n,

$$\boxed{a^{-n} \equiv \frac{1}{a^n} \cdot}$$ (3–19)

We now have the resulting theorems.

Theorem 3–7. For any $a \in R$ ($a \neq 0$) and any n and $m \in I$,

$$a^n a^m \equiv a^{n+m},$$ (3–20)

$$(ab)^n \equiv a^n b^n,$$ (3–21)

$$(a^n)^m \equiv a^{nm},$$ (3–22)

and

$$\frac{a^n}{a^m} \equiv a^{n-m}.$$ (3–23)

Proof. The proofs follow directly from the previous definitions and are left as exercises.

Illustrations

$$5^0 = 1, \qquad 2x^0 = 2 \cdot 1 = 2, \qquad (2x^2 y)^0 = 1,$$

$$x^{-2} \equiv \frac{1}{x^2}, \qquad (x^3)^4 = x^{12}, \qquad \frac{x^3}{x^5} \equiv x^{-2} \equiv \frac{1}{x^2}.$$

PROBLEMS

Remove the negative and zero exponents and simplify the following expressions.

1. $8x^0$

2. $(8x)^0$

3. $3x^{-2} y^4$

4. $5y^{-2} x^3 z^0$

5. $\dfrac{2x^3 y^{-2}}{3x^{-2} y^3}$

6. $\dfrac{4x^{-2} y^4}{6x^{-5} y^{-2}}$

7. $\dfrac{a^{-1} + b^{-1}}{(cd)^{-1}}$

8. $\dfrac{x^{-2} + y^{-2}}{x^{-1} + y^{-1}}$

9. $\dfrac{a^{-1} + b^{-1}}{(a + b)^{-1}}$

10. $(a^{-1} + b^{-1})^{-1}$

11. $(x^n y^2)^m$

12. $(-1)^n (-1)^m (-1)^1$

13. Prove Theorem 3–7, (a) Eq. (3–20); (b) Eq. (3–21).

14. Prove Theorem 3–7, (a) Eq. (3–22); (b) Eq. (3–23).

3–10 RATIONAL EXPONENTS

In the previous article we extended our definitions involving exponents to zero and negative integers, and now we shall extend the definitions to rational exponents.

Definition 3–4. Any number a whose nth power (n is any positive integer) is equal to b and which satisfies the equation $a^n = b$, is called an nth root of b.

We recall, for example, that either 2 or -2 is a square root of 4, since $2^2 = 4$ and $(-2)^2 = 4$. Similarly, since $(-2)^3 = -8$, -2 is a cube root of -8. In general, every number except zero has exactly n distinct nth roots, although most or all of them may be imaginary numbers.* In many cases it is convenient to have a principal nth root defined. The *principal nth root of a positive number* is the positive root. The *principal nth root of a negative number* is the negative root if n is odd. If n is even and the number is negative, no principal nth root is defined, for no real value exists. (Consider, for example, the equation $x^2 = -4$.) The symbol $\sqrt[n]{b}$ means the principal nth root; n is called the index and b the *radicand* of the *radical*.

Illustration 1. $\sqrt{9} = 3$, $\sqrt[3]{-8} = -2$, and $\sqrt[4]{81} = 3$ are the principal square root, cube root, and fourth root of 9, -8 and 81, respectively.

We are now able to extend the theorems concerning exponents to the case where $n \in F$. Consider any rational value p/q, where p and q are any two relatively prime positive integers. If $n = 1/q$ where q is any positive integer, and we wish to have our result consistent with Eq. (3-2), that is, we wish to have

$$\underbrace{b^{1/q} \cdot b^{1/q} \cdot b^{1/q} \cdots b^{1/q}}_{q \text{ factors } b^{1/q}} \equiv b^{q/q} \equiv b, \tag{3-24}$$

we must define $b^{1/q}$ as a qth root of b. In fact, the symbol $b^{1/q}$ is defined as the principal qth root. Likewise, if Eq. (3-3) is to be satisfied, we must define

$$(b^{1/q})^p \equiv b^{p/q}. \tag{3-25}$$

This identity states that $b^{1/q}$ is a pth root of $b^{p/q}$ and that $b^{p/q}$ is the pth power of the principal qth root of b. Also, we can now show, by using Eq. (3-25), that

$$\underbrace{b^{p/q} \cdot b^{p/q} \cdot b^{p/q} \cdots b^{p/q}}_{q \text{ factors } b^{p/q}} \equiv b^p, \tag{3-26}$$

and thus $b^{p/q}$ is also the principal qth root of b^p. Therefore we have, from Eqs. (3-25) and (3-26) and the previous notation,

$$\boxed{b^{p/q} \equiv (b^p)^{1/q} \equiv \sqrt[q]{b^p},} \tag{3-27}†$$

and also

$$\boxed{b^{p/q} \equiv (b^{1/q})^p \equiv (\sqrt[q]{b})^p.} \tag{3-28}$$

It can now be shown that the five theorems on exponents, Eqs. (3-19) through (3-23), hold for all rational exponents (elements of F) as well as for integers (elements of I).

---

* See Chapter 13.
† We must exclude the case where b is negative and q is even, as we did in our definition of principal value.

Illustration 2. $8^{2/3} = \sqrt[3]{8^2} = \sqrt[3]{64} = 4$, or

$$= (\sqrt[3]{8})^2 = 2^2 = 4.$$

Illustration 3. $81^{-3/4} = \dfrac{1}{(\sqrt[4]{81})^3} = \dfrac{1}{3^3} = \dfrac{1}{27}.$

Illustration 4. $x^{1/4} \cdot x^{2/3} \equiv x^{1/4+2/3} \equiv x^{11/12} \equiv \sqrt[12]{x^{11}}.$

Illustration 5. $x^{1/4} \div x^{2/3} \equiv x^{1/4-2/3} \equiv x^{-5/12} \equiv \dfrac{1}{\sqrt[12]{x^5}}.$

Illustration 6. $(x^{-4})^{-3/4} \equiv x^3.$

PROBLEMS

All letters appearing in Problems 10 through 30 represent positive real numbers.

Find the numerical value of the following.

1. $25^{1/2}$ 2. $81^{3/4}$ 3. $(\frac{16}{49})^{1/2}$

4. $(\frac{8}{125})^{-1/3}$ 5. $(\frac{64}{27})^{2/3}$ 6. $32^{-4/5}$

7. $(2^{10})^{-3/5}$ 8. $(2^{-6})^{2/3}$ 9. $3^{7/2} \cdot 3^{1/2}$

Remove the negative exponents, simplify, and express the result in radical form.

10. $x^{1/4} \cdot x^{1/5}$ 11. $x^{1/4} \div x^{1/5}$ 12. $(x^{1/4})^{1/5}$

13. $x^{1/4} \cdot x^{-1/5}$ 14. $(x^{1/4})^{-1/5}$ 15. $(x^{-1/4})^{-1/5}$

Remove the negative and zero exponents and simplify.

16. $(9x^{-4}y^2)^{1/2}$ 17. $(2x^{1/6}y^{5/6})^{-6}$

18. $(2x^{-3}y^4)^3$ 19. $\left(\dfrac{125x^4y^3}{27x^{-2}y^6}\right)^{1/3}$

20. $\left(\dfrac{5^0x^4y^3z}{16x^{-6}yz^5}\right)^{-1/2}$ 21. $(a^{1/2} + b^{1/2})^2$

22. $(a^{1/2} + b^{1/2})(a^{1/2} - b^{1/2})$ 23. $(x^{1/3} + y^{1/3})(x^{2/3} - x^{1/3}y^{1/3} + y^{2/3})$

24. $(x + y)^{-2}(x^{-2} - y^{-2})$ 25. $(x + y^{-1})^2$

26. $\dfrac{a^2 - a^{1/2}}{a^{3/2}}$ 27. $\dfrac{a^2 + 2a^{-1} - a^{-1/2}}{a^{1/2}}$

28. $(x^2 + 6x + 9)^{1/2}$

29. a) Find the value of

$$(x^2 - 2x + 1)^{1/2} + (x^2 + 2x + 1)^{1/2}.$$

b) Show by an example that $2x$ is not always the correct result.

30. a) Find the value of

$$(x^2 + 10x + 25)^{1/2} - (x^2 - 10x + 25)^{1/2}.$$

b) Show by an example that 10 is not always the correct result.

3–11 RADICALS

In many cases it is more advantageous to express a quantity in terms of radicals than in terms of rational exponents. The laws of radicals follow directly from the previous definitions and theorems on exponents. If m and n are positive integers and a and b are positive where m or n are even,

$$(\sqrt[n]{a})^n \equiv a, \tag{3-29}$$

$$\sqrt[n]{ab} \equiv (ab)^{1/n} \equiv a^{1/n} \cdot b^{1/n} \equiv \sqrt[n]{a} \cdot \sqrt[n]{b}, \tag{3-30}$$

$$\sqrt[n]{\frac{a}{b}} \equiv \left(\frac{a}{b}\right)^{1/n} \equiv \frac{a^{1/n}}{b^{1/n}} \equiv \frac{\sqrt[n]{a}}{\sqrt[n]{b}}, \tag{3-31}$$

$$\sqrt[m]{\sqrt[n]{a}} \equiv (a^{1/n})^{1/m} \equiv a^{1/nm} \equiv \sqrt[mn]{a}. \tag{3-32}$$

Illustration 1. $\sqrt{50} = \sqrt{25 \cdot 2} = \sqrt{25} \cdot \sqrt{2} = 5\sqrt{2}.$

Illustration 2. $\sqrt[3]{\dfrac{4}{27}} = \dfrac{\sqrt[3]{4}}{\sqrt[3]{27}} = \dfrac{\sqrt[3]{4}}{3}.$

Illustration 3. $\sqrt[6]{27} = \sqrt{\sqrt[3]{27}} = \sqrt{3}.$

A complete simplification of radicals by the use of these laws will yield: (1) no factors which are perfect nth powers under a radical whose index is n, (2) no fractions under the radical sign, (3) the smallest possible index of the radical.

Any radical that satisfies these conditions is said to be in *simplest form*. In addition to the three illustrations above, which are in simplest form, we give the following examples.

Example 1. Simplify $\sqrt[3]{81x^5y^7}$.

Solution. In this expression it will be necessary to remove from the radicand all factors that are perfect cubes.

$$\sqrt[3]{81x^5y^7} \equiv \sqrt[3]{27x^3y^6 \cdot 3x^2y} \equiv \sqrt[3]{27x^3y^6} \cdot \sqrt[3]{3x^2y} \equiv 3xy^2\sqrt[3]{3x^2y}.$$

Example 2. Simplify $\sqrt{\frac{3}{2}}$.

Solution. For computational reasons, it is important to eliminate any fraction which appears as a radicand. Then the radical may be approximated by only one root extraction and a simple division, rather than by two root extractions and a more complicated division. By introducing a perfect square in the denominator, we may remove it from under the radical.

$$\sqrt{\frac{3}{2}} = \sqrt{\frac{3 \cdot 2}{2 \cdot 2}} = \frac{\sqrt{6}}{2}.$$

Example 3. Simplify $\sqrt[4]{64x^2y^4/z^2}$.

Solution. Problems of this type are usually more easily grasped if rational exponents are introduced. We also must eliminate the denominator under the radical.

$$\sqrt[4]{\frac{64x^2y^4}{z^2}} = \left(\frac{2^6x^2y^4}{z^2}\right)^{1/4} = \frac{2^{3/2}x^{1/2}y}{z^{1/2}} \cdot \frac{z^{1/2}}{z^{1/2}} = \frac{2y}{z}\sqrt{2xz}.$$

PROBLEMS

Simplify each of the following.

1. $\sqrt{8}$

2. $\sqrt{98}$

3. $\sqrt{\frac{75}{12}}$

4. $\sqrt[3]{40}$

5. $\sqrt[3]{-625}$

6. $\sqrt[4]{32}$

7. $\sqrt{27x^3y^5}$

8. $\sqrt{192a^3b^7}$

9. $\sqrt[3]{81z^4x^6y^5}$

10. $\sqrt{\frac{3}{5}}$

11. $\sqrt{\frac{125}{63}}$

12. $\sqrt{\frac{1}{9} + \frac{1}{4}}$

13. $\sqrt{a^2b^2 + b^2c^2}$

14. $\sqrt{a^{-2} + b^{-2}}$

15. $\sqrt{\frac{3x}{y^3}}$

16. $\sqrt{\frac{6}{24}}$

17. $\sqrt[3]{\frac{3}{16}}$

18. $\sqrt{\frac{2x}{3y^3}}$

19. $\sqrt[3]{\frac{27x^4}{2y^2}}$

20. $\sqrt[4]{\frac{4x^5y}{81z^3}}$

21. $\sqrt{x + 6 + \frac{9}{x}}$

22. $\sqrt[3]{\frac{x^4y}{z^2}}$

23. $\sqrt[4]{\frac{x^7y^6}{243}}$

24. $\sqrt{x - 2 + \frac{1}{x}}$

25. $\sqrt[4]{25}$

26. $\sqrt[6]{49x^4}$

27. $\sqrt[3]{\frac{5}{3x^2}}$

28. $\sqrt[6]{\frac{9}{16}}$

29. $\sqrt[4]{\frac{169x^6z^2}{y^4}}$

30. $\sqrt[4]{1 - \frac{4}{x} + \frac{4}{x^2}}$

3–12 ADDITION AND SUBTRACTION OF RADICALS

In addition or subtraction of radicals, all similar radicals (that is, those which result in the same index and radicand) are combined into single terms. Consider the example.

Example. Simplify by combining similar terms,

$$4\sqrt{12} + 5\sqrt{8} - \sqrt{50} - 7\sqrt{48}.$$

Solution

$$4\sqrt{12} + 5\sqrt{8} - \sqrt{50} - 7\sqrt{48} = 4\sqrt{4 \cdot 3} + 5\sqrt{4 \cdot 2} - \sqrt{25 \cdot 2} - 7\sqrt{16 \cdot 3}$$
$$= 8\sqrt{3} - 28\sqrt{3} + 10\sqrt{2} - 5\sqrt{2}$$
$$= 5\sqrt{2} - 20\sqrt{3}.$$

PROBLEMS

Simplify by combining similar terms.

1. $4\sqrt{3} - 5\sqrt{12} + 2\sqrt{75}$

2. $\sqrt[3]{2} + \sqrt[3]{16} - \sqrt[3]{54}$

3. $5\sqrt{2} - \sqrt[4]{64} + 2\sqrt{32}$

4. $\sqrt{x^3} + \sqrt{25x^3} + \sqrt{9x}$

5. $\dfrac{1}{\sqrt{2}} - \sqrt{2}$

6. $2\sqrt{2} - \sqrt{50} + 3\sqrt{32}$

7. $2\sqrt{3} + \sqrt{27} + \sqrt{243}$

8. $2\sqrt{5} - \sqrt{125}$

9. $\sqrt{450} + \sqrt{8} - \sqrt{98}$

10. $\dfrac{1}{\sqrt{3}} - \dfrac{4}{\sqrt{27}} + 2\sqrt{3}$

11. $\sqrt[3]{a^4 b} + \dfrac{1}{\sqrt[3]{a^2 b^2}} + 3\sqrt[3]{ab^4}$

12. $\sqrt[3]{27a^4} + \sqrt[3]{-64a^7} + 7\sqrt[3]{a}$

13. $\sqrt{4(x + y)} - 2\sqrt{9(x + y)} + 3\sqrt{x + y}$

14. $3\sqrt{18} - 3\sqrt{32} + 3\sqrt{12} - 3\sqrt{3}$

15. $\sqrt{a^3 bc^5} + \sqrt{ab^7 c^3} + \sqrt{a^9 b^5 c}$

16. $\sqrt{\dfrac{a-b}{a+b}} - \sqrt{\dfrac{a+b}{a-b}} + \sqrt{\dfrac{a^2}{a^2 - b^2}}$

17. $8\sqrt{\tfrac{1}{3}} + \tfrac{3}{2}\sqrt{108} - \sqrt[4]{9}$

18. $\sqrt{\left(\dfrac{x}{y} - \dfrac{y}{x}\right)\dfrac{1}{xy}} - \sqrt{\dfrac{x + y}{x - y}}$

19. $\dfrac{7 \pm \sqrt{49 - 4 \cdot 10}}{2}$

20. $\dfrac{4 \pm \sqrt{16 - 4 \cdot 2}}{2}$

3–13 MULTIPLICATION AND DIVISION OF RADICALS

The multiplication of two or more radicals is accomplished by using the rule established in Eq. (3–30). If the radicals have the same index, the result follows immediately. If, however, the radicals are of different indices, they must be converted to radicals with the same index before the multiplication takes place. This is always possible, and may be carried out with the aid of equivalent expressions having rational exponents.

Example 1. Find the product of $\sqrt{15ax^3}$ and $\sqrt{45a^2xy^3}$ and simplify.

Solution. Since both radicals have the index 2, we use Eq. (3–30) immediately:

$$\sqrt{15ax^3} \cdot \sqrt{45a^2xy^3} \equiv \sqrt{15^2 \cdot 3a^3x^4y^3} \equiv 15ax^2y\sqrt{3ay}.$$

Example 2. Multiply $\sqrt{6x^3}$ by $\sqrt[3]{4x^4y^2}$ and simplify.

Solution. By converting the radicals to rational exponents, we have

$$\sqrt{6x^3} \cdot \sqrt[3]{4x^4y^2} \equiv (3 \cdot 2x^3)^{1/2} \cdot (2^2 x^4 y^2)^{1/3}$$

$$= (3 \cdot 2x^3)^{3/6} \cdot (2^2 x^4 y^2)^{2/6} \equiv (3^3 \cdot 2^3 \cdot x^9 \cdot 2^4 x^8 y^4)^{1/6}$$

$$= \sqrt[6]{3^3 \cdot 2 \cdot 2^6 x^{12} \cdot x^5 y^4} \equiv 2x^2 \sqrt[6]{54x^5y^4}.$$

Division of two radicals is handled in a similar manner, by using Eq. (3–31). Again, if the radicals are of different indices, they must be converted to the same index.

Example 3. Divide $6\sqrt[3]{5}$ by $2\sqrt{3}$ and simplify.

Solution. Since $\sqrt[3]{5} = \sqrt[6]{25}$ and $\sqrt{3} = \sqrt[6]{27}$, we have

$$\frac{6\sqrt[3]{5}}{2\sqrt{3}} = 3\sqrt[6]{\frac{25}{27}}.$$

Recalling that a radical in simplest form has a denominator free of radicals, we must multiply the numerator and denominator by $\sqrt[6]{27}$. Thus

$$\frac{6\sqrt[3]{5}}{2\sqrt{3}} = 3\sqrt[6]{\frac{25 \cdot 27}{27 \cdot 27}} \equiv 3\sqrt[6]{\frac{25 \cdot 27}{3^6}} = \frac{3}{3}\sqrt[6]{25 \cdot 27} = \sqrt[6]{675}.$$

The process of eliminating radicals from the denominator, illustrated in Example 3, and Example 2, Article 3–11, is called *rationalizing the denominator.* The problem of eliminating all radicals in a denominator may be more complicated.

Example 4. Rationalize the denominator of $(2 + \sqrt{3})/(\sqrt{5} - \sqrt{3})$.

Solution. Since we wish to eliminate both radicals in the denominator, we must find an expression (*rationalizing factor*) which, when multiplied by $\sqrt{5} - \sqrt{3}$, will give a result free of radicals. Since

$$(\sqrt{5} - \sqrt{3})(\sqrt{5} + \sqrt{3}) = 5 - 3,$$

we multiply both numerator and denominator by $\sqrt{5} + \sqrt{3}$.

$$\frac{2 + \sqrt{3}}{\sqrt{5} - \sqrt{3}} \cdot \frac{\sqrt{5} + \sqrt{3}}{\sqrt{5} + \sqrt{3}} = \frac{2\sqrt{5} + \sqrt{15} + 2\sqrt{3} + 3}{5 - 3}$$

$$= \frac{2\sqrt{5} + \sqrt{15} + 2\sqrt{3} + 3}{2}.$$

PROBLEMS

Perform the following multiplications, expressing the result in simplest form.

1. $\sqrt{5} \cdot \sqrt{13}$

2. $\sqrt{14} \cdot \sqrt{21}$

3. $\sqrt[3]{4} \cdot \sqrt[3]{26}$

4. $\sqrt[3]{3x^2} \cdot \sqrt{2x}$

5. $\sqrt{x^2 - y^2} \cdot \sqrt{x - y}$

6. $\sqrt{3x^2y^3} \cdot \sqrt{12x^5y}$

7. $\sqrt{x^3 + y^3} \cdot \sqrt{x + y}$

8. $\sqrt[3]{9x} \cdot \sqrt[6]{27x^4}$

9. $\sqrt{2} \cdot \sqrt[3]{3} \cdot \sqrt[4]{4}$

10. $\sqrt{a} \cdot \sqrt[3]{a} \cdot \sqrt[4]{a}$

11. $\sqrt{2}(\sqrt{6} + \sqrt{14})$

12. $(2 + \sqrt{3})(2 - \sqrt{3})$

13. $(\sqrt{3} + \sqrt{5})(\sqrt{3} - \sqrt{5})$

14. $(2\sqrt{3} - 3\sqrt{2})^2$

15. $(\sqrt{5} + 2\sqrt{3})(\sqrt{5} - 3\sqrt{3})$ **16.** $\sqrt{3 + 2\sqrt{2}} \cdot \sqrt{3 - 2\sqrt{2}}$

17. $\left(\dfrac{\sqrt{5} - 1}{2}\right)^2$ **18.** $\left(\dfrac{\sqrt{6} - \sqrt{2}}{4}\right)^2$

Perform the following divisions, expressing the result in simplest form.

19. $4\sqrt{28} \div 3\sqrt{7}$ **20.** $\sqrt[3]{\frac{4}{5}} \div \sqrt[3]{\frac{108}{25}}$

21. $\sqrt[6]{12} \div \sqrt{3}\sqrt[3]{2}$ **22.** $(2\sqrt{6} + 3\sqrt{14}) \div \sqrt{2}$

23. $\sqrt[4]{24a^3b} \div \sqrt[4]{8ab^3}$ **24.** $\sqrt{xy^2} \div \sqrt[3]{x^2y}$

Rationalize the denominator of each of the following.

25. $\dfrac{2\sqrt{3}}{4\sqrt{5}}$ **26.** $\dfrac{2\sqrt[3]{3}}{4\sqrt[3]{5}}$ **27.** $\dfrac{4}{\sqrt[3]{16}}$

28. $\dfrac{3}{\sqrt{x - 1}}$ **29.** $\dfrac{x^2}{\sqrt{1 - x^2}}$ **30.** $\dfrac{3}{2 + \sqrt{3}}$

31. $\dfrac{5}{\sqrt{7} - \sqrt{3}}$ **32.** $\dfrac{\sqrt{2} + \sqrt{3}}{\sqrt{2} - \sqrt{3}}$ **33.** $\dfrac{x}{x + \sqrt{y}}$

34. $\dfrac{y}{\sqrt{x} - \sqrt{y}}$ **35.** $\dfrac{2\sqrt{7} + \sqrt{3}}{3\sqrt{7} - 5\sqrt{3}}$

36. $\dfrac{2x}{\sqrt{x - 1} + \sqrt{-x + 2}}$ **37.** $\dfrac{x^2}{\sqrt{x^2 - 1} - \sqrt{x + 3}}$

38. $\dfrac{y}{\sqrt{y^2 - 16} - y}$ **39.** $\dfrac{x - \sqrt{x^2 - 9}}{x + \sqrt{x^2 - 9}}$

40. $\dfrac{\sqrt{x} + \sqrt{x + 1}}{\sqrt{x} - \sqrt{x + 1}}$ **41.** $\dfrac{\sqrt{x} + \sqrt{x^2 - 1}}{\sqrt{x} - \sqrt{x^2 - 1}}$

42. $\dfrac{1}{\sqrt[3]{a} + \sqrt[3]{b}}$ *Hint:* $x^3 + y^3 \equiv (x + y)(x^2 - xy + y^2)$.

43. $\dfrac{2}{2 - \sqrt[3]{3}}$ **44.** $\dfrac{1}{\sqrt[3]{9} + \sqrt[3]{6} + \sqrt[3]{4}}$

45. $\dfrac{1}{\sqrt{2} + \sqrt{3} + \sqrt{5}}$ *Hint:* Multiply both numerator and denominator by $(\sqrt{2} + \sqrt{3}) - \sqrt{5}$.

In Problems 46 through 50, use the table of square roots (Table I) to compute the following to three decimal places.

46. $\dfrac{2}{\sqrt{3}}$ **47.** $\dfrac{7}{\sqrt{5}}$ **48.** $\dfrac{1}{\sqrt{2} + \sqrt{3}}$

49. $\dfrac{1}{\sqrt{7} - \sqrt{3}}$ **50.** $\dfrac{1}{2 - \sqrt[3]{5}}$

REVIEW PROBLEMS

1. $\dfrac{(x + h)^2 - x^2}{h}$, where $h \neq 0$, is identical to

   a) h b) $2x$ c) $2x + h$

   d) $\dfrac{2x + h}{h}$ e) none of these

2. $x^4 - y^4$ is identical to

   a) $(x - y)^4$ b) $(x + y)(x - y)(x^2 - y^2)$

   c) $(x + y)(x - y)(x^2 + y^2)$ d) $(x^2 - y^2)^2$

   e) none of these

3. $(x^{1/2} + a^{1/2})^2$ is identical to

   a) $x + a$ b) $x + \sqrt{2ax} + a$ c) $x + 2\sqrt{ax} + a$

   d) $(x^2 + a^2)^{1/2}$ e) none of these

4. $\sqrt{x^2 + y^2}$, where $x > 0$, is identical to

   a) $\sqrt{1 + \left(\dfrac{y}{x}\right)^2}$ b) $x^2\sqrt{1 + \left(\dfrac{y}{x}\right)^2}$ c) $x\sqrt{1 + \left(\dfrac{y}{x}\right)^2}$

   d) $\dfrac{1}{x}\sqrt{1 + \left(\dfrac{y}{x}\right)^2}$ e) $\dfrac{1}{x^2}\sqrt{1 + \left(\dfrac{y}{x}\right)^2}$.

5. $3 \cdot 10^n$ is identical to

   a) 10^{n+3} b) 30^n c) $3^n \cdot 10^n$

   d) 10^{3n} e) none of these

6. $\dfrac{\sqrt{2x}}{x + 4}$ is identical to

   a) $\sqrt{\dfrac{2}{x}} + \dfrac{\sqrt{2x}}{4}$ b) $\dfrac{2}{\sqrt{x}} + \dfrac{\sqrt{x}}{2}$

   c) $\dfrac{2\sqrt{x}}{x + 4}$ d) none of these

Which of the following statements (Problems 7 through 14) are identities?

7. $\dfrac{x}{1 + x^4} \equiv x + \dfrac{1}{x^3}$ **8.** $(a^{2/3} - x^{2/3})^3 \equiv a^2 - x^2$

9. $4x^2 - 12x + 13 \equiv 4[(x - \tfrac{3}{2})^2 + 1]$

10. $\dfrac{x}{(a^2 + x^2)^{3/2}} \equiv \dfrac{x}{a^3 + x^3}$ **11.** $\dfrac{1 + x^4}{x} \equiv \dfrac{1}{x} + x^3$

12. $\dfrac{-\dfrac{1}{x^2}}{\sqrt{1 - \left(\dfrac{1}{x}\right)^2}} \equiv -\dfrac{1}{x\sqrt{x^2 - 1}}$ **13.** $\dfrac{\tfrac{1}{2}}{\sqrt{1 - \left(\dfrac{x - 2}{2}\right)^2}} \equiv \dfrac{1}{\sqrt{4x - x^2}}$

14. $\dfrac{x^4 + 4x^2 - 4}{(x-1)(x^2+4)} \equiv x + 1 + \dfrac{x^2}{(x-1)(x^2+4)}$

15. Simplify $\dfrac{x^2}{(1-x^2)^{3/2}} + \dfrac{2}{(1-x^2)^{1/2}}$.

16. Simplify $[4t(1+t^2)^{-1/2} - 2t^3(1+t^2)^{-3/2}] \div \dfrac{t}{\sqrt{1+t^2}}$.

17. Show that $\sqrt{\left(x - \dfrac{1}{4x}\right)^2 + 1} = x + \dfrac{1}{4x}$ if $x > 0$. Is it true if $x < 0$?

18. If $3x^2 + 3y^2z - 3ay - 3axz = 0$, and $6x - 6az + 6yz^2 + 3y^2w - 3axw = 0$, find w in terms of x, y, and a.

19. If $10x^2 - 6xz - 6y + 10xz = 0$, find z if $x = y = 4\sqrt{2}$.

20. If $x = \dfrac{1}{t+1}$, and $y = t^2$, show that $y = \dfrac{(1-x)^2}{x^2}$.

21. If $y = \dfrac{x}{\sqrt{32 - x^2}}$, express $\sqrt{1 + y^2}$ in terms of x.

22. If $x = \dfrac{3\sqrt{y}}{2\sqrt{3}}$, express $\sqrt{1 + x^2}$ in terms of y.

23. If $y = (ax^2 + bx + c)^{1/2}$, and

$$z = -\dfrac{(2ax + b)^2}{4}(ax^2 + bx + c)^{-3/2} + a(ax^2 + bx + c)^{-1/2},$$

show that $4y^3z = 4ac - b^2$.

24. Show that if $\sqrt{(x+c)^2 + y^2} + \sqrt{(x-c)^2 + y^2} = 2a$, and $a^2 = b^2 + c^2$, then $\dfrac{x^2}{a^2} + \dfrac{y^2}{b^2} = 1$.

25. If $x = \dfrac{2t}{1 - t^2}$, and $y = \dfrac{1 + t^2}{1 - t^2}$, find $y^2 - x^2$.

CHAPTER 4

INEQUALITIES, ABSOLUTE VALUES,
AND COORDINATE SYSTEMS

There are further notions and concepts important in any systematic study of algebra. In Chapter 2 we discussed the field axioms for the real numbers, from which we derived many of the normal properties of the set R. Unfortunately, the ability to compare real numbers does not follow from these field axioms. In addition to them, we must have the four *order axioms*, which we shall give in this chapter, along with the *completeness axiom* (Article 4–3). We shall also consider certain geometric interpretations, together with a brief discussion of other helpful geometric ideas.

4–1 ORDER AXIOMS FOR THE REAL NUMBERS

If any field, such as the real numbers, satisfies the following four axioms, the field is said to be *ordered*. The real numbers are considered the undefined elements. The relation ">" is defined for these elements by the axioms, and is read "is greater than." Recall that a, b, c ... represent *any* real numbers.

Axiom O1. *The trichotomy axiom.* If a and $b \in R$, then one and only one of the following statements is true:

$$a > b, \qquad a = b, \qquad b > a.$$

Axiom O2. *The transitive axiom.* If a, b, and $c \in R$ such that $a > b$ and $b > c$, then $a > c$.

Axiom O3. *The addition axiom.* If a, b, and $c \in R$ such that $a > b$, then $a + c > b + c$.

Axiom O4. *The multiplication axiom.* If a, b, and $c \in R$ such that $a > b$ and $c > 0$, then $ac > bc$.

Since both addition and multiplication are commutative operations, the result in Axiom O3 can read $c + a > c + b$, and in Axiom O4, $ca > cb$. The fact that $c > 0$ is a condition in Axiom O4 should be emphasized.

It is often convenient to say one number "is less than" another, rather than always to use the idea of "is greater than." Consequently, we make the following definition of the relation (is less than) on the set R.

Definition 4–1. If a and $b \in R$, we say $a < b$ (read "a is less than b") if and only if $b > a$.

As a result of this definition, $a > b$ may be read either "a is greater than b" or "b is less than a." In any of our proofs involving these relations (inequalities) we shall assume that any quantity may be substituted for an equal quantity. For example, if $a > b$ and $b = c$, then $a > c$. Further, we shall define $\geq$ to be $>$ or $=$, and similarly $\leq$ to be $<$ or $=$.

One further definition is in order. You noticed in Chapters 2 and 3 that although we discussed $-a$, $a - b$, and so on, we did not mention in our logical process the idea of positive or negative numbers.* We now define such numbers.

Definition 4–2. A real number a is *positive* if $a > 0$ and *negative* if $a < 0$.

It follows immediately from Axiom O1, that zero is neither positive nor negative. Also, because of this definition, Axiom O4 reads, "If $a > b$ and c is positive, then $ac > bc$."

We are now ready to prove several of the more basic theorems.

Theorem 4–1. If a and $b \in R$,

i) $a > b$ if and only if $-a < -b$;
ii) $a < b$ if and only if $-a > -b$.

Proof. We shall prove the statement in (i). The proof of (ii) is similar. If $a > b$, we have by Axiom O3,

$$a + [(-a) + (-b)] > b + [(-a) + (-b)],$$

and by the associative, commutative, and identity axioms, it follows that $0 + (-b) > 0 + (-a)$ or $-a < -b$. Since each of these steps is reversible, the converse follows immediately.

Corollary. If $a > 0$, then $-a < 0$.

Proof. Recall $0 = -0$ (Problem 11, Article 2–3).

Theorem 4–2. $1 > 0$.

Proof. By Axiom O1, $1 > 0$, $1 = 0$, or $1 < 0$. By Axiom 5, we know $1 \neq 0$. We shall assume $1 < 0$, arrive at a contradiction, and thus have our result. If we assume $1 < 0$, $-1 > 0$ by Theorem 4–1, and by Axiom O4,

$$(-1)(-1) > 0(-1) \quad \text{or} \quad 1 > 0,$$

which contradicts our assumption. Therefore, $1 > 0$.

Corollary. $-1 < 0$.

As a result of this theorem, we are able to establish order relations between any pair of natural numbers (see Problems 17 through 20), or, in fact, any integers.

---

* Note the distinction between "negative number" and "negative of a number" (see Axiom 6, Chapter 2).

It should be emphasized that 1 is a positive number, and, as the discussion has implied, this is by no means trivial.

If in the inequality $5 > 3$, we multiply both numbers by -2, the result is $-10 < -6$, and the relation changes from $>$ to $<$. This is always the case if we multiply by a negative number, and can be stated in general.

Theorem 4–3. If $a > b$ and $c < 0$, then $ac < bc$.

Proof. Since $c < 0$, by Theorem 4–1, $-c > 0$. Now, as a direct result of Axiom O4, $a(-c) > b(-c)$, or $-ac > -bc$, which reduces to $ac < bc$ (Theorem 4–1).

Two further theorems, one involving addition and the other multiplication, should be mentioned.

Theorem 4–4. If $a > b$ and $c > d$, then $a + c > b + d$.

Proof. Since $a > b$, $a + c > b + c$ by Axiom O4. Also, since $c > d$, $b + c > b + d$. If we combine these two statements by Axiom O2, we have

$$a + c > b + d.$$

Theorem 4–5. If a, b, c, and d are positive numbers, $a > b$ and $c > d$, then $ac > bd$.

Proof. (Give the reasons for each step.) Since $a > b$, $ac > bc$. Since $c > d$, $bc > bd$. Therefore, $ac > bd$.

Illustrations. Since $4 > 3$ and $5 > 2$, we may say by Theorem 4–4 that $9 > 5$, and by Theorem 4–5, that $20 > 6$.

Some of these properties of the inequality relations will be used in this chapter. Others, together with those stated in the following set of problems, will be used later, especially in the article in which the solution of inequalities is discussed (Article 7–5).

PROBLEMS

1. Verify each of the order axioms *intuitively* by suitable choices of real numbers. For example, in Axiom O1, if $a = 2$ and $b = -3$, $a > b$, since $2 > -3$.

2. Verify each of the general theorems *intuitively* by suitable choices of real numbers.

3. Prove that $a > b$ if and only if $a - b$ is positive. This property is sometimes taken as the definition of $a > b$.

Prove each of the statements in Problems 4 through 6.

4. If c is positive and $a > b$, then $a + c > b$.

5. If a and b are positive and $a > b$, then $(1/a) < (1/b)$.

6. a) If a is positive and $a > 1$, then $a^2 > a$.
   b) If a is positive but $a < 1$, then $a^2 < a$.
   c) If m and n are positive integers, $m \geq n$ and $a > 1$, then $a^m \geq a^n$.

7. Prove that the relation $a > b$ is true if and only if $a + c > b + c$.

8. Prove that the sum of two positive real numbers is positive.

9. Prove that the sum of two negative real numbers is negative.

▶ 10. Prove that the product ab is positive if and only if a and b are both positive or both negative.

11. Prove that the product ab is negative if and only if a is positive and b is negative or a is negative and b is positive.

▶ 12. Prove that $a^2 \geq 0$. *Hint:* Use Problem 10.

13. Prove Theorem 4–2 as a corollary to Problem 12.

14. Prove that if a and b are positive, and $a > b$, then $a^2 > b^2$.

15. Prove that if n is any positive integer, a and b are positive, and $a > b$, then $a^n > b^n$.

16. Prove that if n is any positive integer, a and b are positive, and $a^n > b^n$, then $a > b$. *Hint:* Assume the statement is not true and use Axiom O1.

Problems 17 through 20 indicate a method for ordering the integers.

17. Prove that $2 > 1$. Here we must assume that 2 is the symbol indicating $1 + 1$. *Hint:* $1 > 0$.

18. Prove that $2 > 0$.

19. If we use the symbol 3 to indicate $2 + 1 = (1 + 1) + 1$,

   a) prove that $3 > 2$;   b) prove that $3 > 1$.

20. a) Prove that $-3 < -2$.   b) Prove that $-3 < -1$.

▶ 21. a) If $a > b$, show that

$$a > \frac{a + b}{2} > b.$$

   b) Show that $0 < \frac{1}{2} < 1$.   c) Show that $\frac{1}{2} < \frac{3}{4} < 1$.

22. If $a > b > 0$, show that $a > \sqrt{ab} > b$. *Hint:* Use Problem 16.

23. Show that the statement in Problem 22 is not necessarily true if $0 > a > b$.

24. We recall that $a - c = a + (-c)$. State a property for subtraction, analogous to Axiom O3, and explain why it is true.

25. We recall that if $c \neq 0$,

$$a \cdot \frac{1}{c} = \frac{a}{c}.$$

State a property for division, analogous to Axiom O4, and explain why it is true.

4–2 A ONE-DIMENSIONAL COORDINATE SYSTEM

The method of associating numbers with points on a line is of considerable help in mathematics and has resulted in great progress in the application of mathematics to science. Any scale which measures quantities, such as a yardstick or thermometer, makes use of an association of this kind. To each numerical value assumed by the physical quantity there corresponds a position on the scale, and to each position on the scale there corresponds a real number. Such a correspondence establishes a coordinate system. The simplest and most useful coordinate system in one dimension employs a one-to-one correspondence between the set R of real numbers and the set of points on a straight line. Let us consider such a system.

On a fixed straight line of reference of unlimited length, we choose any point O, called the origin, and lay off equal divisions* of arbitrary length in both directions from O. We now associate zero with the origin, the positive integers with the successive points on one side, and the negative integers with the successive points on the other (see Fig. 4–1). The usual convention on such a horizontal line is to consider the integers to the right as positive and those to the left as negative.

The point associated with any rational number can be determined by the simple geometric construction used to divide any line segment into b equal parts. Thus the number $\frac{3}{4}$ is represented by a point three-fourths of the way from 0 to the point identified with 1. Also, $-1\frac{3}{8}$ is represented by a point at a distance $1\frac{3}{8}$ units to the left of 0.

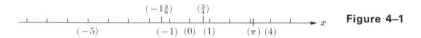

Figure 4–1

The points associated with some irrational numbers may also be found by geometric construction. For example, the point associated with $\sqrt{2}$ may be located, because $\sqrt{2}$ is the hypotenuse of an isosceles right triangle with each leg one unit in length. Although geometric construction is not possible for all real numbers, *we shall assume that the correspondence can be extended to all real numbers*. This is done by associating every line segment with a real number which represents its length. Thus, with each real number, we have associated one point on the line and, conversely, with each point on the line there is associated one real number.

The *coordinate* of a point is defined to be the number associated with that point. It is written (x) and will be referred to as "the point x."

The coordinate system gives us a graphic interpretation of the relative magnitude of numbers. Thus $5 > 3$ corresponds to the fact that (5) lies to the right of (3), while $-5 < -3$ corresponds to the fact that (-5) is to the left of (-3). The notation $x < y < z$ indicates that y is greater than x but less than z.

To express the distance between any two points in this system, we need only subtract the coordinate of the left-hand point from the coordinate of the right-hand point. Thus, if $x_1 < x_2$, where the subscripts 1 and 2 merely denote two distinct values of x, the distance between (x_1) and (x_2) is $x_2 - x_1$, but if $x_2 < x_1$, the distance must be $x_1 - x_2$, since we wish to have the distance always positive. We can avoid the inconvenience of having to distinguish between the two points by employing the notion of absolute value.

The absolute value of x, denoted by $|x|$, indicates its size or magnitude without regard to its sign. For example, $|3| = 3$, and $|-3| = 3$.

---

* There are systems where the subdivisions are not equal. Consider the slide-rule scale.

Definition 4–3. The absolute value of a real number x is defined as

$$|x| \equiv \begin{cases} x & \text{if } x > 0, \\ -x & \text{if } x < 0, \\ 0 & \text{if } x = 0. \end{cases} \qquad (4\text{–}1)$$

Here we should recall the definition of the square-root sign, $\sqrt{}$. For any positive number a, $\sqrt{a}$ denotes the positive square root of a. Let us emphasize this by the following consistent definition.

Definition 4–4. For any real number x, x^2 is positive (or zero if $x = 0$) and

$$\sqrt{x^2} \equiv \begin{cases} x & \text{if } x > 0, \\ -x & \text{if } x < 0, \\ 0 & \text{if } x = 0. \end{cases} \qquad (4\text{–}2)$$

Thus $\sqrt{7^2} = 7$, and $\sqrt{(-7)^2} = -(-7) = 7$, and in general $|x| = \sqrt{x^2}$. Since Eqs. (4–1) and (4–2) define the same values, either expression can be used to indicate absolute value.

As an immediate consequence of the definition of the absolute value, we have the following theorem.

Theorem 4–6. For any $a \in R$,

$$-|a| \leq a \leq |a|. \qquad (4\text{–}3)$$

Proof. Right-hand inequality: If $a \geq 0$, $a = |a|$, but if $a < 0$, (that is, $0 < -a$), $|a| = -a$ so that $0 < |a|$, $a < 0 < |a|$. Thus $a \leq |a|$ for all a.

Left-hand inequality: If $a \geq 0$, $-a = -|a| \leq 0 \leq a$. If $a < 0$, $|a| = -a$ or $-|a| = a$, so that for all a, $-|a| \leq a$.

Since two basic properties of absolute value will be used later in work with inequalities, we shall mention them now.

Theorem 4–7. If a and b are any two real numbers, the absolute value of their product (or quotient) is equal to the product (or quotient) of their absolute values:

$$|ab| \equiv |a| \cdot |b|, \qquad (4\text{–}4)$$

$$\left|\frac{a}{b}\right| \equiv \frac{|a|}{|b|}, \qquad b \neq 0. \qquad (4\text{–}5)$$

Proof of (4–4). By Definitions 4–3 and 4–4, $|ab| = \sqrt{(ab)^2}$. Thus,

$$|ab| = \sqrt{(ab)^2} = \sqrt{a^2 b^2} = \sqrt{a^2}\sqrt{b^2} = |a| \cdot |b|.$$

Theorem 4–8. If a and b are any two real numbers, the absolute value of their sum is less than or equal to the sum of their absolute values:

$$|a + b| \leq |a| + |b|. \tag{4–6}$$

Proof. See Problem 10 below.

We are now able to give the general expression for the distance between any two points P_1 and P_2.

Theorem 4–9. The distance between any two points P_1 and P_2 with coordinates (x_1) and (x_2) may be expressed

$$d = P_1 P_2 = |x_1 - x_2| \equiv \sqrt{(x_1 - x_2)^2}. \tag{4–7}$$

For example, the distance between the two points (5) and (−3) is given either by the expression $d = \sqrt{[5 - (-3)]^2} = 8$ or by the expression $d = \sqrt{(-3 - 5)^2} = 8$.

PROBLEMS

1. Arrange the following numbers in ascending order of magnitude and plot them on a linear coordinate system such as that of Fig. 4–1: 2.3, 0.333, 2^3, 4, $\frac{1}{3}$, −5, −1, 0, −6.5.

2. State the conditions on a and b in Theorem 4–8, so that the $=$ sign will hold.

3. State in words the geometrical interpretation of the following.

a) $a < b$ b) $a < 2$

c) $a > b$ d) $a > b > c$

e) $a - b = 1$ f) $3.14 < \pi < 3.15$

g) $1.41 < \sqrt{2} < 1.42$ h) $|5 - 2| > |1 - 3|$

i) $|a - b| > 0$ j) $|x - 2| < 3$

k) $|x - 1| > 4$ l) $-1 < x < 1$

4. If the coordinates of two points, P_1 and P_2, on a line are (2) and (8) respectively, show that the coordinate of the midpoint of the segment $P_1 P_2$ is (5).

5. Find the coordinate of the midpoint of the line joining (4) and (−4), (3) and (−5), (−1.7) and (3.7), ($\sqrt{2}$) and ($\sqrt{3}$), (x_1) and (x_2).

6. Solve the following equations for x.

a) $x = |10|$ b) $x = |2 - 5|$

c) $x = \sqrt{3^2}$ d) $x = \sqrt{(-4)^2}$

e) $x = |-\frac{3}{2}|$ f) $x = \sqrt{(-1)^2}$

g) $x = |\frac{1}{3} - \frac{5}{3}|$ h) $x = |\frac{1}{3}| + |-\frac{5}{3}|$

7. Solve the following equations for all possible values of x.

a) $|x| = 2$

b) $|x| = \sqrt{5}$

c) $\sqrt{x^2} = 3$

d) $\sqrt{x^2} = \frac{1}{4}$

e) $|x - 2| = 5$

f) $|x - 4| = 0$

g) $|3 - x| = 6$

h) $\sqrt{(x - 1)^2} = 5$

i) $\sqrt{(2 - x)^2} = 4$

j) $|x - 2| = -3$

k) $\sqrt{(x - 4)^2} = -1$

l) $\sqrt{(x - 5)^2} = 3$

8. Prove Eq. (4–5), Theorem 4–7.

▶ **9.** If $d \geq 0$, then $|c| \leq d$ if and only if $-d \leq c \leq d$. Give the reasons for each step in the proof of this property, which must consist of two parts:

a) Proof of the statement that if $|c| \leq d$, then $-d \leq c \leq d$. We know $c \leq |c|$ and $|c| \leq d$, so that $c \leq d$. We know $-d \leq -|c|$ and $-|c| \leq c$, so that $-d \leq c$. Therefore, $-d \leq c \leq d$.

b) Proof of the statement that if $d \geq 0$ and $-d \leq c \leq d$, then $|c| \leq d$. If $c \geq 0$, $|c| = c$. Since $c \leq d$, we have $|c| \leq d$. If $c < 0$, $|c| = -c$. Since $-d \leq c$ or $-c \leq d$, we again have $|c| \leq d$.

▶ **10.** Prove Theorem 4–8. *Hint:* $-|a| \leq a \leq |a|$ and $-|b| \leq b \leq |b|$. Add these inequalities and use the result in Problem 9.

▶ **11.** Prove $|a - b| \leq |a| + |b|$. *Hint:* Let b in Theorem 4–8 be equal to $-b$.

12. Solve the following inequalities for all possible values of x.

a) $|x - 1| \leq 2$. By the statement in Problem 9, this is equivalent to

$$-2 \leq x - 1 \leq 2.$$

The left inequality, $-2 \leq x - 1$, gives $x \geq -1$; the right inequality $x - 1 \leq 2$, gives $x \leq 3$. The result may be written $-1 \leq x \leq 3$.

b) $|3 - x| \leq 5$

c) $|2x + 5| < 6$

d) $|4 + 3x| < 2$

▶ **13.** Prove that if $d \geq 0$, then $|c| \geq d$ if and only if $c \geq d$ or $c \leq -d$. *Hint:* See the proof in Problem 9.

14. Solve the following inequalities for all possible values of x.

a) $|x - 1| \geq 2$. By the statement in Problem 13, this is equivalent to $x - 1 \geq 2$ or $x - 1 \leq -2$. The first inequality says $x \geq 3$, while the second says $x \leq -1$. Compare these answers with those in Problem 12(a).

b) $|3 - x| \geq 5$

c) $|2x + 6| > 4$

d) $|3x + 1| > 8$

15. a) Prove or disprove that $|x^2| = |x|^2$.

b) Prove or disprove that $|x^3| = |x|^3$.

16. Solve the following inequalities for x.

a) $\dfrac{1}{|x - 1|} > 3$

b) $\dfrac{1}{|2x + 3|} < \dfrac{1}{4}$

17. Recall from plane geometry that a circle is the locus (totality) of points at a given distance from a given point, where the distance is called the radius and the given point is called the center. In this geometry of one dimension, how many points are at a given distance from a fixed point? Of how many points would a "circle" consist?

18. If (1) is a given point and 2 a given distance, explain how $|x - 1| = 2$ would be the condition that any point (x) must be 2 units distant from (1). This is the condition that the point (x) lies on the "circle" with center (1) and radius 2, and is called the equation of the "circle."

19. In terms of "circles in one dimension," give the geometric significance of each of the equations in Problem 7.

20. Give the equation of a "circle in one dimension" with its center at the point (a) and with radius r.

4–3 THE COMPLETENESS PROPERTY

Since we wish to characterize the set R completely, it is necessary to give one axiom in addition to the field axioms and order axioms.

Consider the set of rational approximations for $\sqrt{2}$, obtained by the ordinary process of finding a square root. This set $A = \{1, 1.4, 1.41, 1.414, \ldots\}$ is a subset of the set $B = \{x | x \in R \text{ and } x^2 < 2\}$. In neither of these sets is there any element equal to or greater than $\sqrt{2}$, so that $\sqrt{2}$ is called an upper bound of either set. Of course there are many such upper bounds. The numbers 2, $2\frac{1}{2}$, 3, and 4 are also upper bounds, although $\sqrt{2}$ appears to be "the best upper bound," in the sense that it is the smallest of all the upper bounds.

> **Definition 4–5.** The number v is called an *upper bound* of a set S if $x \leq v$ for all $x \in S$. Similarly, the number u is called a *lower bound* of a set S if $u \leq x$ for all $x \in S$.

In the examples above, v could be $\sqrt{2}$, 2, $2\frac{1}{2}$, 3, and so on. For the set A, u could be 1, 0, -3, and so on. Are these lower bounds of B? (Why?)

We are not only interested in the bounds of any set, but we also wish to emphasize the smallest of the upper bounds and the largest of the lower bounds, if they exist.

Consider any set of numbers $X = \{x | a < x < b\}$. If $c \in X$, we have, by definition, that $a < c$ and $c < b$. Since, by Problem 21, Article 4–1,

$$a < \frac{a + c}{2} < c,$$

we know that c is not a lower bound of X. Also, since

$$c < \frac{c + b}{2} < b,$$

c is not an upper bound of X. Consequently, b is the smallest upper bound of X, and similarly, a is its largest lower bound.

Definition 4–6. An upper bound b of a set S is the *least upper bound* if no upper bound is less than b. Similarly, a lower bound a is the *greatest lower bound* if no lower bound is greater than a.

In the set $X = \{x|a < x < b\}$, b is the least upper bound and a is the greatest lower bound.

The least upper bound and greatest lower bound may or may not be in the set. In the set X they are not in the set, but they are in the set $Y = \{x|a \le x \le b\}$. The set of real numbers $\{x|x \ge 0\}$ has a greatest lower bound zero, but no least upper bound. If we recall Theorem 1–1, the set of real numbers

$$\{x|x \ge 0, \ x \text{ is rational, and } x^2 \le 2\}$$

has zero for its greatest lower bound, and $\sqrt{2}$ for its least upper bound. Its greatest lower bound, zero, is in the set, but its least upper bound, $\sqrt{2}$, is not. (Why?)

We are now prepared to state the rather intuitive completeness property as our final axiom for the set of real numbers R.

Axiom C. Every set S where $S \subset R$ and has an upper bound has a least upper bound. Similarly, every such set S that has a lower bound has a greatest lower bound.

Example. Show that the set of *positive* integers I_+ has no upper bound.

Solution. We shall show this by assuming the statement is not true and arriving at a contradiction. Let us assume that the set of positive integers I_+ has an upper bound. Since $I_+ \subset R$, it has a *least* upper bound (by Axiom C), which we shall denote by b. Thus, there exists a b such that if $x \in I_+$, $x \le b$, and b is the least such number. But if $x \in I_+$, $x + 1 \in I_+$, so that $x + 1 \le b$ for all $x \in I_+$. Therefore, $x \le b - 1$, which contradicts the fact that b was the least upper bound. This contradiction shows that I_+ has no upper bound.

PROBLEMS

1. Give the least upper bound and the greatest lower bound of each of the following sets (if they exist).

a) $\{x|x \in R \text{ and } x < -3\}$

b) $\{x|x \in F, \ x > 0 \text{ and } x^2 > 2\}$

c) $\{x|x \in I \text{ and } -3 \le x < 1\}$

d) $\left\{\dfrac{1}{n} \middle| n \in I \text{ and } n > 0\right\}$

2. Give an example of a subset of R such that

a) it has neither an upper nor a lower bound;

b) it has an upper but no lower bound;

c) it does not contain its upper or lower bound;

d) it contains both its upper and lower bound.

3. Show why the set $\{-1, 0, 1\}$ contains its least upper and greatest lower bound. What are they?

4. Show that any finite set $\{a_1, a_2, \ldots, a_n\}$ can be ordered, by recalling Axiom O1. With this knowledge, show that any finite set contains its least upper bound (and greatest lower bound).

5. Let b be the least upper bound of the set S of real numbers. If $x \in S$ and $x < b$, there exists a number $y \in S$ such that $x < y \leq b$. If this were not the case, x would be an upper bound of S, contradicting the fact that b is the least upper bound. What is an analogous property for a, the greatest lower bound of the set S of real numbers? Explain.

6. If $r \in R$ and $r > 0$, show that the set $S = \{nr | n \in I_+\}$ has no upper bound. *Hint:* Assume the statement is not true. Thus there exists some real number t such that $nr \leq t$ for all $n \in I_+$. Therefore, $n \leq (t/r)$ must hold for all $n \in I_+$. Does this contradict the result of the example?

7. If $r > 0$, $s > 0$, and r and $s \in R$, there exists a positive integer n such that $nr > s$. Show that this statement is true. *Hint:* If it were not true, $n \leq (s/r)$ for all $n \in I_+$.

8. If a, b, and c are real numbers such that $a < c < b$, we say c lies between a and b. Show that there is always some rational number between any two unequal rational numbers. *Hint:* See Problem 21, Article 4–1.

9. If a and $b \in R$, and $0 < a < b$, show that there is always some *rational* number between a and b. Although the proof of this important result is somewhat involved, each step is comparatively simple. Give the reasons for each step in the proof that follows.

i) Since a and 1 are positive, there exists a positive integer n' such that $n'a > 1$.

ii) Since $b - a$ and 1 are positive, there exists a positive integer n'' such that $n''(b - a) > 1$.

iii) If n is the larger of n' and n'', we have $na > 1$ and $nb > 1 + na$.

iv) Since na and 1 are positive, there exists a positive integer m' such that $m' > na$.

v) If m is the smallest such m', we have $na + 1 \geq m > na$.

vi) Therefore, $nb > m > na$, so that $b > (m/n) > a$.

10. Under the same conditions as those stated in Problem 9, show that there is always an irrational number between a and b. *Hint:* If x is some positive irrational number such as $\sqrt{2}$, $a(1/x) < b(1/x)$, and by Problem 9, there exists an m and an n such that $a/x < m/n < b/x$. Therefore $a < mx/n < b$. What can be said about mx/n?

4–4 A TWO-DIMENSIONAL COORDINATE SYSTEM

In Article 4–2 we observed a coordinate system that not only enabled us to view the relative magnitudes of numbers in a graphic way, but also allowed us to represent the distance between two points by the magnitude of their differences. But the usefulness of a one-dimensional coordinate system is limited. One of the more important concepts in mathematics is the relation or dependence of two sets of numbers. The corresponding values of two such related sets can be regarded as pairs of numbers; hence a system which produces an association between a point and an ordered pair of numbers would be most advantageous in studying such a relationship. A two-dimensional system provides the association.

We recall the definition of the *cartesian product* of two sets. We are particularly interested here in the case where $X = Y$, and, in fact, where X and Y are both the set of real numbers R. Symbolically this is

$$R \times R = \{(x, y) | x \in R \text{ and } y \in R\}.$$

Each member of the set is an ordered pair (x, y). We are able to set up an association between this set of all ordered pairs (x, y) of $R \times R$ and the set of all points in the plane. (The student should review the important notion of product set, given in Problem 12, Article 1–3.)

The most frequently used system that sets up an association between each point in a plane and pair of real numbers is the *rectangular cartesian system of coordinates*. In 1637 René Descartes, a French mathematician and philosopher, used this method of associating points with numbers, and by so doing, associated a curve with its equation. Great progress in mathematics and the application of mathematics in science resulted from this unification of algebra and geometry.

Let us construct two perpendicular straight lines and, for convenience, let one of them be horizontal. We shall call these *coordinate axes*. Using the point of intersection as the origin O, set up on each line a one-dimensional system. Ordinarily, the same unit of length is used on both lines, although in some cases it is convenient to do otherwise. We now denote by the expression $(x, 0)$ the point on the horizontal line corresponding to the number x in its one-dimensional system. Similarly, we denote the point on the vertical line corresponding to the number y in its one-dimensional system by the symbol $(0, y)$. The horizontal line is called the *x-axis*, or *axis of abscissas*, while the vertical line is referred to as the *y-axis* or *axis of ordinates*. As is customary, the point on the *y*-axis $(0, y)$ is above the *x*-axis when y is positive.

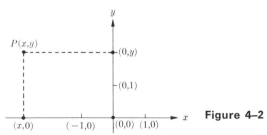

Figure 4–2

In the reference system of axes shown in Fig. 4–2, consider any specific pair of values of x and y, x_1 and y_1. To find the point corresponding to this ordered pair of values, we draw lines parallel to the axes through the point $(x_1, 0)$ on the *x*-axis and the point $(0, y_1)$ on the *y*-axis. These lines intersect at a point P, a distance x_1 from the *y*-axis (to the right or left, depending upon whether x_1 is positive or negative) and a distance y_1 from the *x*-axis (above or below, depending upon whether y_1 is positive or negative). These distances can be called *directed distances*. The point P, determined by the ordered pair of values x_1 and y_1, is denoted by the ordered pair, expressed (x_1, y_1), where x_1 and y_1 are called *coordinates* of P. As might be expected, the x-value is called the *abscissa* of P and the y-value is called its *ordinate*. Clearly, there is only one point determined by any ordered pair of values (x, y). Conversely, for each point there is only one ordered pair of values (x, y), since the point has unique directed distances from the axes. *Thus a one-to-one correspondence is established between all the points in the plane and the set of all ordered number pairs (x, y).* In the discussion which follows it will be convenient to refer to the ordered pair (x, y) as the point (x, y), with coordinates x and y.

The two coordinate axes divide the plane into four parts, called the *first, second, third,* and *fourth quadrants.* It is helpful to verify that the coordinates of points located in the different quadrants have the signs shown in the table.

Quadrants	Abscissa	Ordinate
I	+	+
II	−	+
III	−	−
IV	+	−

In Fig. 4–3 the plotting of several points is shown.

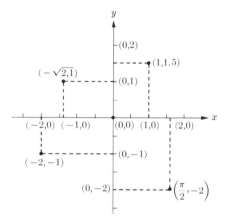

Figure 4–3

PROBLEMS

1. Plot the following points:

   a) with abscissa 4 and ordinate 3   b) $(4, -3)$ c) with $x = -4$ and $y = 3$

2. Plot the points whose coordinates are:

   a) $(2, 6)$, $(-1, 4)$, $(3, -2)$, $(-1, -3)$
   b) $(4, 0)$, $(-4, 0)$, $(0, 4)$, $(0, -4)$, $(0, 0)$

3. What are the coordinates of a point

   a) three units to the right of the y-axis, and two above the x-axis?
   b) four units to the left of the y-axis, and six above the x-axis?
   c) five units to the right of the y-axis, on the x-axis?

4. a) What is the abscissa of any point on the y-axis?

   b) What is the ordinate of any point on the x-axis?

5. Without plotting, indicate the quadrant in which each of the following points lies:
   $(-1, 2)$, $(2, -4)$, $(-3, -7)$, $(4, 6)$, $(-5, 2)$, $(28, -2)$.

6. a) Give the coordinates of four points which are the vertices of a rectangle.

   b) Give the coordinates of three points which are the vertices of a right triangle.
   c) Give the coordinates of four points on a circle with its center at $(2, 3)$ and with radius 4.

7. In each of the following, three vertices of a parallelogram are given. Give the three possible sets of coordinates for the fourth vertex.

a) (0, 0), (2, 4), and (6, 0)   b) (−2, 1), (1, 2), and (0, −3)

8. Three vertices of a parallelogram are (a, b), (0, 0), and $(c, 0)$. What are the possible coordinates of the fourth vertex?

9. Indicate in a rectangular coordinate system the location of the set of all the points (x, y) whose coordinates satisfy the following conditions.

a) $x = 2$ b) $y = -3$ c) $x > 2$ d) $y > 4$
e) $x < -1$ f) $x = y$ g) $x > 2$,   h) $x > y$
                                     $y = 3$

i) $x < y$ j) $x > 2$,   k) $x = 2$,   l) $x = 2$,
                 $y < 4$ $y < -1$ $y = 3$

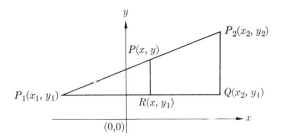

Figure 4–4

▶ **10.** If, in Fig. 4-4, $P(x, y)$ is the midpoint of the line segment joining $P_1(x_1, y_1)$ and $P_2(x_2, y_2)$, and the line PR is drawn parallel to the y-axis, the coordinates of R will be (x, y_1). Since $RP_1 = QR$, $x - x_1 = x_2 - x$. Using this fact, and a similar construction, show that the coordinates of the midpoint of the line joining P_1 and P_2 are

$$x = \frac{x_1 + x_2}{2}, \qquad y = \frac{y_1 + y_2}{2}. \qquad (4\text{--}8)$$

11. Find the coordinates of the midpoint of the line joining

a) (1, 2) and (−3, 5)   b) (6, −2) and (5, −7)
c) (−4, 3) and (2, −3)

12. Let $A = (4, -3)$. Find the coordinates of B if line segment $\overline{AB}$ has midpoint

a) (0, 0)   b) (2, −1)   c) (1, −2)   d) (0, 3)   e) (3, 0)

13. If $A = \{1, 2\}$ and $B = \{-1, 0, 1\}$, plot the set of ordered pairs of

$$A \times B = \{(x, y) | x \in A \text{ and } y \in B\}$$

in a rectangular coordinate system.

14. a) Describe and plot the points which are members of the set

$$I \times I = \{(x, y) | x \in I \text{ and } y \in I\}.$$

b) Describe the set of points which are members of the set

$$F \times F = \{(x, y) | x \in F \text{ and } y \in F\}.$$

15. It is sometimes desirable to consider sets of ordered pairs in which the first element is not equal to the second element in any one pair. Such a "deleted cartesian product" has no members of the form (x, x). If $A = \{1, 2, 3\}$, list the members of the deleted cartesian product of A with itself.

▶ **16.** The concept of a cartesian product may easily be extended to include any finite number of sets. For example, $R \times R \times R = \{(x, y, z)|x, y, \text{ and } z \in R\}$ has for its members ordered triples. Explain how such a set of triples could be put into one-to-one correspondence with all the points in three-dimensional space. *Hint:* How did we proceed from a one- to a two-dimensional system?

4–5 THE DISTANCE FORMULA

We are now prepared to obtain a formula which has many applications in the mathematics dealt with in this book. To obtain an expression for the distance d between any two points $P_1(x_1, y_1)$ and $P_2(x_2, y_2)$, where the same unit lengths are used on both axes, we make use of the famous theorem of Pythagoras. Considering $P_1(x_1, y_1)$ and $P_2(x_2, y_2)$ any two points in the plane, construct a right triangle, as in Fig. 4–5, with P_1P_2 the hypotenuse, and the two legs parallel to the axes. Call their point of intersection, where the right angle is formed, $P_3(x_3, y_3)$. Since $x_3 = x_1$ and $y_3 = y_2$, the distance between P_2 and P_3 is

$$P_2P_3 = \sqrt{(x_1 - x_2)^2}$$

and the distance between P_1 and P_3 is

$$P_1P_3 = \sqrt{(y_1 - y_2)^2}.$$

Recalling the theorem of Pythagoras, which states that

$$\overline{P_1P_2^2} = \overline{P_2P_3^2} + \overline{P_1P_3^2},$$

we obtain

$$\overline{P_1P_2^2} = (x_1 - x_2)^2 + (y_1 - y_2)^2.$$

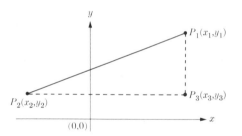

Figure 4–5

This results in the following theorem.

> **Theorem 4–10.** The distance between any two points $P_1(x_1, y_1)$ and $P_2(x_2, y_2)$ is given by

$$d = P_1P_2 = \sqrt{(x_1 - x_2)^2 + (y_1 - y_2)^2}. \qquad (4\text{–}9)$$

Example 1. The distance between the points $P_1(-4, 2)$ and $P_2(3, -1)$ is

$$P_1P_2 = \sqrt{[3 - (-4)]^2 + (-1 - 2)^2}$$
$$= \sqrt{58}.$$

Example 2. The distance between the origin $(0, 0)$ and any point (x, y) is

$$d = \sqrt{(x - 0)^2 + (y - 0)^2}$$
$$= \sqrt{x^2 + y^2}.$$

Example 3. The triangle with the points $P_1(-5, -1)$, $P_2(2, 3)$, and $P_3(3, -2)$ as vertices is isosceles:

$$P_1P_2 = \sqrt{(-5 - 2)^2 + (-1 - 3)^2}$$
$$= \sqrt{49 + 16} = \sqrt{65},$$

$$P_1P_3 = \sqrt{(-5 - 3)^2 + (-1 + 2)^2}$$
$$= \sqrt{64 + 1} = \sqrt{65}.$$

PROBLEMS

In each of the following exercises, draw the figure on coordinate paper.

1. Find the distance between the given points:
   a) $(3, 2)$ and $(6, 7)$ b) $(-4, 3)$ and $(5, -2)$
   c) $(\frac{5}{2}, -\frac{3}{4})$ and $(\frac{7}{4}, -\frac{3}{2})$

2. Find the distance between the given points:
   a) $(0, 0)$ and $(5, -12)$ b) $(-3, 7)$ and $(5, 7)$
   c) $(-1, 3)$ and (x, y)

3. Find the length of the line segment joining the points
   a) $P(6, 14)$ and $Q(1, 2)$ b) $P(-4, 1)$ and $Q(6, -5)$

4. By proving that two sides of the triangle are equal, show that the triangle whose vertices are $(2, 1)$, $(5, 5)$, and $(-2, 4)$ is an isosceles triangle.

5. Show that the points $(8, 1)$, $(-6, -7)$, and $(2, 7)$ are the vertices of an isosceles triangle.

6. Show that the points $(6, 1)$, $(5, 6)$, $(-4, 3)$, and $(-3, -2)$ are the vertices of a parallelogram.

7. Prove that the points $(2, 3)$, $(-4, -3)$, and $(6, -1)$ are the vertices of a right triangle. Note that we must use the converse of the theorem of Pythagoras to prove this.

8. Show that the points $(12, 9)$, $(20, -6)$, $(5, -14)$, and $(-3, 1)$ are the vertices of a square. What is the length of a diagonal?

9. Test algebraically to see whether or not the following triples of points are collinear (lie on the same line): $(6, 2)$, $(1, 1)$, $(-4, 0)$; $(-6, 5)$, $(3, -10)$, $(-2, -2)$.

10. Show that the three points $A(-2, 1)$, $B(2, 3)$, and $C(10, 7)$ lie on a straight line.

11. If $D(h, 5)$ is on the straight line described in Problem 10, what condition must the coordinate h satisfy?

12. If a circle had its center at the point $(2, 3)$ and passed through $(8, -5)$, what would be its radius? Would it pass through $(-6, 9)$?

13. Consider the circle with its center at the origin and with a radius of 1. Through which of the following points does it pass: $(1, 0)$, $(0, -1)$, $(1, 1)$, $(1/\sqrt{2}, 1/\sqrt{2})$, $(\frac{1}{2}, \frac{1}{2})$, $(-\frac{1}{2}, \sqrt{3}/2)$?

▶ 14. By giving the expression for the distance between the origin and the point (x, y), and equating this distance to 1, we have stated the algebraic condition on x and y which must be satisfied by the coordinates of any point (x, y) lying on the circle whose center is $(0, 0)$ and whose radius is 1. Show that this condition, when simplified, becomes $x^2 + y^2 = 1$. This is called the equation of the unit circle in the plane.

15. If a point lies on a curve, its coordinates must satisfy the equation representing that curve. Check the results of Problem 13 by determining whether the coordinates of the points satisfy the equation of the unit circle obtained in Problem 14, namely, $x^2 + y^2 = 1$.

16. Note that Eq. (4–9) is a generalization of Eq. (4–7). What would be the corresponding generalization in the three-dimensional space described in Problem 16, Article 4–4?

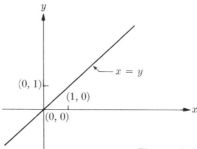

Figure 4–6

In any two-dimensional rectangular coordinate system a locus or curve, such as a straight line or circle, may be considered a set of points. The two coordinates of each point in this set satisfy some stated condition* involving these coordinates. Conversely, if the coordinates of any point satisfy this condition, that point must be in this set. For example, let us consider the set of points (ordered pairs) which are members of the set A, where

$$A = \{(x, y)|x = y\}.$$

The set A, whose members are the points (x, y) which satisfy the condition $x = y$, is a *locus* or *curve*.† The *equation* of this locus or curve is the condition $x = y$, which the coordinates of the points (and only those points) must satisfy. The *graph* of this locus or curve is the figure we see in Fig. 4–6, namely, the geometric representation of the set of points A in the cartesian coordinate plane.

We have the following three important definitions, and we should distinguish between any two of them.

Definition 4–7. A *locus* (or *curve*) is the set of points, and only those points, whose coordinates satisfy certain conditions.

Definition 4–8. The *equation* of a locus (or curve) is the *condition* which the coordinates of each of the points of that locus, and only those points, must satisfy.

---

* This condition will be in addition to the fact that $(x, y) \in R$, which we shall always assume unless otherwise stated.
† The word *curve* is used in this restrictive sense in two dimensions.

Definition 4–9. The *graph* of a locus (or curve) is the geometric representation of the set of points of the locus.

In this article we are concerned with the distance formula and its simple applications, one of which is the equation of a circle.

We recall the definition of a circle as the locus of all points in the plane that are a constant distance from a fixed point. We are, therefore, interested in the set

$C = \{(x, y) | \text{the distance between } (x, y) \text{ and some fixed point is constant}\}.$

If we use the distance formula (Eq. 4–9), it is possible to obtain a general equation of a circle.

With $C(h, k)$ as the center and r as the radius (Fig. 4–7), the condition that any point $P(x, y)$ lying on the circle must satisfy is

$$CP = r,$$

which is the same as having the coordinates of P satisfy the condition

$$\sqrt{(x - h)^2 + (y - k)^2} - r.$$

Conversely, if $CP = r$, then P is on the circle. We therefore have

$$\boxed{(x - h)^2 + (y - k)^2 = r^2,} \quad (4\text{–}10)$$

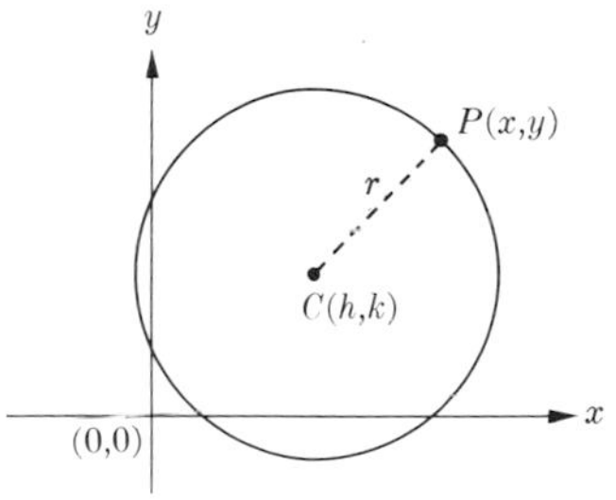

Figure 4–7

which is a general equation of the circle with center (h, k) and with radius r.

The circle itself is the set

$$\boxed{C = \{(x, y) | (x - h)^2 + (y - k)^2 = r^2\}.} \quad (4\text{–}11)$$

Example 4. An equation of the circle with its center at $(2, -3)$ and radius 4 is

$$(x - 2)^2 + (y + 3)^2 = 16.$$

The circle itself is the set

$$\{(x, y) | (x - 2)^2 + (y + 3)^2 = 16\}.$$

Example 5. An equation of the circle with its center at the origin and a radius of 1 is

$$(x - 0)^2 + (y - 0)^2 = 1,$$

or

$$\boxed{x^2 + y^2 = 1.}$$

This is called an equation of the unit circle. Recall Problem 14. This unit circle is the set $\{(x, y) | x^2 + y^2 = 1\}$.

PROBLEMS

1. Write an equation of the following circles:
   a) center at $(3, 1)$ and radius 5,
   b) center at $(4, -2)$ and radius 3,
   c) center at $(-1, 3)$ tangent to the x-axis,
   d) center at $(2, -4)$ and passing through $(5, -8)$.

2. Find an equation of the circle with its center at $(2, 3)$
   a) tangent to the x-axis,
   b) tangent to the y-axis,
   c) through the origin,
   d) tangent to the line whose equation is $x = 5$,
   e) tangent to the line whose equation is $y = 7$,
   f) through the point $P(4, 5)$.

3. Write an equation of the circle with its center at the origin and radius r.

4. Describe the following sets.
   a) $A = \{(x, y) | (x - 1)^2 + (y - 1)^2 = 4\}$
   b) $B = \{(x, y) | (x - 2)^2 + (y + 7)^2 \leq 9\}$
   c) $C = \{(x, y) | (x - 2)^2 + (y + 7)^2 \geq 1\}$
   d) $D = \{(x, y) | (x - 3)^2 + (y + 1)^2 = 0\}$
   e) $E = \{(x, y) | (x + 2)^2 + (y - 5)^2 < 0\}$

5. Describe in words the following sets, where reference is made to Problem 4:
   a) $B \cup C$ b) $B \cap C$

6. Write in set notation the set of points (x, y) such that the points
   a) lie outside the circle with center at $(2, 3)$ and radius 4;
   b) lie on or inside the circle with center $(-1, 3)$ and radius $\sqrt{2}$.

CHAPTER 5

FUNCTIONS AND THEIR
GRAPHICAL REPRESENTATION

In mathematics, the concept of a *function* is very important and useful. It appears in almost every branch of the subject. The idea in mathematics, however, has a slightly different meaning than that in ordinary language. We shall use the word *function* to denote a certain specific type of correspondence or association between the elements of two sets. In this book the elements of the two sets will be real numbers, although in the general mathematics context this is not always the case.

5–1 FUNCTIONS AND RELATIONS

In considering the unit circle, discussed in Example 5, Article 4–5, we found its equation to be $x^2 + y^2 = 1$. If we subtract x^2 from both members of this equality and take the positive square root, we have

$$y = \sqrt{1 - x^2}, \qquad (5\text{--}1)$$

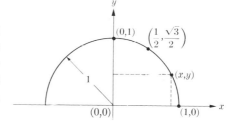

Figure 5–1

the equation of the "top" half of the circle (Fig. 5–1). From the graph of this half-circle, we see that for a particular point to be on the curve, its y-coordinate is determined *uniquely* if its x-coordinate is given. Similarly, from the equation (5–1), there must be a certain value of y which corresponds to any specific value of x. For example, if $x = 0$, y must be 1; if $x = 1$, y must be 0; or if $x = \frac{1}{2}$, y must be $\sqrt{3}/2$. This association or correspondence, which in fact constitutes a specific function, is, of course, more precise than that of any arbitrary product set if no further condition is imposed. Note that the above example satisfies the general definition of a function.

> **Definition 5–1.** If there is associated with each element of a set X *exactly* one element of another set Y, then this association constitutes a *function* from X to Y.

This is usually written $f : X \to Y$, and is read "the function f from X to Y."

In algebra we usually wish to emphasize the elements of the sets as well as the sets themselves. In this case we will write $f : x \to y$, and read "f takes x into y," where we assume $x \in X$ and $y \in Y$. The set X is called the *domain* of the function f, and the set Y is called its *range*.

The method of association may be accomplished in many ways, although it usually is done by an equation such as $y = \sqrt{1 - x^2}$, by a table of values, or by a graph. The important point is that a function pairs *one and only one* element of Y with each element of X. In the above example, the domain is the set

$$X = \{x | x \in R \text{ and } -1 \leq x \leq 1\},$$

and the range is the set

$$Y = \{y | y \in R \text{ and } 0 \leq y \leq 1\}.$$

Frequently we may be more specific. If we combine the symbol f for the function with the elements, x, of the domain and regard $f(x)$ as the corresponding element of the range, we may write $f\!:\!x \rightarrow f(x)$. The symbol $f(x)$* is, therefore, considered to be the value of f at x, and is read "f of x." In our example, when $x = 0$, $f(0) = 1$; when $x = 1$, $f(1) = 0$, and when $x = \frac{1}{2}$, $f(\frac{1}{2}) = \sqrt{3}/2$. In many cases we may even go further. If the method of defining the association for the function f is an explicit equation for y in terms of x, such as $y = \sqrt{1 - x^2}$, we may write $f\!:\!x \rightarrow \sqrt{1 - x^2}$. It should be emphasized that in this discussion x stands for any element in the domain of f, and y [or $f(x)$] stands for the corresponding element in the range. Of course, other letters, such as u, v, or t, may also represent elements of the domain with the corresponding elements $f(u)$, $f(v)$, or $f(t)$ in the range. Any such usage will be clear from the context. There is nothing special about the letter f for denoting a function. Other letters, such as g or h, may also represent the function. In general, a function $f\!:\!X \rightarrow Y$, might be indicated as in Fig. 5–2, where two different elements in X may be associated with the same element in Y, but *no two* distinct elements in Y are the correspondent of the same element in X.

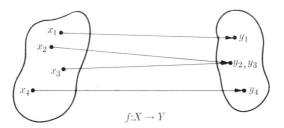

$$f\!:\!X \rightarrow Y$$

Figure 5–2

Let us summarize the concept of function. There are *three* important parts: the domain X, or set of x-values, the range Y, or set of y-values, and the rule, relationship, or correspondence which associates these two sets in a certain way. Unless otherwise stated, both the domain and range of any function will be the largest possible set of suitable real numbers.

Illustration 1. Consider the function defined by the equation $y = 2x - 6$ for all positive integers less than 10. Thus, $f\!:\!x \rightarrow 2x - 6$, where $X = \{1, 2, \ldots, 9\}$.

---

* This symbol, $f(x)$, is not to be confused with f multiplied by x.

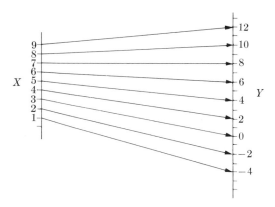

Figure 5–3

For this function, $f(1) = -4$, $f(2) = -2$, and so on. The function f is illustrated in Fig. 5–3.

Illustration 2. We recall that the area A of a circle of radius r is given by the expression $A = \pi r^2$. Since π is a quantity which remains fixed in value (called a *constant*), we can consider $A(r) = \pi r^2$ as an equation which defines the function expressing the association between values of the radius and the corresponding area for any circle. This function may be written $A : r \rightarrow \pi r^2$, $(r \geq 0)$. For example, $A(0) = 0$, $A(1) = \pi$, $A(2) = 4\pi$, and so on. The function has for its domain and its range all positive real values, and zero.

Illustration 3. An important, and yet almost trivial, function is the one which associates all real numbers with the same fixed number. Such a function, called a *constant function*, might be written $f : x \rightarrow c$. As a result of this definition, $f(0) = c$, $f(1) = c$, or $f(\pi) = c$ and, in fact, $f(x) = c$ for all $x \in R$, so that the domain of the function is the set R, but its range is the single real number c.

Illustration 4. Recall in Article 2–2 that for each real number x, $(x \neq 0)$ there existed a unique inverse with respect to multiplication, $1/x$ (the reciprocal). This association describes the function $r : x \rightarrow 1/x$, whose domain and range are the set R except for zero.

With these illustrations in mind, it should be clear that a function defines a set of ordered pairs, with the added condition that no two pairs have the same first element. For example, in Illustration 4, $(1, 1)$, $(2, \frac{1}{2})$, $(-3, -\frac{1}{3})$, and $(\sqrt{2}, 1/\sqrt{2})$ are specific ordered pairs which belong to this function r. If this point of view is taken, the set X consists of the first members in the ordered pair, and Y the second. We could use the following equivalent definition.

Definition 5–2. A function from X to Y is a set of *ordered pairs* (x, y) such that to each $x \in X$, there corresponds a unique $y \in Y$.

We may, therefore, use the set notation to describe a function:

$$\{(x, y) | y = f(x)\}.$$

If the ordered pair (a, b) belongs to the function, that is, if $f(a) = b$, we say b is the *image* of a under f, so that, in general, the range is the image of its domain.

Illustration 5. If $y = a(x)$ is defined so that

$$a(x) = \begin{cases} x & \text{for } x \geq 0, \\ -x & \text{for } x < 0, \end{cases}$$

the function, defined by different expressions over different subsets of the domain, may be written $a:x \rightarrow |x|$. What is the domain and range of this function? The ordered pairs $(3, 3)$ and $(-4, 4)$ belong to this function. Give several other such ordered pairs which also belong to a.

In the definition of a function $f:x \rightarrow y$, the value of y is unique, corresponding to any specific value of x. Other possibilities exist, however, so that for a given value of x there may exist two, three, or even an infinite number of corresponding values of y. For example, if we solve the equation of the unit circle, $x^2 + y^2 = 1$, for y, we have

$$y = \pm\sqrt{1 - x^2}.$$

If this is the equation which sets up the association between X and Y, there are two values of y which correspond to any value of x between -1 and 1. Although this might be called a double-valued (and, in general, multiple-valued) function, we prefer to call such a correspondence a *relation*, and not a function of any kind. It could be symbolized by

$$\{(x, y)|x^2 + y^2 = 1\}.$$

More generally, we define a relation as any set of ordered pairs. In most cases, the pairing is accomplished by a defining equation or inequality.

Definition 5–3. A relation from X to Y is a set of ordered pairs (x, y) such that to each $x \in X$ there corresponds at least one $y \in Y$.

It should be clear that any function is a relation, but there exist many relations which are not functions. As in the case of a function, a relation has a domain and range. Although relations will be mentioned in this book, we shall restrict our discussion to functions whenever possible.

PROBLEMS

1. Give the domain and range of the following functions, where $x, y \in R$.

a) $f:x \rightarrow x$ b) $g:x \rightarrow \sqrt{x}$ c) $p:x \rightarrow x^2$

d) $f:x \rightarrow \sqrt{4 - x^2}$ e) $g:x \rightarrow \sqrt{x^2 - 1}$ f) $h:x \rightarrow \dfrac{x}{1 - x}$

g) $f:x \rightarrow \dfrac{1}{x^2 - 1}$ h) $g:x \rightarrow |x| - 2$

2. Which of the following sets describe a function, and which describe only a relation?

a) $\{(1, 2), (2, 3), (3, 4)\}$

b) $\{(1, 2), (1, 3), (2, 4)\}$

c) $\{(x, y)|y = 2x + 4\}$

d) $\{(x, y)|2x + 3y = 6\}$

e) $\{(x, y)|x + y^2 = 1\}$

f) $\{(x, y)|y + x^2 = 1\}$

g) $\{(x, y)|(x - 2)^2 + (y - 3)^2 = 9\}$

h) $\{(x, y)|x \leq y\}$

i) $\left\{(x, y)\left|x + \dfrac{1}{y - 3} = 7\right.\right\}$

j) $\{(x, y)|\ |x| + |y| = 1\}$

3. What is the domain and the range of each of the functions and relations in Problem 2?

Find the domain and range of each of the following. State whether the given relation is a function.

4. a) $\{(x, y)|x + y = 4\}$

b) $\{(x, y)|y^2 + 1 = x\}$

c) $\{(x, f(x))|f(x) = x^2 + 1\}$

5. a) $\{(x, y)|y = |x|\}$

b) $\{(x, f(x))|f(x) - x = (x + 1)^2\}$

c) $\{(x, y)|x = |y|\}$

6. If $f:x \rightarrow 2x - 5$, find

a) $f(0)$ b) $f(1)$ c) $f(3)$ d) $f(-1)$

7. If $f:x \rightarrow x^2 - 7x + 10$, find

a) $f(2)$ b) $f(5)$ c) $f(3)$ d) $f(0)$

8. If $f:x \rightarrow 1/(x - 3)$, find

a) $f(4)$ b) $f(2)$ c) $f(-1)$

d) What can be said about $f(3)$?

9. If $e:x \rightarrow 2^x$, where the domain is the set I, find

a) $e(0)$ b) $e(1)$ c) $e(5)$ d) $e(-5)$

10. If $g:x \rightarrow x^{1/2}$, find

a) $g(0)$ b) $g(2)$ c) $g(4)$ d) $g(\frac{1}{9})$

11. Consider the function described by the set $\{(x, y)|10^y = x\}$. If $y = f(x)$, find

a) $f(1)$ b) $f(10)$ c) $f(100)$ d) $f(\frac{1}{100})$

12. If $a:x \rightarrow |x - 2|$, find

a) $a(0)$ b) $a(2)$ c) $a(4)$ d) $a(-2)$

13. If f is a constant function, find $f(2)$ if

a) $f(1) = 6$ b) $f(6) = -3$ c) $f(-3) = 4$

14. If x is the length of one side of a square, express the perimeter P in terms of x. By using this expression for P we are able to establish a correspondence between the length x and the perimeter of the square. What specific function does this association describe?

15. In Problem 14, express the area A in terms of x. What specific function does this association describe?

16. If x is the length of one side of an equilateral triangle, express the perimeter P in terms of x. Express the area A in terms of x. *Hint:* In a 30°–60° triangle, the hypotenuse is double the shorter leg. Use the Pythagorean Theorem to find the altitude, and recall that $A = \frac{1}{2}(\text{base}) \cdot (\text{altitude})$.

Each of these equations defines a different function. What are these two functions?

17. With s measured in feet and t in seconds, the equation $s = f(t) = -16t^2 + 32t$ expresses the height of a ball above the ground after t seconds if it were thrown upward with a velocity of 32 ft/sec. Find $f(0)$, $f(\frac{1}{2})$, $f(1)$, $f(\frac{3}{2})$, $f(2)$, and explain the result.

▶ **18.** If a function f is defined so that $f(x) = x^2$, show that $f(-x) = f(x)$. Any function satisfying the condition $f(-x) = f(x)$ is called an *even function*. Give another example of such a function.

▶ **19.** If a function f is defined so that $f(x) = x^3$, show that $f(-x) = -f(x)$. Any function satisfying this condition is called an *odd function*. Give another example of an odd function.

20. Find an expression for $[f(x) - f(a)]/(x - a)$, where $x \neq a$, if

a) $f(x) = a$ b) $f(x) = x$ c) $f(x) = 3x$

21. Simplify the expression for $[f(x) - f(a)]/(x - a)$, where $x \neq a$, if

a) $f(x) = 1/x$ b) $f(x) = x^2$ c) $f(x) = \sqrt{x}$

To describe the behavior of functions more accurately, it is helpful to consider certain basic combinations of functions. In dealing with combinations, the domains of the functions involved must be taken into consideration at all times, so that the combinations will be clearly defined.

The more important combinations of functions are defined as follows:

Definition 5–4. The sum function of two functions f and g is defined as the function $f + g$, where the functional value

$$y = f(x) + g(x). \tag{5–2}$$

Definition 5–5. The product function of two functions f and g is defined as the function fg, where the functional value

$$y = f(x) \cdot g(x). \tag{5–3}$$

Definition 5–6. The quotient function of two functions f by g is defined as the function f/g, where the functional value

$$y = \frac{f(x)}{g(x)}. \tag{5–4}$$

Definition 5–7. The composite function of two functions f by g is defined as the function $f \circ g$, where the functional value

$$y = f(g(x)). \tag{5–5}$$

Because of Definition 5–6, the quotient function of g by f is defined by $y = g(x)/f(x)$. Similarly, by Definition 5–7, the composite function of g by f is written $g \circ f$ and defined by $y = g(f(x))$.

The domain of $f + g$, fg, and f/g is the set of all real numbers contained in the domains of both f and g, that is, the intersection of the domains of f and g, except in the case of the quotient, which is not defined for any x where $g(x) = 0$. The domain of $f \circ g$ consists of the set of x's for which $g(x)$ is contained in the domain of f. Unless the function is defined for all real values, its domain should be clearly stated.

Illustration 6. If $f(x) = 2x - 1$ and $g(x) = 6 - x - x^2$ for all values of x, the sum function of f and g is defined by

$$y = (2x - 1) + (6 - x - x^2) = 5 + x - x^2;$$

the product function of f and g is defined by

$$y = (2x - 1)(6 - x - x^2) = -2x^3 - x^2 + 13x - 6;$$

the quotient function of f by g is defined by

$$y = \frac{2x - 1}{6 - x - x^2}, \qquad (x \neq 2 \text{ or } -3);$$

the composite function of f by g is defined by

$$f(g(x)) = 2(6 - x - x^2) - 1 = 11 - 2x - 2x^2;$$

and the composite function of g by f is defined by

$$g(f(x)) = 6 - (2x - 1) - (2x - 1)^2$$
$$= 2(3 + x - 2x^2).$$

PROBLEMS

In Problems 1 through 5, where f and g are given, find $f + g$, fg, f/g, $f \circ g$, and $g \circ f$. Give the domain for each combination.

1. $f(x) = 2x - 3$, $g(x) = 3x + 2$
2. $f(x) = x^2 - x$, $g(x) = x + 4$
3. $f(x) = 4 - 3x$, $g(x) = 2x - 3x^2$
4. $f(x) = 2/x$, $g(x) = x - 3$
5. $f(x) = \sqrt{x}$, $g(x) = x^3$
6. If $f(g(x)) = 1 - x^2$ and $g(x) = 1 - x^2$, find $f(x)$.
7. If $f(g(x)) = 1 - x^2$ and $g(x) = x$, find $f(x)$.
8. If $f(g(x)) = x^2 + 2x + 1$ and $f(x) = x^2$, find $g(x)$.
9. If $f(g(x)) = x^2$ and $f(x) = x - 1$, find $g(x)$.
10. If $f(x) = x$, $g(x) = x + 1$, $h(x) = x + 2$, find $(f \circ g) \circ h$ and $f \circ (g \circ h)$. Are the two composite functions the same?
11. If $f(x) = x - 2$, $g(x) = x + 2$, $h(x) = x^2$, find $(f \circ g) \circ h$ and $f \circ (g \circ h)$. Are the two composite functions the same?
12. If $f(x) = 2x + 1$, find $(f(x))^2$, $f(x^2)$, and $f(f(x))$. Are the three expressions equal?

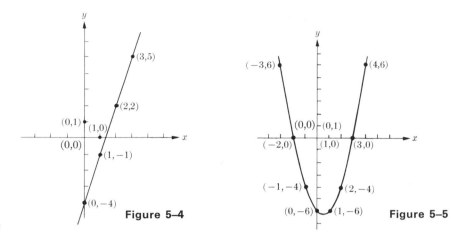

Figure 5–4   **Figure 5–5**

5–2 GRAPHICAL REPRESENTATION OF FUNCTIONS AND RELATIONS

Using the rectangular coordinate system discussed in Article 4–4, we are able to exhibit the association between x and y (or any two variables) in the case of any particular function. Although all the points (x, y) whose coordinates satisfy a given equation $y = f(x)$ cannot be plotted, usually a sufficient number may be so that a good approximation to a picture of the function may be obtained. The aggregate of all such points forms the graph of the function f, or the curve which represents this function. (Recall Definition 4–9.)

Example 1. Draw the graph of the function $f: x \to 3x - 4$.

Solution. By assigning arbitrary values for x and computing the corresponding y-values, we can obtain any number of points (x, y) whose coordinates satisfy the equation $y = 3x - 4$. The points, arranged in the table below, are then plotted and joined by a smooth curve. This function is represented by a straight line (Fig. 5–4).

x	0	1	2	3	4
$y = f(x)$	-4	-1	2	5	8

Example 2. Draw the graph of the function $q: x \to x^2 - x - 6$.

Solution. Again assign values to x, compute the corresponding values of $y = q(x)$, and arrange the results in a table.

x	0	1	2	3	4	-1	-2	-3
$y = q(x)$	-6	-6	-4	0	6	-4	0	6

If we draw a smooth curve through these points (x, y), starting with the point whose abscissa is -3, then -2, -1, and so on, we obtain the result shown in Fig. 5–5. This curve, called a *parabola*, is the required graph. Often, to complete the graph correctly, additional points [e.g., $(\frac{1}{2}, -6\frac{1}{4})$] whose coordinates satisfy the required condition must be found. Although many different curves could be drawn through whatever points are located, the required curve is obtained by sensible "interpolation" between the plotted points.

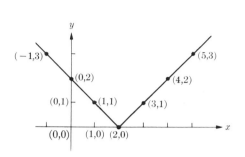

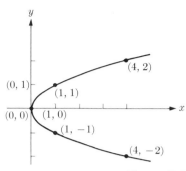

Figure 5–6   Figure 5–7

We have noticed in both Examples 1 and 2 that the graph of the function crosses the x-axis. At any such point, the y-coordinate is zero. The x-value at such points is called a *zero of the function*. In Example 1, the zero of the function is $x = 4/3$; in Example 2, there are two zeros of the function, -2 and 3. In general, a zero of a function is the abscissa of a point where the graph of the function crosses or touches the horizontal axis.

Example 3. Draw the graph of the function represented by the set of ordered pairs $\{(x, y)|y = |x - 2|\}$.

Solution. We construct the table,

x	0	1	2	3	4	5	-1
y	2	1	0	1	2	3	3

plot the points, and draw the graph. (See Fig. 5–6.) Note that $x = 2$ is the zero of this function, although the curve does not cross the x-axis.

A relation may be represented graphically by exactly the same method. Such a graph was given in Fig. 4–7 for the relation

$$\{(x, y)|(x - h)^2 + (y - k)^2 = r^2\}.$$

It should be remarked that any vertical line intersects the graph of a function only once at most, although it may intersect a relation's graph any number of times (why?).

Example 4. Sketch the graph of the relation $\{(x, y)|y^2 = x\}$.

Solution. If we solve $y^2 = x$ for y, we have $y = \pm\sqrt{x}$, so that the table is relatively easy to construct.

x	0	1	2	4
y	0	± 1	$\pm\sqrt{2}$	± 2

We see, as we would expect, that for each value of x, there are two associated values of y. The graph is shown in Fig. 5–7.

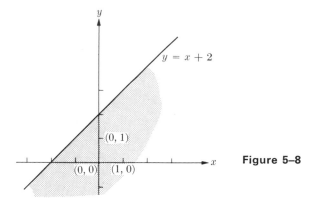

Figure 5–8

Example 5. Draw the graph of the relation $\{(x, y) | y \leq x + 2\}$.

Solution. For the graph of this relation, we first plot the line $y = x + 2$ and then realize that for any particular x the point (x, y) is a member of the required set if its y-coordinate is equal to or less than it would be if the point lay on the line. The required set is thus the line $y = x + 2$, and all points *below* this line. The shaded area indicates the graph (Fig. 5–8) of this relation.

PROBLEMS

Draw the graph of each of the functions defined by the equations in Problems 1 through 12. Show the scales on both axes and give the zeros of the function in each case.

1. $y = 2x + 5$ 2. $y = 6 - 3x$

3. $y = x^2/16$ 4. $y = -4x^2$

5. $y = x^2 - 7x + 10$ 6. $y = -x^2 - x + 30$

7. $y = |x - 1|$ 8. $y = |2x - 3|$

9. $y = \sqrt{x - 1}$. *Hint:* y is never negative.

10. $y = x^3$ 11. $y = x^3 - x$

12. $y = \sqrt{x(2 - x)}$. What is the domain and the range of this function?

13. Draw the graph of each of the functions in Problem 1, First Set, Article 5–1.

14. In Fig. 5–9, which graphs represent functions and which represent only relations? Why?

15. Draw the graph of each of the sets defined in Problem 2, First Set, Article 5–1.

16. Draw the graph of each of the following sets. Which is a function?

    a) $\{(x, y) | yx^2 = 1\}$ b) $\{(x, y) | y^2x = 1\}$

17. Consider the sets defined in Problem 4, Second Set, Article 4–5. Draw the graph of

    a) A b) B c) C d) D

18. If we refer to the sets defined in Problem 4, Second Set, Article 4–5, draw the graph of

    a) $B \cap C$ b) $A \cup B \cup D$

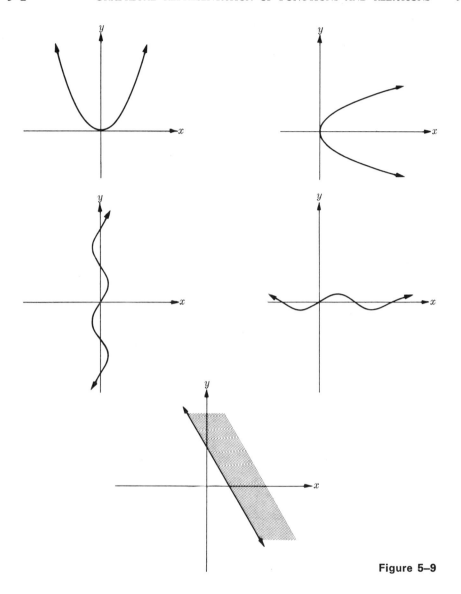

Figure 5–9

19. Draw the graph of the relations

    a) $\{(x, y)|x + y < 2\}$ b) $\{(x, y)|2x - 3y < 6\}$

20. Draw the graph of the relation

$$\{(x, y)|x - 3y + 3 > 0\} \cap \{(x, y)|y > x^2 - 7x + 10\}$$

CHAPTER 6

LINEAR AND QUADRATIC FUNCTIONS

6–1 THE LINEAR FUNCTION

In the last chapter we considered the concept of function in general. Probably the simplest function defined in mathematics by means of a nontrivial algebraic expression, is the function defined by the equation, $y = mx + b$.

Definition 6–1. The function f, defined by the first degree equation

$$f(x) = mx + b,$$

where m and b are constants, and written

$$f = \{(x, y)|y = mx + b\}, \tag{6–1}$$

is called a *linear function*.

The function derives its name from the fact that its graph is a straight line.* Moreover, any straight line other than $x = k$ (a straight line parallel to the y-axis) can be represented by such an equation with the appropriate m and b. We shall concern ourselves with the linear function's algebraic properties and its zeros, rather than the geometric properties.

We recall (Article 5–2) that the zero of a function is the x-coordinate or x-value for which y, the value of the function, is zero. Hence, we let $y = 0$, and we can find the zero of a linear function by solving the equation $mx + b = 0$ for x. In general, the zeros of a function are the *roots* or *solution* of the equation $f(x) = 0$. Before considering the solving of such a linear equation specifically, let us consider the problem of solving any equation.

Various methods are used in solving an equation. Any device that produces an *equivalent equation*, one which has the same roots, and only those roots, is permitted. Some procedures, such as squaring, may introduce new factors, and some, such as dividing, may lose some factors, so that extreme care should be exercised in using such procedures. Furthermore, it is always wise to check any purported solution, for the ultimate test of a number as a root of any equation is not how it is obtained, but whether it satisfies the equation. The following opera-

---

* The fact that $y = mx + b$ represents the equation of a straight line is proved in analytic geometry and will be assumed here.

tions are called *permissible*, since they always result in equations which are equivalent to the original, that is, the new equation has exactly the same roots.

1) The same number or algebraic expression may be added to or subtracted from both members of an equation.

2) Both members of an equation may be multiplied or divided by any nonzero number.

Illustration 1. In the solving of $4x - 5 = x + 7$, 5 is added and x is subtracted from both members, giving $3x = 12$. Then, division by 3 yields $x = 4$.

It should be clear that any permissible operation is reversible.

In addition to the permissible operations mentioned, an operation such as squaring both members of an equation is sometimes used. This device, however, is not reversible. Although no root of the original equation will be lost by the process, certain values may be introduced which are roots of the new equation, but not of the original one. If this type of operation is employed, the roots of the final equation *must* be examined to determine whether they are roots of the original equation.

Illustration 2. If in the equation $x - 1 = 3$, which has the root $x = 4$, both members are squared $(x - 1)^2 = 9$. If this equation is solved, one of its roots is -2, although it does not satisfy the original equation.*

Illustration 3. In solving the equation $x^2 - 3x = 0$ for values of x, we find $x = 0$ or 3. If we were to divide both members by x, however, we would have only the solution $x = 3$. The value $x = 0$ would have been "lost."†

Now let us consider the solution of linear equations.

Example 1. Solve the equation

$$\frac{2x + 5}{2} - \frac{5x}{x - 1} = x$$

for all possible values of x.

Solution. We first clear the equation of fractions by multiplying by the LCD, $2(x - 1)$,

$$(2x + 5)(x - 1) - (5x)(2) = (x)(2)(x - 1),$$

or

$$2x^2 + 3x - 5 - 10x = 2x^2 - 2x.$$

Combining similar terms, we have

$$-7x - 5 = -2x.$$

Adding $2x + 5$ to both members, we have $-5x = 5$, and dividing by -5, we get $x = -1$. This result should be verified by substituting $x = -1$ in the original equation.

---

* Any equation which, because of some mathematical process, has acquired an extra root is sometimes called a *redundant equation*.
† Any equation which, because of some mathematical process, has fewer roots than its original is sometimes called a *defective equation*.

Example 2. Solve the equation

$$s = \frac{a - rl}{1 - r}$$

for r.

Solution. This equation, one in which some or all of the known quantities are represented by letters, is called a *literal* equation. Each step in the solution should be verified;

$$s = \frac{a - rl}{1 - r},$$

$$s(1 - r) = a - rl,$$

$$s - rs = a - rl,$$

$$rl - rs = a - s,$$

$$r(l - s) = a - s,$$

$$r = \frac{a - s}{l - s}, \qquad \text{if } s \neq l.$$

PROBLEMS

Find the zeros of the linear functions f, defined by the following expressions for $f(x)$.

1. $2x + 4$ 2. $-5x + 10$ 3. $10 - 12x$

4. $6x - 9$ 5. $8x + 24$ 6. $5x - 17$

Solve the following linear equations and check.

7. $4x - 2 = 6x + 12$

8. $3x + 7 = 5x - 13$

9. $5 + 2(3 - x) = 4 + 2(x - 2) + 5x$

10. $x^2 - 7x + 10 = x^2 + 5x - 6$

11. $\dfrac{3x + 5}{12} - \dfrac{4 - x}{6} = \dfrac{x - 2}{3}$ 12. $\dfrac{3x - 6}{5} = \dfrac{2x - 5}{10} + \dfrac{x - 4}{2}$

13. $\dfrac{3x + 2}{x - 1} - \dfrac{6}{5} = 0$ 14. $\dfrac{2}{6x - 7} - \dfrac{5}{3x - 4} = 0$

15. $\dfrac{2x - 3}{3x} + \dfrac{5}{x - 1} = \dfrac{2}{3}$ 16. $\dfrac{x - 2}{3} = 3 - \dfrac{x + 9}{3}$

17. $\dfrac{1 + x}{1 - x} = 2$ 18. $\dfrac{x - 3}{2} + \dfrac{2 - x}{3} = \dfrac{4x}{5} - 4$

19. $\dfrac{4(2x + 3)}{5} = \dfrac{4 + (2x + 3)}{10}$ 20. $\dfrac{1}{2(x + \pi)} = \dfrac{2}{x + \pi} + 1$

Solve the following equations for the letters indicated.

21. $ax - bx = c$, for x 22. $ay + by = c + dy$, for y

23. $A = \frac{1}{2}bh$, for b 24. $A = \frac{1}{2}(b_1 + b_2)h$, for b_1

25. $l = a + (n - 1)d$, for d

26. $l = a + (n - 1)d$, for n

27. $S = \dfrac{a - rl}{1 - r}$, for l

28. $S = \dfrac{a - rl}{1 - r}$, for a

29. $S = \dfrac{n}{2}(a + l)$, for l

30. $S = v_0 t + \frac{1}{2}gt^2$, for v_0

31. $\dfrac{y}{K_1} = \dfrac{a + y}{K_2}$, for y

32. $K_1\left(\dfrac{x}{K_2} + a\right) = x$, for x

In Problems 33 through 40 sketch the graph of the linear function $f:x \rightarrow y$, where $y = f(x)$ is given by the following expressions.

33. $f(x) = 2x - 7$

34. $f(x) = (x/3) + 5$

35. $f(x) = -4x + 8$

36. $f(x) = 6 - (x/2)$

37. $f(x) = 4$

38. $f(x) = 3x + 6$

39. $f(x) = 20x - 30$

40. $f(x) = -(x/50) + (1/100)$

In solving the following problems, *read the problem carefully*, let one of the unknown quantities be x, and express all other unknown quantities in terms of x. Find two expressions or quantities that are equal, equate these, and solve the resulting equation. Check *all* answers.

41. A man 42 years old has a son 12. In how many years will the father be twice as old as his son?

42. The tens digit of a number is 3 less than the units digit. If the number is divided by the sum of the digits, the quotient is 4 and the remainder 3. What is the original number? *Hint:* If x equals the units digit, $x - 3$ is the tens digit, and the number may be written $10(x - 3) + x$.

43. A man left $\frac{1}{2}$ of his estate to his wife, $\frac{1}{6}$ to his daughter, and the remainder, an amount of \$15,000, to his son. How large was the entire estate?

44. A starts walking along a road at 3 mi/hr. Two hours later B starts in the same direction at 3.5 mi/hr. How far from the starting point will B overtake A? *Hint:* Rate × time = Distance.

45. A can do a certain job in 3 hours, while the same job takes B 4 hours. How long will it take both of them working together? *Hint:* If $x = $ number of hours for both to complete the work, $1/x$ will be the amount of the work done by both in 1 hour.

46. If the larger of two integers, whose sum is 88, is divided by the smaller, the quotient is 5 and the remainder is 10. What are the two numbers?

6–2 ARITHMETIC PROGRESSIONS

Let us consider the linear function defined by the equation $f(x) = 2x - 1$, where the domain of the function consists of the positive integers. In this case the function assumes the values $1, 3, 5, \ldots, 2n - 1, \ldots$. Similarly, if the function whose defining equation is $y = 2^x$ has as its domain the positive integers, the corresponding functional values are $2, 4, 8, \ldots, 2^n, \ldots$. Both of these sets of functional values are examples of sequences. In general, a *sequence* is the range of some function whose domain is either all or a part of the set of positive integers.

The functional value of the integer 1 is the first term of the sequence, of 2 the second term, of 3 the third term, and so on. In this way, the first, second, third, etc., values in the sequence are specifically determined. If the entire set of integers is considered, the sequence is *infinite;* but if only the first n positive integers make up the domain of the function, the sequence is *finite.* We are concerned in this article with one specific type of sequence.

> **Definition 6-2.** An *arithmetic progression* is a sequence in which each term after the first is obtained by adding the same fixed number, called the common difference, to the preceding term.

> **Alternative Definition 6-2.** An *arithmetic progression* is any sequence for which the "defining function" is linear. (See Problem 33.)

Illustration 1. The finite sequence 2, 5, 8, 11, 14 is an arithmetic progression with the common difference of 3. The function defining this sequence is $f: x \to 3x - 1$, with the domain $\{1, 2, 3, 4, 5\}$.

Illustration 2. The infinite sequence 7, 2, -3, -8, -13, ... is an arithmetic progression with the common difference $-5 : f(x) = 12 - 5x$.

Let us use the following general notations for any arithmetic progression:

$$t_1, \text{ the first term,} \qquad d, \text{ the common difference,}$$

$$n, \text{ the number of terms,} \qquad t_n, \text{ the last or } n\text{th term.}$$

Thus, in Illustration 1, $t_1 = 2$, $d = 3$, $n = 5$, and $t_n = 3n - 1$, while for Illustration 2, $t_1 = 7$, $d = -5$, and $t_n = 12 - 5n$. Note that the nth term really represents the function which defines the sequence.

In general, the first n terms of an arithmetic progression may be represented by

$$t_1, \quad t_1 + d, \quad t_1 + 2d, \quad t_1 + 3d, \quad \ldots, \quad t_1 + (n - 1)d.$$

The last value also gives us the expression for the nth term t_n, in terms of t_1, n, and d,

$$\boxed{t_n = t_1 + (n - 1)d.} \tag{6-2}$$

Example 1. Find the 25th term of the arithmetic progression 2, 5, 8, 11, ...

Solution. In this progression, since $t_1 = 2$ and $d = 3$, we have

$$t_{25} = t_1 + (n - 1)d = 2 + (24)3 = 74.$$

Example 2. If the 6th term of an arithmetic progression is 27 and the 12th term is 48, find the first term.

Solution. We have the two relations,

$$t_6 = 27 = t_1 + 5d$$

and

$$t_{12} = 48 = t_1 + 11d.$$

Subtracting the respective members of the first equation from those of the second, we obtain $21 = 6d$, or

$$d = \tfrac{7}{2}.$$

Substituting this value in the first equation, we have

$$27 = t_1 + 5(\tfrac{7}{2}),$$

and we find

$$t_1 = 9\tfrac{1}{2}.$$

Example 3. Find the arithmetic progression of 6 terms if the first is $\tfrac{2}{3}$ and the last is $7\tfrac{1}{3}$.

Solution. Using Eq. (6–2), we have

$$t_5 = \tfrac{22}{3} = \tfrac{2}{3} + 5d,$$

and solving,

$$d = \tfrac{4}{3}.$$

Therefore the required progression is

$$\tfrac{2}{3}, \quad 2, \quad \tfrac{10}{3}, \quad \tfrac{14}{3}, \quad 6, \quad \tfrac{22}{3}.$$

We are often interested in the sum of the general finite arithmetic progression. We let

$$S_n = t_1 + (t_1 + d) + (t_1 + 2d) + \cdots + [t_1 + (n - 1)d]. \qquad (6\text{–}3)$$

We may also write this expression in reverse order:

$$S_n = [t_1 + (n - 1)d] + [t_1 + (n - 2)d] + \cdots + (t_1 + d) + t_1.$$

If we add the respective members of these equations and group the corresponding terms,

$$2S_n = [2t_1 + (n - 1)d] + [2t_1 + (n - 1)d]$$
$$+ [2t_1 + (n - 1)d] + \cdots + [2t_1 + (n - 1)d].$$

Since there are n terms, $2t_1 + (n - 1)d$, on the right side of this equation, we have

$$2S_n = n[2t_1 + (n - 1)d],$$

or

$$S_n = \frac{n[2t_1 + (n - 1)d]}{2}. \qquad (6\text{–}4)^*$$

Recalling that $t_n = t_1 + (n - 1)d$, we may also write Eq. (6–4) as

$$S_n = \frac{n(t_1 + t_n)}{2}. \qquad (6\text{–}5)$$

---

* This relation can also be proved by mathematical induction. (See Problem 17, Article 11–1.)

Example 4. Find the sum of the first 30 terms of the arithmetic progression $-15, -13, -11, \ldots$

Solution. Since $t_1 = -15$, $d = 2$, and $n = 30$, we have

$$S_{30} = \frac{30[2(-15) + (30 - 1)2]}{2}$$

$$= \frac{30(-30 + 58)}{2} = 420.$$

Example 5. The sum of the first 15 terms of an arithmetic progression is 270. Find the first term and the common difference if the 15th term is 39.

Solution. By using Eq. (6–5), we obtain

$$270 = \frac{15(t_1 + 39)}{2}.$$

Solving for t_1, we have

$$15t_1 + 585 = 540, \qquad 15t_1 = -45, \qquad t_1 = -3.$$

Since $t_{15} = t_1 + (n - 1)d$,

$$39 = -3 + 14d, \qquad \text{or} \qquad d = 3.$$

PROBLEMS

Write the next three terms in each of the following arithmetic progressions, and find t_n and S_n.

1. $1, 4, 7, \ldots$ to 9 terms.   2. $27, 25, 23, \ldots$ to 30 terms.

3. $10, 7, 4, \ldots$ to 15 terms.   4. $-\frac{5}{4}, -\frac{1}{4}, \frac{3}{4}, \ldots$ to 8 terms.

In Problems 5 through 11, three of the elements t_1, t_n, d, n, and S_n of the arithmetic progression are given. Find the missing elements in each case.

5. $t_1 = 2, d = 4, n = 12$ 6. $t_1 = 3, n = 4, t_n = 12$

7. $t_1 = -2, n = 14, S_n = 20$ 8. $d = 3, n = 5, t_n = 14$

9. $d = \frac{1}{2}, n = 14, S_n = 30$ 10. $t_1 = 4, d = 4, S_n = 40$

11. $t_1 = 6, d = 5, t_n = 36$

12. Find the value of k so that $8k + 4$, $6k - 2$, and $2k - 7$ will form an arithmetic progression.

13. What are the first three terms of an arithmetic progression whose 9th term is 16 and 40th term is 47?

14. The 18th and 52nd terms of an arithmetic progression are 3 and 173, respectively. Find the 25th term.

15. Find the sum of all the even integers from 12 to 864, inclusive.

16. Find the sum of all the odd integers from 27 to 495, inclusive.

▶ 17. The terms between any two terms of an arithmetic progression are called the *arithmetic means* between these two terms. Insert four arithmetic means between -1 and 14.

18. Insert five arithmetic means between 14 and 86.

19. Insert three arithmetic means between -18 and 4.

▶ **20.** Insert one arithmetic mean between 24 and 68. Such a number is called the *arithmetic mean* of the two numbers.

21. Find the arithmetic mean of

     a) 7 and -15 b) $\frac{3}{5}$ and $\frac{5}{3}$

▶ **22.** A *harmonic progression* is a sequence of numbers whose reciprocals form an arithmetic progression. Insert two harmonic means between 4 and 8.

23. For any sequence of numbers forming an arithmetic progression, show that the products formed by multiplying each term by any constant also form an arithmetic progression.

24. If a^2, b^2, and c^2 form an arithmetic progression, show that $a + b$, $c + a$, and $b + c$ form a harmonic progression.

25. How many numbers between 10 and 200 are exactly divisible by 7? Find their sum.

26. How many numbers between 25 and 400 are exactly divisible by 11? Find their sum.

27. If a clock strikes the appropriate number of times on each hour, how many times will it strike in one week?

28. A man accepts a position at the rate of $3600 a year with the understanding that he will receive an increase of $250 every six months. What will his salary be after working 15 years? How much will his entire earnings be?

29. The force of gravity causes a body to fall 16.1 feet during the first second, 48.3 the next second, 80.5 the third, and so on. How far will the body fall in 10 seconds?

30. A man bought a house at the beginning of 1952 for $10,000. If it increased $500 in value each year, how much was it worth at the end of 1966?

31. A piece of equipment cost a certain factory $29,000. If it depreciates in value 15% the first year, 13.5% the second, 12% the third, and so on, what will its value be at the end of 10 years, all percentages applying to the original cost?

32. A certain antique originally worth $1600 is evaluated at $5660 after 80 years. Find the value at the end of each ten-year period if the increase in value during each such period was $125 more than during the preceding ten years.

33. By using Eq. (6–2), prove that the two definitions of an arithmetic progression are equivalent.

6–3 THE QUADRATIC FUNCTION

The second type of algebraic function usually considered, is one in which the defining equation is of the second degree.

     Definition 6–3. The function f, defined by the second degree equation $f(x) = ax^2 + bx + c$, where a, b, and c are constants, and $a \neq 0$, and written

$$f = \{(x, y) | y = ax^2 + bx + c\}, \tag{6–6}$$

is called a *quadratic function*.

The graph of such a function was briefly considered in Example 2, Article 5–2. Another example seems appropriate.

Example 1. Draw the graph of the quadratic function

$$q:x \rightarrow -2x^2 + 12x - 14.$$

Solution. The graph (Fig. 6–1) is drawn by tabulating a sufficient number of points whose coordinates satisfy the equation $y = -2x^2 + 12x - 14$.

x	0	1	2	3	4	5	6
y	-14	-4	2	4	2	-4	-14

Comparing this curve with that in Fig. 5–5, we see that both have the same general shape. The graph of any quadratic function is of this type and is called a *parabola*. Although we shall not prove it, when the coefficient of x^2 is positive, the curve opens upward, while the curve opens downward if the coefficient of x^2 is negative. Compare the two examples.

The graph of the general quadratic function may be sketched by the more direct process of expressing the quadratic function in terms of the square of a linear function. Consider

$$y = ax^2 + bx + c. \tag{6–7}$$

Factoring out a, and grouping the x^2 and x terms together, we have

$$y = a\left[\left(x^2 + \frac{b}{a}x\right) + \frac{c}{a}\right].$$

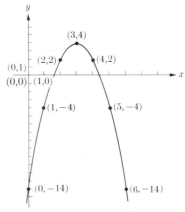

Recalling Eq. (3–13), we must add $(b/2a)^2$ to $x^2 + (b/a)x$ in order to form a perfect square. Thus, adding and subtracting $b^2/4a^2$ within the bracket,

$$y = a\left[\left(x^2 + \frac{b}{a}x + \frac{b^2}{4a^2}\right) + \frac{c}{a} - \frac{b^2}{4a^2}\right],$$

and simplifying, we have

$$y = a\left[\left(x + \frac{b}{2a}\right)^2 + \frac{4ac - b^2}{4a^2}\right]. \tag{6–8}$$

Figure 6–1

Since the squared quantity $(x + b/2a)^2 \geq 0$, the expression within the bracket has its least value when $x = -b/2a$. If $a > 0$, the function also has its least value at $x = -b/2a$. This least value of the function, $(4ac - b^2)/4a$, is called its *minimum*. If, however, $a < 0$, when $x = -b/2a$, the function has its greatest value, called its *maximum*, and is also equal to $(4ac - b^2)/4a$. In either case, the point

$$\left[\frac{-b}{2a}, \frac{4ac - b^2}{4a}\right]$$

is called the *vertex* of the parabola. With this point found, and an additional point or two, the graph can be sketched. It is usually simpler to complete the square in each case than to use the formulas in this discussion.

Example 2. Find the vertex of the parabola represented by the equation

$$y = x^2 - x - 6.$$

Compare with Example 2, Article 5–2.

Solution. Grouping the first two terms on the right and completing the square, we obtain

$$y = (x^2 - x) - 6 = (x^2 - x + \tfrac{1}{4}) - 6 - \tfrac{1}{4} = (x - \tfrac{1}{2})^2 - \tfrac{25}{4}.$$

The vertex is $(\tfrac{1}{2}, -\tfrac{25}{4})$. Since $a = 1$, which is positive, the minimum value of the function is $-\tfrac{25}{4}$, and this occurs when $x = \tfrac{1}{2}$. The graph of this function appears in Fig. 5–5.

PROBLEMS

For each of the following functions f, where $f(x)$ is given by the following expressions, find the maximum or minimum and draw the graph.

1. $x^2 + 6x + 5$
2. $x^2 + x - 6$
3. $2x^2 + 5x - 12$
4. $-2x^2 + 11x - 15$
5. $6x^2 - 17x + 5$
6. $-2x^2 + 5x + 8$
7. $x^2 + 6x + 11$
8. $-3x^2 + 5x - 4$

9. Find two numbers whose sum is 16 and whose product is a maximum. *Hint:* Letting x be one number, and $16 - x$ the other, we can express the product y in terms of x, namely, $y = x(16 - x) = 16x - x^2$.

10. Divide 40 into two parts such that the sum of the squares of these parts is a minimum.

11. A man with 160 ft of fencing wishes to fence off an area in the shape of a rectangle. What should be the dimensions of the area if the enclosed space is to be as large as possible?

12. A man with 160 ft of fencing wishes to fence off an area in the shape of a rectangle. If one side of the area will not require fencing, what should be the dimensions to ensure the largest area possible?

6–4 SOLUTION OF THE QUADRATIC EQUATION

We are now in a position to find the zeros of any quadratic function. Recalling the definition of the zeros of a function (Article 5–2), we are interested in finding the abscissas of the points where the graph $y = ax^2 + bx + c$ crosses or meets the x-axis. This may be found graphically by sketching the curve. For example, from Fig. 5–5, the zeros of $x^2 - x - 6$ are -2, and 3. Likewise, from Fig. 6–1, the zeros of $-2x^2 + 12x - 14$ are approximately 1.3 and 4.7. Such values can, of course, be checked by substituting in the original function, set equal to zero.

There are more accurate methods for finding the zeros of the function $f:x \rightarrow ax^2 + bx + c$. In finding its zeros or, equivalently, in solving the equation

$$ax^2 + bx + c = 0 \quad (a \neq 0), \tag{6–9}$$

we may be able to factor the left member. This method, known as the *factoring method*, depends upon the fact that either factor is zero if the product is zero (Theorem 2–5).

Example 1. Solve the quadratic equation $x^2 - 7x + 10 = 0$ by factoring.

Solution. Since $x^2 - 7x + 10 \equiv (x - 5)(x - 2)$, [see Eq. (3–14)], the equation may be written

$$(x - 5)(x - 2) = 0.$$

We wish to find a value such that when it is substituted for x in the member on the left, the product is zero. Such may be found by solving either of

$$x - 5 = 0 \quad \text{and} \quad x - 2 = 0.$$

For these, we find $x = 5$ or $x = 2$, either of which is a root of the original equation. All answers should be checked.

Example 2. Solve the equation $ax^2 - px + aqx - pq = 0$ for all possible values of x in terms of a, p, and q.

Solution. If we factor the left-hand member of this equation, by recalling Eq. 3–15, we have

$$ax^2 - px + aqx - pq = (ax - p)(x + q),$$

so that the equation becomes

$$(ax - p)(x + q) = 0.$$

Thus, we have two equations

$$ax - p = 0 \quad \text{and} \quad x + q = 0$$

to solve for x, and we obtain $x = p/a$ or $-q$.

PROBLEMS

1–8. From the graphs of the functions listed in Problems 1 through 8 Article 6–3, give the roots of the corresponding equations. Check these by substituting the results into the original equations.

Solve Problems 9 through 26 by factoring and check by substitution.

9. $9x^2 - 16 = 0$ 10. $2x^2 - 5x - 12 = 0$

11. $4x^2/a^2 = 1$ 12. $4y^2/b^2 = 3$

13. $6x^2 - 5x = 50$ 14. $2x^2 - 2 = x - 4x$

15. $2x^2 - 5x - 12 = 0$ 16. $6x^2 + 7x - 3 = 0$

17. $3x^2 - x = 10$ 18. $4x^2 - 12x + 9 = 0$

19. $3x^2 + x - 2 = 0$ 20. $2x^2 + x = 0$

21. $x^2 + 2ax = b^2 - a^2$ 22. $8x^2 + 14ax + 3a^2 = 0$

23. $2x^2 - rx + 2sx - rs = 0$ 24. $prx^2 - qrx + ptx - qt = 0$

25. $\dfrac{x - 2}{x + 3} - 3 = \dfrac{4(x + 3)}{x - 2}$ 26. $(x - 2)(x + 3) = 6$

The quadratic expression in an equation may be difficult to factor. Moreover, in many cases factors may not exist. As a result, the most useful method of solving any quadratic equation is *by the quadratic formula*. We obtain this formula by completing the square, as was done in finding the vertex of the parabola.

Theorem 6–1. The two roots of any quadratic equation,

$$ax^2 + bx + c = 0 \qquad (a \neq 0), \tag{6–9}$$

are

$$x = \frac{-b \pm \sqrt{b^2 - 4ac}}{2a}. \tag{6–10}$$

Proof. If we divide by the coefficient of x^2 in Eq. (6–9) and transpose the constant term to the right side of the equation, we have

$$x^2 + \frac{b}{a}x = -\frac{c}{a}.$$

We may complete the square of the left member by adding $b^2/4a^2$ to both sides of the equation,

$$x^2 + \frac{b}{a}x + \frac{b^2}{4a^2} = \frac{b^2}{4a^2} - \frac{c}{a}, \qquad \text{or} \qquad \left(x + \frac{b}{2a}\right)^2 = \frac{b^2 - 4ac}{4a^2}.$$

If we extract the square root, this becomes

$$x + \frac{b}{2a} = \frac{\pm\sqrt{b^2 - 4ac}}{2a}, \qquad \text{or} \qquad x = \frac{-b \pm \sqrt{b^2 - 4ac}}{2a}.$$

The use of the plus and then the minus sign gives the two roots of the quadratic equation $ax^2 + bx + c = 0$, which completes the proof. The reader should verify that each of these roots is actually a solution by substituting them in Eq. (6–9).

Although any quadratic equation can be solved by the *method of completing the square* used to obtain this formula, direct substitution into Eq. (6–10) is more frequently employed because of its efficiency. Consider the following examples.

Example 3. Solve the quadratic equation $4x^2 + 5x = 21$.

Solution. Transposing all the members to the left side to put the equation in the form $ax^2 + bx + c = 0$, and comparing the two, we have $a = 4$, $b = 5$, and $c = -21$. Substituting these values into Eq. (6–10), we have

$$x = \frac{-5 \pm \sqrt{(5)^2 - 4(4)(-21)}}{2(4)}.$$

Simplification yields

$$x = \frac{-5 \pm \sqrt{25 + 336}}{8} = \frac{-5 \pm \sqrt{361}}{8} = \frac{-5 \pm 19}{8}.$$

Therefore, choosing the plus and then the minus sign, we obtain

$$x = \tfrac{7}{4} \quad \text{or} \quad -3.$$

Both answers should be checked by substituting them in the original equation. The fact that the number under the radical sign is a perfect square guarantees that the roots are rational. Thus the equation could have been solved by the method of factoring. Specifically,

$$4x^2 + 5x - 21 \equiv (4x - 7)(x + 3).$$

Example 4. Solve $3 + 5y = y^2$ for all values of y.

Solution. It is possible to rewrite this equation in the form of Eq. (6–9),

$$y^2 - 5y - 3 = 0.$$

If we use Eq. (6–10), we find $a = 1$, $b = -5$, and $c = -3$. Therefore,

$$y = \frac{5 \pm \sqrt{25 + 12}}{2} = \frac{5 \pm \sqrt{37}}{2},$$

or, if approximate answers are desired,

$$y = \frac{5 \pm 6.0828}{2}, \quad \text{or} \quad y = 5.5414 \quad \text{or} \quad -0.5414.$$

The general procedure in solving any quadratic equation is:

1) Try to solve the equation by the method of factoring.
2) If this method fails, either because the factors are not immediately evident or because they actually do not exist as rational factors, use the quadratic formula.

PROBLEMS

Solve the equations of Problems 1 through 19 by using the quadratic formula. Check all answers.

1. $2x^2 + 5x - 12 = 0$

2. $4x^2 - 2x = 7$

3. $x^2 + x - 1 = 0$

4. $2x^2 + x - 12 = 0$

5. $x^2 - 3x + 2 = 0$

6. $2(1 - x^2) + 3x = 0$

7. $x^2 - (a + b)x + ab = 0$

8. $6x^2 + 17x + 12 = 0$

9. $(a - b)x^2 + (b - c)x + (c - a) = 0$

10. $4(1 - x^2) - 3x - 2 = 0$

11. $3(1 + x^2) + x - 5 = 0$

12. $x^2 - 2x + 1 = 4a^2$

13. $\dfrac{x - 1}{x^2 - 9} - \dfrac{3x + 5}{x + 3} = \dfrac{x + 3}{x - 3}$

14. $1/x = 2 + x$

15. $4(1 - x^2) + 2x = 3$

16. $6ax^2 - 2bx + 3b = 9ax$

17. $s = v_0 x - gx^2/2$

18. $x + 5 = 3(1 + x^2)$

19. $\dfrac{1}{x^2 + 3x + 2} - \dfrac{1}{1 - x} = \dfrac{2}{x^2 - 1}$

20. The product of two consecutive positive integers is 72. Find the integers.

21. The sum of a number and its reciprocal is $34/15$. Find the number.

22. A man traveling 40 miles finds that by traveling one more mile per hour, he would make the journey in 2 hr less time. How many miles per hour did he actually travel?

23. If $(6 - x)$, $(13 - x)$, and $(14 - x)$ are the lengths of the sides of a right triangle, find the value of x.

24. By how much must a radius of 24 in. be reduced in order to decrease the area of a circle by 49π in^2?

25. A rectangular flower bed 30 yards long by 24 yards wide has a walk of uniform width around it. If the area of the path is one-fourth that of the flower bed, find the width of the path.

26. Working together, two men can do a job in 20 days. Working alone, however, it would take one man 9 days longer than it would take the other to complete the job. How long would it take each separately?

6–5 INEQUALITIES

Since most of the inequalities discussed in this book involve either first or second degree algebraic expressions, it seems appropriate to consider them in this chapter. The student should review the order axioms and basic theorems in Article 4–1.

A statement that one mathematical expression is greater than or less than another is called an *inequality*. As is true for equations (Article 1–6), there are two general types of inequalities in mathematics, the conditional inequality, corresponding to the conditional equation, and the absolute inequality, corresponding to the identity.

> **Definition 6–4.** An inequality is called an *absolute inequality* if it is true for all permissible values of the variables involved.

Although frequently an inequality may be true for an entire set of values, if it is not true for every permissible value, the inequality is not absolute.

> **Definition 6–5.** An inequality is called a *conditional inequality* if it is not true for all permissible values of the variables involved.

Illustration. The inequality $a^2 + b^2 + 1 > 0$ is an absolute inequality. The expression $-4 < 3$ is also of this type. But $2x - 6 > 0$ is a conditional inequality, since it is true only for values of x greater than 3.

As is true in dealing with equations, there are certain important properties to be remembered in working with inequalities. The proofs of the theorems below follow directly from the axioms and theorems in Article 4–1.

Theorem 6–2. The sense of an inequality is not changed if both members are increased or decreased by the same number.

Proof. This is a direct result of Axiom O3, where c may be either positive or negative. The usefulness of this property lies in the fact that a term may be transposed from one member of an inequality to the other member by changing the sign of the term without changing the sense of the inequality.

Theorem 6–3. The sense of an inequality is not changed if both members are multiplied or divided by the same *positive* number.

This is a restatement of Axiom O4.

Theorem 6–4. The sense of an inequality is reversed if both members are multiplied or divided by the same *negative* number.

This is a restatement of Theorem 4–3.

Since we wish to confine our discussion to inequalities in one variable, we are interested in those inequalities which may be written $f(x) > 0$ or $f(x) < 0$. First let us consider conditional inequalities. To solve such an inequality, *we must find the set of values of x for which the inequality is true.* When $f(x)$ is linear or quadratic, this set may be found by either an algebraic or graphical method.

Example 1. Solve

$$\frac{x}{3} - 2 < \frac{5x + 9}{2}$$

both algebraically and graphically.

Algebraic solution. Multiplying both members by 6, we have

$$2x - 12 < 15x + 27.$$

Transposing and collecting terms, we obtain

$$-13x < 39.$$

If we divide by -13,

$$x > -3,$$

so that the solution is $\{x | x > -3\}$.

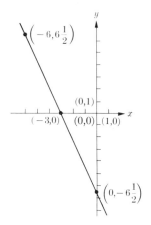

Figure 6–2

Graphical solution. If we transpose all terms to the left side of the inequality, we have

$$\frac{x}{3} - 2 - \frac{5x + 9}{2} < 0.$$

Denoting this left member by $f(x)$, we get

$$f(x) \equiv \frac{2x - 12 - 15x - 27}{6} \equiv \frac{-13x - 39}{6}.$$

From the graph of $y = f(x)$ in Fig. 6–2, which can easily be drawn from the table below, it is clear that the inequality is satisfied for $x > -3$, since for these values of x, $y = f(x)$ is below the x-axis, that is, $f(x) < 0$. The graphical method is more frequently used for quadratic inequalities.

x	0	-3	-6
y	$-6\frac{1}{2}$	0	$6\frac{1}{2}$

Example 2. For what values of x does the inequality $x^2 - x - 6 > 0$ hold?

Solution. If we factor the expression, we have

$$x^2 - x - 6 \equiv (x - 3)(x + 2).$$

Since the product of two terms will be positive only if both are positive or both negative (Problem 10, Article 4-1), $x - 3$ and $x + 2$ must both be greater than zero or both less than zero. We see that

$$\left\{\begin{matrix} x - 3 > 0 \\ \text{and} \\ x + 2 > 0 \end{matrix}\right\} \quad \text{or} \quad \left\{\begin{matrix} x > 3 \\ \text{and} \\ x > -2 \end{matrix}\right\} \text{ will both be true if } x > 3,$$

and

$$\left\{\begin{matrix} x - 3 < 0 \\ \text{and} \\ x + 2 < 0 \end{matrix}\right\} \quad \text{or} \quad \left\{\begin{matrix} x < 3 \\ \text{and} \\ x < -2 \end{matrix}\right\} \text{ will both be true if } x < -2.$$

Thus the solution for the inequality is

$$\{x|x > 3 \text{ or } x < -2\}.$$

This may be checked graphically by Fig. 5–5. It is often helpful to test some value in the set for which the inequality holds. Although this will not guarantee the proper complete solution, it is usually a helpful check of the work.

Example 3. For what values of x does the inequality $-2x^2 + 12x - 14 > 0$ hold?

Solution. Since the left member is not factorable rationally, we use the graphical method. In Fig. 6–1 we have the graph of the function

$$y = f(x) = -2x^2 + 12x - 14,$$

whose zeros we may approximate as 1.6 and 4.4. Thus the inequality holds for the set

$$\{x|1.6 < x < 4.4\}.$$

Should we wish to determine the zeros more accurately, we could use the quadratic formula for the equation $-2x^2 + 12x - 14 = 0$, or the equivalent equation $x^2 - 6x + 7 = 0$,

$$x = \frac{6 \pm \sqrt{36 - 28}}{2} = \frac{6 \pm 2\sqrt{2}}{2} = 3 \pm \sqrt{2}.$$

Hence, $x = 4.414$ or 1.586, approximately, and as a result the solution would be written

$$\{x|1.586 < x < 4.414\}.$$

Example 4. Determine the values of y which satisfy the inequality

$$2(1 - y^2) + y < 2.$$

Solution. If we simplify the inequality $2(1 - y^2) + y < 2$, we have

$$2 - 2y^2 + y - 2 < 0, \quad \text{or} \quad y(1 - 2y) < 0.$$

Since the product of two quantities will be negative if one is negative while the other is positive (Problem 11, Article 4–1), we may have

$$\text{either} \quad \left\{ \begin{array}{c} y < 0 \\ \text{and} \\ 1 - 2y > 0 \end{array} \right\}, \quad \text{which gives} \quad \left\{ \begin{array}{c} y < 0 \\ \text{and} \\ y < \frac{1}{2} \end{array} \right\},$$

$$\text{or} \quad \left\{ \begin{array}{c} y > 0 \\ \text{and} \\ 1 - 2y < 0 \end{array} \right\}, \quad \text{which gives} \quad \left\{ \begin{array}{c} y > 0 \\ \text{and} \\ y > \frac{1}{2} \end{array} \right\}.$$

The first set is satisfied if $y < 0$, while the second is satisfied if $y > \frac{1}{2}$. The solution set is

$$\{y|y < 0 \text{ or } y > \tfrac{1}{2}\}.$$

PROBLEMS

Find the values of x for which the following inequalities are satisfied. Use either the algebraic or graphical method.

1. $3x - 27 > 0$

2. $2x - 12 < 0$

3. $2x + 5 > 4x - 9$

4. $5x - 3 < 8x - 12$

5. $x^2 + 2x > 99$

6. $2x^2 + 3x < 14$

7. $6x^2 + x < 1$

8. $6x^2 - x > 35$

9. $x^2 + 2x > 12$

10. $x^2 + 2x + 4 > 0$

11. $x^4 + x^2 < 0$

12. $\dfrac{x - 2}{x - 5} > 0$

13. $\dfrac{1}{x} < \dfrac{1}{5}$

14. $\dfrac{1}{x - 2} < \dfrac{1}{3}$

15. $|x - 4| < 1$
      Hint: Problem 9, Article 4–2.

16. $|x - 3| > 2$
      Hint: Problem 13, Article 4–2.

17. $|2x - 3| \leq 4$

18. $\left|\dfrac{x}{3} - 7\right| \leq 5$

19. $\left|\dfrac{x}{4} + 6\right| \geq \dfrac{1}{2}$

20. $|5x + 1| \geq 4$

Absolute inequalities, of course, will also satisfy the properties mentioned in this section as well as those in Article 4–1. The usual problem in dealing with absolute inequalities is to establish the validity of the given inequality for all permissible values. Since we must start with a valid inequality in any proof, it is often convenient to assume tentatively the proposition we are proving and reduce it to a simpler inequality which is known to be valid. Then the actual proof will consist of retracing the steps. The method is illustrated below.

Example 5. Prove that for all real values of x, $x^2 + 1 \geq 2x$.

Solution. We wish to find an inequality known to be true. By subtracting $2x$ from both members of

$$x^2 + 1 \geq 2x, \tag{6–11}$$

we have

$$x^2 - 2x + 1 \geq 0, \tag{6–12}$$

which is known to be true, since $x^2 - 2x + 1 \equiv (x - 1)^2$ (Problem 12, Article 4–1). Our proof therefore starts with inequality (6–12). Since

$$x^2 - 2x + 1 \geq 0,$$

for all real values of x, by adding $2x$ to both members, we obtain the desired result,

$$x^2 + 1 \geq 2x.$$

Example 6. Prove that the sum of any *positive* number and its reciprocal is greater than or equal to 2.

Solution. If we let x be any positive number, we wish to prove

$$x + \frac{1}{x} \geq 2. \tag{6–13}$$

Although this is not an absolute inequality, we shall use one to establish it. If we divide both members of Eq. (6–11) by x, which is positive, we get the required inequality.

PROBLEMS

Prove each of the following inequalities. The letters in the problems represent unequal positive numbers. Tell which are conditional and which are absolute inequalities.

1. $a^2 + b^2 > 2ab$

2. $\dfrac{a}{b} + \dfrac{b}{a} > 2$

3. $\dfrac{x + y}{2} > \sqrt{xy}$

4. $\dfrac{a + b}{2} > \dfrac{2ab}{a + b}$

5. $\dfrac{x^2}{y} + \dfrac{y^2}{x} > x + y$

6. $x^3 + y^3 > x^2y + xy^2$

7. $x^2 + y^2 + z^2 < (x + y + z)^2$

8. $a^2 + 2a + 2 > 0$

9. $|a + b| \leq |a| + |b|$

10. $|a - b| \geq |a| - |b|$

6-6 RELATIONS BETWEEN ZEROS AND COEFFICIENTS OF THE QUADRATIC FUNCTION

In addition to Eq. (6–10), which gives the zeros of the quadratic function

$$f:x \rightarrow ax^2 + bx + c$$

in terms of the coefficients, there are other relations between the zeros and the coefficients. By letting r_1 and r_2 be the zeros of $ax^2 + bx + c$, where

$$r_1 = \frac{-b + \sqrt{b^2 - 4ac}}{2a},$$

$$r_2 = \frac{-b - \sqrt{b^2 - 4ac}}{2a}, \tag{6–14}$$

we have the sum of the two zeros,

$$r_1 + r_2 = -\frac{b}{a}. \tag{6–15}$$

Likewise, we have the product

$$r_1 \cdot r_2 = \frac{(-b)^2 - (\sqrt{b^2 - 4ac})^2}{4a^2}$$

$$= \frac{b^2 - (b^2 - 4ac)}{4a^2},$$

or

$$r_1 \cdot r_2 = \frac{c}{a}. \tag{6–16}$$

Since the zeros of the function $f:x \rightarrow ax^2 + bx + c$ and the roots of the equation formed by setting the functional value $f(x)$ equal to zero are the same, Eqs. (6–15) and (6–16) are useful in forming such an equation. The following theorem will clarify this remark.

Theorem 6–5. If any quadratic equation $ax^2 + bx + c = 0$ is written

$$x^2 + \frac{b}{a}x + \frac{c}{a} = 0, \tag{6–17}$$

so that the coefficient of x^2 is unity, (1) the sum of its roots is equal to the negative of the coefficient of x, and (2) the product of its roots is equal to the constant term.

Proof. We establish this result by comparing the coefficient of x with Eq. (6–15), and the constant term with Eq. (6–16).

Example 1. Without obtaining the zeros, find the sum and product of the zeros of $f:x \rightarrow 3x^2 - 4x + 8$.

Solution. Since $a = 3$, $b = -4$, and $c = 8$, the sum is $-(-4/3) = \frac{4}{3}$, and the product is $\frac{8}{3}$.

Example 2. Write a quadratic equation whose roots are $3 + \sqrt{2}$ and $3 - \sqrt{2}$.

Solution. Since

$$(3 + \sqrt{2}) + (3 - \sqrt{2}) = 6,$$

and

$$(3 + \sqrt{2})(3 - \sqrt{2}) = 9 - 2 = 7,$$

an equation of this type is

$$x^2 - 6x + 7 = 0.$$

Example 3. Without solving, form a quadratic equation whose roots are the squares of the roots of $2x^2 + x - 6 = 0$.

Solution. By letting r_1 and r_2 be the roots of the given equation, we have

$$r_1 + r_2 = -\tfrac{1}{2}, \qquad r_1 r_2 = -3.$$

Since $(r_1 + r_2)^2 \equiv r_1^2 + 2r_1 r_2 + r_2^2$, the sum of the roots for the new equation will be

$$r_1^2 + r_2^2 \equiv (r_1 + r_2)^2 - 2r_1 r_2 = \tfrac{1}{4} + 6 = \tfrac{25}{4},$$

and the product will be

$$(r_1 r_2)^2 = 9.$$

Therefore the required equation is

$$x^2 - \tfrac{25}{4}x + 9 = 0$$

or, clearing fractions,

$$4x^2 - 25x + 36 = 0.$$

The expression $b^2 - 4ac$, under the radical in Eq. (6–14), is another quantity which, in terms of the coefficients, is important in considering the nature of the zeros of the function. If this expression, called the *discriminant*, is negative, no real square root will exist. The zeros will be *imaginary*. Such numbers will be considered in Chapter 13. If $b^2 - 4ac$ is equal to zero, $r_1 = r_2$ and the zeros are equal; while if $b^2 - 4ac$ is positive, the zeros are real and unequal. Since the zeros of the function $f : x \rightarrow ax^2 + bx + c$ and the roots of the equation $ax^2 + bx + c = 0$ are the same, we have immediately the following theorem.

Theorem 6–6. Consider the quadratic equation $ax^2 + bx + c = 0$.

1. If $b^2 - 4ac < 0$, no real roots exist.
2. If $b^2 - 4ac = 0$, the roots are real and equal.
3. If $b^2 - 4ac > 0$, the roots are real and unequal.

If we wished to emphasize the graph of $y = f(x) = ax^2 + bx + c$, rather than the roots of $ax^2 + bx + c = 0$, we could give the following theorem.

Theorem 6–7. Consider the quadratic function $f(x) = ax^2 + bx + c$.

1) If $b^2 - 4ac < 0$, the graph of the parabola does not touch or cross the x-axis.

2) If $b^2 - 4ac = 0$, the graph of the parabola has its vertex on the x-axis.

3) If $b^2 - 4ac > 0$, the graph of the parabola intersects the x-axis in two real points.

Example 4. Without solving equations, determine the nature of the zeros of $f\colon x \to 2x^2 - 9x - 35$.

Solution. Since $a = 2$, $b = -9$, and $c = -35$,

$$b^2 - 4ac = (-9)^2 - 4(2)(-35) = 81 + 280 = 361.$$

Since $361 > 0$, the zeros are real and unequal. Moreover, since $b^2 - 4ac = 361$, a perfect square, the zeros will be rational. Is this always true when $b^2 - 4ac$ is a perfect square?

Example 5. On the same coordinate axis, sketch graphs of

a) $y = x^2 - 6x + 5$,

b) $y = x^2 - 6x + 9$,

c) $y = x^2 - 6x + 13$.

Check the results by finding $b^2 - 4ac$ in each case.

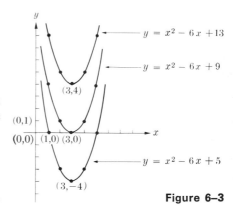

Solution. The graphs of each are shown in Fig. 6–3. These are consistent with the values for $b^2 - 4ac$, since we have

a) $b^2 - 4ac = (-6)^2 - 4(1)(5) = 16$,

b) $b^2 - 4ac = (-6)^2 - 4(1)(9) = 0$,

c) $b^2 - 4ac = (-6)^2 - 4(1)(13) = -16$.

Figure 6–3

PROBLEMS

1. Without solving, find the sum and product of the zeros of the functions given in Problems 1 through 8, Article 6–3.

Find quadratic equations with integral coefficients having the following given numbers as roots.

2. $2, -3$

3. $-5, 4$

4. $\frac{2}{3}, -2$

5. $-\frac{3}{4}, \frac{2}{3}$

6. $+\sqrt{3}, -\sqrt{3}$

7. $2 + \sqrt{3}, 2 - \sqrt{3}$

8. $\dfrac{-1 + \sqrt{5}}{2}, \dfrac{-1 - \sqrt{5}}{2}$

9. $\dfrac{-3 + \sqrt{7}}{4}, \dfrac{-3 - \sqrt{7}}{4}$

10. Find a quadratic equation whose roots are the squares of the roots of

$$4x^2 + 8x - 5 = 0.$$

11. Find a quadratic equation whose roots are the reciprocals of the roots of

$$4x^2 + 8x - 5 = 0.$$

$$\textit{Hint:} \quad \frac{1}{r_1} + \frac{1}{r_2} = \frac{r_1 + r_2}{r_1 r_2}.$$

12. Find a quadratic equation whose roots are the squares of the roots of

$$3x^2 - 5x - 2 = 0.$$

13. Find a quadratic equation whose roots are the reciprocals of the roots of

$$3x^2 - 5x - 2 = 0.$$

14. Find a quadratic equation whose roots are twice the roots of $4x^2 + 8x - 5 = 0$.

15. Find a quadratic equation whose roots are one-third the roots of

$$4x^2 + 8x - 5 = 0.$$

16. Find a quadratic equation whose roots are three times the roots of

$$3x^2 - 5x - 2 = 0.$$

17. Find a quadratic equation whose roots are half the roots of $3x^2 - 5x - 2 = 0$.

Find the value of k so that the equation:

18. $4x^2 + kx + 6 = 0$ has one root $= -2$.

19. $2x^2 + kx - 15 = 0$ has one root $= 3$.

20. $3x^2 + kx - 2 = 0$ has roots whose sum is equal to 6.

21. $5x^2 - 8x + k = 0$ has roots whose product is equal to $\frac{1}{5}$.

22. $4x^2 + 20x + k = 0$ has equal roots.

23. $3x^2 - 7x + k = 0$ has equal roots.

24. $2x^2 + (4 - k)x - 17 = 0$ has roots numerically equal but opposite in sign.

25. $3x^2 - 5x + 8 = kx$ has roots numerically equal but opposite in sign.

26. $3x^2 - 7x + 6 = k$ has one root equal to zero.

27. $4x^2 + 20x + k = 0$ has one root equal to zero.

Find the range of values of k so that the equation:

28. $3x^2 - 4kx + k = 0$ will have real roots.

29. $2x^2 + 3kx - 9 = 0$ will have real roots.

30. $x^2 + (k - 2)x + 4 = 0$ will have real roots.

31. $2x^2 - kx + 8 = 0$ will not have real roots.

32. $kx^2 + 4\sqrt{3}x + k = 1$ will not have real roots.

Find the range of values of k or value of k so that the graph of the function where y equals:

33. $3x^2 - 9x + k$ will touch (have its vertex on) the x-axis.

34. $x^2 + 2kx + \frac{3}{4} - k$ will not intersect the x-axis.

35. $4x^2 + 4\sqrt{2}kx + k + 3$ will intersect the x-axis in two real points.

36. Show that there are no real values of x and y such that

$$\frac{1}{x} + \frac{1}{y} = \frac{1}{x + y}.$$

6–7 EQUATIONS IN QUADRATIC FORM

In the last few articles, we have discussed the quadratic function and quadratic equations. Generally, any equation which can be written in the form

$$av^2 + bv + c = 0 \qquad (a \neq 0), \tag{6–18}$$

where v is expressed in terms of another variable, is called an *equation in quadratic form*. The methods developed in the last articles apply equally to any equation of this type.

Example 1. Solve $9x^4 - 37x^2 + 4 = 0$.

Solution. Letting $v = x^2$, and substituting, we have

$$9v^2 - 37v + 4 = 0,$$

or

$$(9v - 1)(v - 4) = 0.$$

Thus,

$$v = x^2 = \tfrac{1}{9} \quad \text{or} \quad 4,$$

and

$$x = \pm\tfrac{1}{3}, \quad \pm 2.$$

Example 2. Solve $(x^2 - 5x)^2 + (x^2 - 5x) - 30 = 0$.

Solution. With $v = x^2 - 5x$, we wish to solve

$$v^2 + v - 30 = 0,$$

a quadratic equation in v, whose roots are

$$v = 5 \quad \text{or} \quad -6.$$

Hence, we must solve

$$x^2 - 5x - 5 = 0$$

and

$$x^2 - 5x + 6 = 0.$$

Our solution is $x = (5 \pm 3\sqrt{5})/2$, 3, and 2.

PROBLEMS

Solve the following equations for x.

1. $x^4 - 11x^2 + 28 = 0$

2. $9x^4 + 5x^2 - 4 = 0$

3. $x^{-4} - 13x^{-2} + 36 = 0$

4. $x^{-4} - 8x^{-2} + 15 = 0$

5. $x^6 + 7x^3 - 8 = 0$

6. $8x^{-6} + 7x^{-3} = 1$

7. $x^{2/3} + 2x^{1/3} - 8 = 0$

8. $x + x^{1/2} = 20$

9. $(x^2 - 7x)^2 + 9(x^2 - 7x) - 10 = 0$

10. $(x^2 + 2x)^2 + (x^2 + 2x) = 12$

11. $\dfrac{2 + x}{2 - x} + \dfrac{2 - x}{2 + x} = 2$

12. $\left(x + \dfrac{1}{x}\right)^2 - 2\left(x + \dfrac{1}{x}\right) + 1 - 0$

13. $3(x + 3) + \sqrt{x + 3} = 2$

14. $2x - 9\sqrt{x + 2} + 14 = 0$

15. $2x^2 - 5x + 10 = 7\sqrt{2x^2 - 5x}$

16. $x^2 - x - 4 = \sqrt{x^2 - x - 2}$

6–8 EQUATIONS INVOLVING RADICALS

The last four problems of Article 6–7 contain radicals. Fortunately, they are of a special form, and it is possible to solve them by the method prescribed. Many equations involving radicals are not solvable by this method, and the radical or radicals must first be eliminated. Then the usual methods may be used. Extreme care must be taken, however, to substitute all possible roots in the original equation, since the method of eliminating radicals involves raising both members of an equality to some power. This process (recall Illustration 2, Article 6–1) may introduce roots of the final equation which are not roots of the original one.

Example 1. Solve $\sqrt{2x + 5} = 3$.

Solution. In an equation involving one radical, we must first eliminate the radical by squaring both members of the equation,

$$2x + 5 = 9.$$

Solving, we find

$$x = 2.$$

By substituting, we find that $x = 2$ does satisfy the original equation

$$\sqrt{2(2) + 5} = \sqrt{9} = 3,$$

so that $x = 2$ is the only root of the original equation.

Example 2. Solve $\sqrt{1 - 5x} + \sqrt{1 - x} = 2$.

Solution. With two radicals, it is simpler to transpose one to the opposite side before squaring. Thus,

$$\sqrt{1 - 5x} = 2 - \sqrt{1 - x}.$$

Squaring, we find

$$1 - 5x = 4 - 4\sqrt{1 - x} + 1 - x,$$

and we have

$$-4x - 4 = -4\sqrt{1 - x} \qquad \text{or} \qquad 1 + x = \sqrt{1 - x}.$$

Squaring again, we obtain

$$1 + 2x + x^2 = 1 - x, \qquad x^2 = -3x, \qquad x = 0, -3.$$

Therefore, no numbers other than 0 or -3 are roots of the original equation. By substitution, we find that 0 satisfies the original equation, but -3 does not. Therefore, $x = 0$ is the only solution.

PROBLEMS

Solve and check the following equations.

1. $\sqrt{2x + 5} = 4$

2. $\sqrt{6x - 3} = 7$

3. $\sqrt{8x - 7} - x = 0$

4. $\sqrt{3x + 1} + 1 = x$

5. $\sqrt{1 - 4x} + 4 = x + 9$

6. $\sqrt{x + 10} + x = 2x - 2$

7. $\sqrt{3x + 1} = \sqrt{x} + 3$

8. $2\sqrt{4x + 5} = \sqrt{8 - x} - 1$

9. $\sqrt{11 - x} - \sqrt{x + 6} = 3$

10. $\sqrt{3 - x} - \sqrt{2 + x} = 3$

11. $\sqrt{10 - 2x} + \sqrt{3x - 5} = 4$

12. $2\sqrt{10 - 2x} - \sqrt{3x - 5} = 2$

13. $\sqrt{2x + \sqrt{2x + 4}} = 4$

14. $\sqrt{2x + \sqrt{7 + x}} = 3$

6-9 VARIATION

Many applications in physical and social science make use of a functional dependence known as *proportion* or *variation*. Often the relations are linear or quadratic (although this is by no means always the case). For example, Ohm's law for an electrical circuit states that the current *varies directly* as the electromotive force, and *varies inversely* as the resistance. Thus the current is a function of both the electromotive force and the resistance. We may write this functional equation

$$I = k \cdot \frac{E}{R},$$

where k is called the *proportionality constant*. Let us define the three different common types of variation.

Definition 6-6. If the two variables x and y are so related (no matter how their values change) that the quotient of y divided by x, called the ratio of y to x, is constant, then y is said to *vary directly* as x. This relationship may be written $y/x = k$, or

$$\boxed{y = kx.} \qquad\qquad (6\text{-}19)$$

Definition 6-7. If the two variables, x and y, are so related (no matter how their values change) that the product of y and x is constant, then y is said to *vary inversely* as x. This relationship may be written $yx = k$, or

$$y = \frac{k}{x}. \tag{6–20}$$

Definition 6–8. If the variable z varies directly as x when y is held constant, and varies directly as y when x is held constant, then z is said to *vary jointly* as x and y, and is written

$$z = kxy. \tag{6–21}$$

Example 1. Express z as a specific functional equation of x and y if z varies directly as x and inversely as the square of y, and $z = 18$ when $x = 3$ and $y = 2$.

Solution. The given proportion may be written

$$z = k\frac{x}{y^2}.$$

Substituting the values for x, y, and z, we have $18 = k(\frac{3}{4})$, and $k = 24$. Therefore the functional equation may be written

$$z = \frac{24x}{y^2}.$$

Example 2. At constant temperature, the resistance of a wire varies directly as its length and inversely as the square of its diameter. If a piece of wire 0.1 in. in diameter and 50 ft long has a resistance of 0.1 ohm, what is the resistance of a piece of wire of the same material, 2000 ft long, 0.2 in. in diameter?

Solution. Letting R, L, and d represent the resistance, the length, and the diameter, respectively, of the wire, we have $R = kL/d^2$. By substitution, $0.1 = k(50)/(0.1)^2$, or $k = (0.1)^3/50$. Thus,

$$R = \frac{(0.1)^3}{50} \cdot \frac{L}{d^2}.$$

Therefore,

$$R = \frac{(0.1)^3}{50} \cdot \frac{(2000)}{(0.2)^2} = \frac{(0.001)(2000)}{50(0.04)} = 1 \text{ ohm.}$$

Note that all the measurements need not be expressed in the same unit, although we must be consistent for each variable.

Example 3. If y varies inversely as the square of x, how is y affected if x is increased 25%?

Solution. We have $y = k/x^2$. If $x = x_1$, then $y = k/x_1^2$. But $x = 5x_1/4$.
Thus,

$$y = \frac{k}{(5x_1/4)^2} = \frac{16}{25} \cdot \frac{k}{x_1^2} = 0.64 \frac{k}{x_1^2}.$$

Therefore y is 0.64 of its original value.

PROBLEMS

In Problems 1 through 8, express the functional equation as a single algebraic equation, giving the specific value of k if possible.

1. The variable z varies directly as x and inversely as y.

2. The variable z varies directly as x and inversely as the square of y.

3. The variable z varies jointly as x and y, and $z = 72$ when $x = 4$ and $y = 3$.

4. The variable z varies inversely as x, and $z = 8$ when $x = 16$.

5. The area of a circle varies directly as the square of the diameter.

6. The area of any triangle varies jointly as the product of the base and altitude.

7. The area of an equilateral triangle varies directly as the square of one side. (Compare Problem 14, Article 5–1.)

8. The distance a falling body travels (neglecting air resistance) varies as the square of the time traveled, and a body starting from rest falls 64 feet in 2 seconds.

9. a) If $y = f(x)$ varies directly with x, and the point $(3, 2)$ is on its graph, find the specific equation for y in terms of x.
   b) Give the coordinates of another point on the graph.

10. a) If $y = f(x)$ varies inversely with x, and the point $(3, 2)$ is on its graph, find the specific equation for y in terms of x.
    b) Give the coordinates of another point on the graph.

11. If z varies jointly as x^2 and y, and $z = 24$ when $x = 2$ and $y = 3$, find the value of z when $x = 3$ and $y = 5$.

12. If z varies directly as x and inversely as y, and if $z = 5$ when $x = 2$ and $y = 3$, find z when $x = 4$ and $y = 2$.

13. The surface area of a sphere varies directly as the square of the radius. If the surface is 36π in^2 when the radius is 3 in., what is the surface area when the radius is 12 in.?

14. With the information in Problem 8,
    a) find the distance the body has fallen in 5 sec,
    b) find the distance the body fell during the fifth second.

15. The kinetic energy K varies jointly as the mass m and the square of the velocity v. If K is 36 ergs when m is 8 gm and v is 3 cm/sec, find K if $m = 4$ gm and $v = 6$ cm/sec.

16. The vibrating frequency, or pitch, of a vibrating string varies directly as the square root of the tension of the string. If a string vibrates 216 times/sec due to a tension of 3 pounds, find its rate of vibration caused by a tension of 12 pounds.

17. The intensity of light varies inversely as the square of the distance from its source. How much farther from the light must an object be moved to receive one-fourth the amount of light it now receives if it is now 2 ft from the light?

18. If z varies directly as the square of x and inversely as y, what effect on z does doubling x and tripling y have?

19. The gravitational attraction F between two bodies varies jointly as their masses m_1 and m_2 and inversely as the square of the distance d between them. What is

the effect on the gravitational attraction between two bodies if the masses are each doubled and the distance between them is halved?

20. The stiffness of a beam varies jointly as its breadth and depth and inversely as the square of the length.

a) Find the change in stiffness if each of the three dimensions is increased 10%.
b) Find the change in the length that is necessary to increase the stiffness 20% if the breadth and depth are unaltered.

21. Draw the graph of $y = kx$ for $k > 0$. Note that on the graph y increases as x increases. *Hint:* Use units of k length on the y-axis.

22. Draw $y = k/x$ for $k > 0$. Note that y decreases as x increases.

23. a) If $y = f(x)$ varies directly as x, show that

$$\frac{f(x_1)}{f(x_2)} = \frac{x_1}{x_2}.$$

b) If $y = f(x)$ varies inversely as x, show that

$$\frac{f(x_1)}{f(x_2)} = \frac{x_2}{x_1}.$$

24. The law of divine proportion, according to early Egyptians and Greeks, states, "the most beautiful division of a line segment into two parts is such that the ratio of the longer part to the total length is equal to the ratio of the length of the shorter part to that of the longer part."

a) If we consider the length of the line to be one unit and call t the length of the longer of the two parts, find t.
b) What is the proportionality constant for this ratio?

6–10 SOLUTION OF TWO LINEAR EQUATIONS

We recall the general definition of a function (Definition 5–1) $f:P \rightarrow Z$, which associated with each element of P exactly one element of Z. If we consider the elements of P as the set of all ordered pairs of real numbers and Z the set of all real numbers, we might write this function

$$f:(x, y) \rightarrow z, \qquad\qquad (6\text{–}22)$$

where the correspondence is from an ordered pair to a real number. This is frequently done, where z is expressed algebraically in terms of x and y.* Our special interest is the linear case where z is equal to a first degree expression of this type, namely, $z = ax + by + c$. As a simple generalization of Eq. (6–1), our main concern is to find "the zeros" of this function. In a manner analogous to that in Article 6–1, we set $z = 0$, and wish to find the set of ordered pairs (x, y)

---

* In many books this is referred to as a function of two variables and is written $z = f(x, y)$.

such that $ax + by + c = 0$. This set

$$\{(x, y)|ax + by + c = 0\} \qquad (6\text{-}23)$$

is called the *solution set*, while any particular member of this set is a solution to the equation

$$ax + by + c = 0. \qquad (6\text{-}24)$$

In Article 6–1, we sketched the graph of equations such as $ax + by + c = 0$*
(Problems 33 through 40) by solving for y and obtaining an equivalent equation
in the form $y = mx + b$,† which represented a straight line. There are, clearly,
infinitely many solutions to the equation $ax + by + c = 0$, for there are infinitely many points (x, y) which lie on the line. Any arbitrary value of x will
determine a corresponding value of y. For example, the linear equation

$$3x - 2y - 5 = 0$$

has one solution $(3, 2)$ since $x = 3$, $y = 2$ satisfies the equation. Another is
$(1, -1)$, another $(-1, -4)$, and so on. In this case the solution set is

$$\{(x, y)|3x - 2y - 5 = 0\}.$$

We are frequently interested in the solution not of one equation but of a pair
of linear equations in x and y, such as

$$\boxed{\begin{aligned} a_1x + b_1y &= c_1, \\ a_2x + b_2y &= c_2. \end{aligned}} \qquad (6\text{-}25)‡$$

Thus, we are interested in finding any ordered pairs (x, y) whose values satisfy
both equations. If we put our problem in the context of sets by letting

$$A = \{(x, y)|a_1x + b_1y = c_1\} \quad \text{and} \quad B = \{(x, y)|a_2x + b_2y = c_2\},$$

we wish to find the intersection of A and B, namely,

$$A \cap B = \{(x, y)|a_1x + b_1y = c_1 \text{ and } a_2x + b_2y = c_2\}.$$

From a geometrical point of view, the graph of each of the equations in (6–25)
is a straight line, and hence we must find the coordinates of the points (x, y)
which lie on both lines. Since, in general, two straight lines intersect in one point,
their solution usually consists of one element. By drawing a graph of each line,
we can approximate the coordinates of the point of intersection.

---

* If $b = 0$, $x = -c/a$ is a straight line parallel to the y-axis. If $b \neq 0$, by $= -ax + c$
or $y = -(a/b)x + c/b$.
† The two b's are not the same in Eq. (6–1) and Eq. (6–24). The reader should differentiate
between them.
‡ Since it is often more convenient to write the constant term as the right member of such
an equation, we have chosen to write these equations in this form.

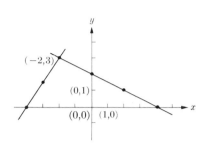

Figure 6–4

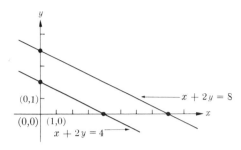

Figure 6–5

Example 1. Solve graphically the pair of equations

$$x + 2y = 4 \quad \text{and} \quad 3x - 2y = -12.$$

Solution. The graph of each of these straight lines is shown in Fig. 6–4. It appears that the two lines intersect at the point $(-2, 3)$. This is actually the case as may be verified by direct substitution, so that the solution is, $x = -2$, $y = 3$, where the ordered pair is $(-2, 3)$. If we consider

$$A = \{(x, y)|x + 2y = 4\} \quad \text{and} \quad B = \{(x, y)|3x - 2y = -12\},$$

then the solution set is $A \cap B = \{(-2, 3)\}$, which contains the one element $(-2, 3)$.

We should remark that two parallel lines such as $x + 2y = 4$ and $x + 2y = 8$, when plotted, will not intersect. (Fig. 6–5.) The fact that the equations of two such lines have no points of intersection is, of course, apparent from the equations, since there can be no pair of numbers such that the first number plus twice the second is equal to 4 and also 8. If we consider the intersection of

$$\{(x, y)|x + 2y = 4\} \quad \text{and} \quad \{(x, y)|x + 2y = 8\},$$

the result is the null set $\emptyset$. Two equations of this type are called *inconsistent*.

If two lines such as $x + 2y = 4$ and $3x + 6y = 12$ coincide when their graphs are plotted (Fig. 6–6), any pair of values (x, y) which satisfies one equation will also satisfy the other. Any two equations of this type have an infinite number of solutions and are said to be *dependent*.

In summary, the two equations (6–25) either

1) have a unique solution, when their graphs are two straight lines which intersect in one point;

2) have no solution, when their graphs are two parallel but not coincident straight lines; or

3) have infinitely many solutions, when their graphs are two straight lines which are parallel and coincide.

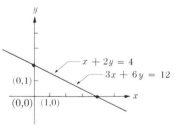

Figure 6–6

Since the graphical method of solution is only approximate, we must also consider some exact method. One of the variables may be eliminated by a proper combination of the two equations (or equations equivalent to them), and the resulting equation may be solved in terms of the other variable. The eliminated variable may then be found by substitution.

Example 2. Solve algebraically the two equations of Example 1.

Solution. Since the coefficients of y are equal, but opposite in sign, the members of the first equation may be added to those of the second, and thereby the y is eliminated.

$$\begin{aligned} x + 2y &= 4 \\ 3x - 2y &= -12 \\ \hline 4x &= {-8} \end{aligned}$$

Solving this equation in one variable, we have $x = -2$. When this value is substituted in either of the two original equations, we find $y = 3$. Therefore the required solution is

$$x = -2, \qquad y = 3,$$

or $(-2, 3)$. We might have found y by multiplying each member of the first equation by -3, adding the members of the resulting equation, $-3x - 6y = -12$, to those of the second equation, $3x - 2y = -12$, and finding $-8y = -24$, or $y = 3$.

Example 3. Solve the pair of two general equations (6–25) for x and y in terms of the coefficients.

Solution. If we multiply each member of the first equation by b_2, and of the second by b_1, we have

$$a_1 b_2 x + b_1 b_2 y = c_1 b_2,$$
$$a_2 b_1 x + b_1 b_2 y = c_2 b_1.$$

Subtracting the members of the second from those of the first, we obtain

$$a_1 b_2 x - a_2 b_1 x = c_1 b_2 - c_2 b_1.$$

Solving this equation for x, we find

$$(a_1 b_2 - a_2 b_1) x = c_1 b_2 - c_2 b_1,$$
$$x = \frac{c_1 b_2 - c_2 b_1}{a_1 b_2 - a_2 b_1} \qquad (a_1 b_2 - a_2 b_1 \neq 0).$$

By multiplying each member of the first equation by a_2, of the second by a_1, and so on, we find

$$y = \frac{a_1 c_2 - a_2 c_1}{a_1 b_2 - a_2 b_1} \qquad (a_1 b_2 - a_2 b_1 \neq 0).$$

Although not used in this form, these values for x and y can be considered a *solution by formula.*

PROBLEMS

Solve the following pairs of linear equations algebraically. The graphical method might be used as an approximate check.

1. $2x - y = 5$, $x - 3y = 5$
2. $3x - 2y = -14$, $2x + 3y = 8$
3. $4x + 3y = 27$, $2x - 5y + 19 = 0$
4. $2x - 5y + 43 = 0$, $6x - y + 31 = 0$
5. $3x + 4 = 4y$, $9x + 2y = 9$
6. $6x + 9y = 7$, $3x - 6y + 14 = 0$
7. $4x + y = 3$, $6x - 2y = 1$
8. $\sqrt{3}x - y = 1$, $x - 3\sqrt{3}y = -\sqrt{3}$
9. $2x - 4y = 0$, $x + y = \sqrt{3}$

*10. $\dfrac{2}{x} + \dfrac{3}{y} = 2$, $\quad \dfrac{4}{x} - \dfrac{9}{y} + 1 = 0$

11. $\dfrac{15}{x} + \dfrac{4}{y} - 1$, $\quad \dfrac{5}{x} \quad \dfrac{12}{y} \quad 7$

12. $\dfrac{15}{2x} - \dfrac{16}{3y} = \dfrac{23}{6}$, $\quad \dfrac{4}{3x} + \dfrac{7}{2y} + \dfrac{31}{72} = 0$

13. $ax + by = a^2 + 2ab + b^2$, $bx - ay = b^2 + 2ab - a^2$
14. $ax - by = a^2 - b^2$, $bx + ay = 2ab$

15. $k_1 = \dfrac{y}{x}$, $\quad k_2 = \dfrac{y + a}{x}$

▶ 16. $k_1 = \dfrac{a}{y}$, $\quad k_2 = \dfrac{a}{y + x}$

▶ 17. Solve the pair of equations
$$x = x'b - y'a, \qquad y = x'a + y'b$$
for x' and y' in terms of x and y, where $a^2 + b^2 = 1$.

Find $A \cap B$ in Problems 18 through 20 if:

18. $A = \{(x, y)|3x - 4y = -7\}$, $B = \{(x, y)|x + y = 7\}$.
19. $A = \{(x, y)|x + y = 1\}$, $B = \{(x, y)|2x + 3y = 4\}$.
20. $A = \{(x, y)|3x + y = 5\}$, $B = \{(x, y)|6x + 2y = 7\}$.
21. Sketch the graph of $\{(x, y)|x - y = 3$ and $x + 2y > 4\}$.
22. Sketch the graph of $\{(x, y)|x + 2y = 6$ and $x - y < 3\}$.
23. Sketch the graph of
   a) $A = \{(x, y)|2x + y > 3\}$, $\qquad$ b) $B = \{(x, y)|x - y > 6\}$.
   c) Show algebraically that
$$A \cap B = \{(x, y)|x > 3 \text{ and } 3 - 2x < y < x - 6\}.$$
   d) Sketch the graph of $A \cap B$.

---

* Although Problems 10 through 12 are not linear, they may be solved by the method discussed in this article.

24. Sketch the graph of

$$A = \{(x, y)\,|\,x > 0,\ y > 0,\ x + 3y < 15,\ \text{and}\ 2x + y < 10\}.$$

25. Sketch the graph of $|x| + |y| = 1$.

26. Sketch the graph of $|x - 4| + |y - 3| = 2$.

27. Sketch the graph of $4|x| + 3|y| = 12$.

28. The sum of the digits of a two-digit number is 9. If the digits are reversed, the new number is 9 less than the original number. Find the two numbers.

29. A certain fraction has the value $\frac{3}{4}$. If its numerator is decreased by 7 and its denominator increased by 4, the resulting fraction has the value $\frac{1}{2}$. Find the original fraction.

30. The sum of the two nonright angles in a right triangle is, of course, 90°. If twice the first is 40° more than 3 times the second, find the angles.

31. With the wind, an airplane travels 1120 miles in 7 hours. Against the wind, however, it takes 8 hours. Find the rate of the plane in still air and the velocity of the wind.

32. The sum of the reciprocals of two numbers is 9. Twice the reciprocal of the first is 12 less than 4 times the reciprocal of the second. Find the numbers.

33. A and B, working together, can do a job in $6\frac{2}{3}$ hours. A became ill after 3 hours of working with B, and B finished the job, continuing to work alone in $8\frac{1}{4}$ more hours. How long would it take each working alone to do the job?

34. Find the coordinates of the vertices of the triangle formed by the lines

$$x - y + 1 = 0, \qquad x + 4y + 1 = 0, \qquad 3x + 2y - 5 = 0.$$

35. Find the coordinates of the vertices of the triangle formed by the lines

$$x - y = -3, \qquad 3x + 4y = 5, \qquad 6x + y = 17.$$

36. Check the coordinates found in Problem 35 in the equations.

37. Show that the lines

$$2x - y = 4, \qquad x + 3y = 6, \qquad 2x - y = 8, \qquad x + 3y = -1$$

form a parallelogram, and find its vertices.

38. We recall that $y = mx + b$ represents an equation of any straight line (not parallel to the y-axis). Find the values of m and b so that $y = mx + b$ passes through $(-3, 1)$ and $(1, 9)$. (If a point lies on a line, its coordinates satisfy the equation.) If these values for m and b are substituted in the equation $y = mx + b$, we have found an equation of the straight line which passes through two given points.

39. By the method of Problem 38, find an equation of the straight line that passes through

  a) $(2, 3)$ and $(-1, 4)$ b) $(-4, 2)$ and $(6, -1)$

40. An equation of the form $(x^2/a^2) + (y^2/b^2) = 1$ represents an equation of an *ellipse* with its center at the origin. Find the equation of the particular ellipse of this type which passes through $(2, 4)$ and $(-1, 3)$.

41. Find the linear relation between the centigrade temperature C and the Fahrenheit temperature F of any body. *Hint:* $F = mC + b$. Also $F = 32$ when $C = 0$, and $F = 212$ when $C = 100$.

6–11 ALGEBRAIC SOLUTION OF THREE LINEAR EQUATIONS

Any equation of the form

$$ax + by + cz = d, \tag{6–26}$$

where a, b, c, and d are constants and a, b, and c are not all equal to zero, is called a *linear equation in three variables*. A solution of such an equation is any set of three numbers x, y, and z that satisfies the equation. As was the case for Eq. (6–24), there are an infinite number of solutions for one equation of this type.

Although we shall not prove it in this book, the geometric interpretation of Eq. (6–26) is a plane in a three-dimensional rectangular coordinate system.* Two nonparallel planes intersect in a straight line, and this line intersects a third plane, parallel to neither of the first two, in a point. In general, then, three planes have one point in common. Algebraically, this may be interpreted by the fact that the system of equations

$$
\begin{aligned}
a_1x + b_1y + c_1z &= d_1, \\
a_2x + b_2y + c_2z &= d_2, \\
a_3x + b_3y + c_3z &= d_3
\end{aligned}
\tag{6–27}
$$

has a single solution for x, y, and z.

To solve such a system, we follow a method which is a generalization of that used to solve the pair of equations (6–25). We choose a pair from the three equations and eliminate one of the variables from the pair, obtaining an equation in two variables. Repeating this procedure for another pair of the equations, we obtain a second equation in the same two variables. We now solve the two resulting equations for the two variables and, by substitution in any one of the original equations, find the complete solution. Let us illustrate.

Example. Solve the system of equations

$$
\begin{aligned}
2x - y + z &= 8, \\
x + 2y + 3z &= 9, \\
4x + y - 2z &= 1.
\end{aligned}
$$

Solution. Let us eliminate z by combining the first two equations, and then by combining the first and third. Multiply each member of the first equation by -3 and add the result, member by member, to the second equation;

$$
\begin{array}{rcr}
-6x + 3y - 3z &=& -24 \\
x + 2y + 3z &=& 9 \\
\hline
-5x + 5y &=& -15
\end{array}
$$

or $x - y = 3$.

---

* A three-dimensional rectangular coordinate system is a generalization of the one- and two-dimensional systems discussed in Articles 4–2 and 4–4. For example, each point in the space has three coordinates and is denoted (x, y, z), an ordered triple, and so on. (Recall Problem 15, Article 4–4.)

Multiply each member of the first equation by 2 and add the result, member by member, to the third equation.

$$4x - 2y + 2z = 16$$
$$\underline{4x + y - 2z = 1}$$
$$8x - y = 17$$

We now solve the two resulting equations. Give the reasons for each step.

$$8x - y = 17$$
$$\underline{x - y = 3}$$
$$7x = 14$$

Therefore, $x = 2$ and $y = -1$. Substituting these values in the first of the original equations, we have

$$2(2) - (-1) + z = 8, \qquad z = 3$$

Therefore the complete solution is $x = 2$, $y = -1$, $z = 3$ and may be written $(2, -1, 3)$. All solutions should be checked.

PROBLEMS

Solve each system of equations.

1. $x + 3y - z = 4$
   $3x - 2y + 4z = 11,$
   $2x + y + 3z = 13$

2. $3x - y - 2z = -13$
   $5x + 3y - z = 4$
   $2x - 7y + 3z = -36$

3. $2x - y + 3z = 19$
   $5x - 2y + 4z = 33$
   $3x + 3y - z = 2$

4. $6x + 4y - z = 13$
   $5x - 2y + 7z = 18$
   $x + y - 8z = -35$

5. $3x + 5y + 2z = 0$
   $12x - 15y + 4z = 12$
   $6x + 25y - 8z = -12$

6. $7x - 3y + 4z = 18$
   $13x + 6y + 8z = 30$
   $11x - 9y - 12z = 16$

7. $2x + 3y = 28$
   $3y + 4z = 46$
   $4z + 5x = 53$

8. $x - 3y = -11$
   $2y - 5z = 26$
   $3z - 7x = 2$

9. $\dfrac{3}{x} - \dfrac{4}{y} + \dfrac{6}{z} = 1$

   $\dfrac{9}{x} + \dfrac{8}{y} - \dfrac{12}{z} = 3$

   $\dfrac{9}{x} - \dfrac{4}{y} + \dfrac{12}{z} = 4$

10. $x + y + z = a + b + c$
    $bx - ay + cz = b^2$
    $ax - ay + cz = ab$

11. If three given sets of ordered triples are given

$$A = \{(x, y, z) \mid x - 2y + 3z = 4\},$$
$$B = \{(x, y, z) \mid 2x - y + z = -1\}, \quad \text{and}$$
$$C = \{(x, y, z) \mid 4x + y + 2z = 4\},$$

find $(A \cap B) \cap C$.

12. The sum of the digits of a three-digit number is 13. If the tens and hundreds digits are interchanged, the new number is 90 less than the original, and if the units and hundreds digits are interchanged, the resulting number is 99 less than the original. Find the original number.

13. Twenty-five coins, whose value is $2.75, are made up of nickels, dimes, and quarters. If the nickels were dimes, the dimes were quarters, and the quarters nickels, the total value would be $3.75. How many coins of each type are there?

14. We recall that the sum of the angles of any triangle is 180°. What are the three angles if the sum of two is equal to the third angle, but the difference of these two is only two-thirds of the third angle?

15. If the general equation (4–10) of the circle is expanded, it can be written in the form $x^2 + y^2 + Ax + By + C = 0$. Recalling that the coordinate of any point on the circle must satisfy its equation, find the values of A, B, and C and, thereby, the circle which passes through the points $(1, 1)$, $(-2, 3)$, $(3, 4)$.

16. If A, B, and C work together on a job, it will take $1\frac{1}{3}$ hours. If only A and B work, it would take $1\frac{5}{7}$ hours, but if B and C work, it would take $2\frac{2}{5}$ hours. How long would it take each man, working alone, to complete the job?

17. We recall from the footnote in this section that $ax + by + cz = d$ represents the equation of a plane in a three-dimensional coordinate system. At least one of the coefficients is not zero. We can divide by this coefficient, and, for example, the equivalent equation might be in the form $x = ey + fz + g$. Find an equation of the plane that passes through the three points $(4, 1, 2)$, $(3, 2, 1)$, and $(-6, -1, -2)$.

18. Find an equation of the plane that passes through the three points $(1, -5, -2)$, $(0, 5, 2)$, and $(3, 2, -1)$.

6–12 SOLUTION OF ONE LINEAR AND ONE QUADRATIC EQUATION

In Articles 6–10 and 6–11 we discussed systems of linear equations. These systems may be generalized either by considering more variables than two or three, or by considering functions of higher degree than the linear ones. The solutions of such systems, if they exist, are often difficult to obtain. We shall consider one simple but useful generalization in two variables, namely, the case in which one equation is linear and one is of the second degree, or quadratic. Such a system, in general, might be written

$$ax^2 + bxy + cy^2 + dx + ey + f = 0,$$
$$gx + hy + k = 0, \qquad\qquad (6\text{–}28)$$

where a, b, c, d, e, f, g, h, and k are constants, a, b, and c not all zero, and g and h not both zero. If each of the equations (conditions) in Eq. (6–28) is considered as defining a set of points, whose coordinates satisfy the equation, again, as in Article 6–10, the intersection of these two sets has for its elements, the points of intersection of the two curves representing these equations.

It is possible to solve such a system either graphically or algebraically, as in the case of two linear equations. The graph of the quadratic equation may best be plotted by solving for one variable in terms of the others, before the table of values is obtained. The points of intersection of the graphs of the quadratic equation and the linear equation may be approximated and their coordinates taken as solutions, since the points lie on both curves.

The simplest algebraic method is carried out by eliminating one of the variables. More specifically, we solve the linear equation for one variable in terms of the other, substitute this value in the quadratic equation, and solve the resulting quadratic equation in one variable. With these results substituted in the original linear equation, we obtain our complete solution.

Since this system reduces to the problem of solving one quadratic equation, we shall have two real, distinct ordered pairs, one real ordered pair, or no real ordered pair. (Recall Article 6–6.)

Example 1. Solve the system of equations

$$x^2 - 5x - y + 4 = 0,$$
$$x - 4y = 1.$$

Algebraic solution. Although we are able to eliminate x or y, we choose to solve the linear equation for y in terms of x, and substitute this value in the quadratic, since this approach appears to be simpler;

$$4y = x - 1$$

or

$$y = \frac{x - 1}{4}.$$

Therefore,

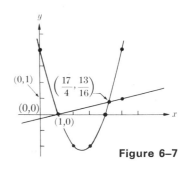

$$x^2 - 5x - \left(\frac{x - 1}{4}\right) + 4 = 0,$$

$$4x^2 - 20x - x + 1 + 16 = 0,$$

$$4x^2 - 21x + 17 = 0,$$

$$(4x - 17)(x - 1) = 0.$$

Figure 6–7

Thus $x = 1$ or $\frac{17}{4}$. Substitution of these values in the linear equation gives the corresponding values $y = 0$, $\frac{13}{16}$. The two solutions are $x = 1$, $y = 0$, and $x = \frac{17}{4}$, $y = \frac{13}{16}$ or $(1, 0)$ and $(\frac{17}{4}, \frac{13}{16})$.

Graphical solution. The given equations represent the parabola and straight line whose graphs are shown in Fig. 6–7. The intersections of the two curves show the solutions found by the algebraic method.

Example 2. Solve the system of equations

$$x^2 - 2y^2 + 3x - 4y + 20 = 0,$$
$$2x - y = 1.$$

*Solution.** Although we are able to eliminate x or y, we choose to solve the linear

---

* A graphical solution involves the plotting of $x^2 - 2y^2 + 3x - 4y + 20 = 0$. Problems of this kind will be discussed in Article 9–2.

equation for y and thus work with x, since the work appears to be simpler. Substituting $y = 2x - 1$ in the first equation, we have

$$x^2 - 2(2x - 1)^2 + 3x - 4(2x - 1) + 20 = 0.$$

Simplifying, we obtain

$$x^2 - 8x^2 + 8x - 2 + 3x - 8x + 4 + 20 = 0,$$
$$-7x^2 + 3x + 22 = 0,$$
$$7x^2 - 3x - 22 = 0,$$
$$(7x + 11)(x - 2) = 0.$$

Therefore,

$$x = 2, \qquad -\tfrac{11}{7}.$$

Substitution of these values in the linear equation yields the corresponding values $y = 3$, $-\tfrac{29}{7}$.   The two solutions are then $x = 2$, $y = 3$, and $x = -\tfrac{11}{7}$, $y = -\tfrac{29}{7}$ or $(2, 3)$ and $(-\tfrac{11}{7}, -\tfrac{29}{7})$.

PROBLEMS

Solve each of the systems in Problems 1 through 6 both graphically and algebraically.

1. $y = 4x^2$
    $y = 8x$

2. $x - 2y = 10$
    $y = x^2 + 2x - 15$

3. $y^2 = 4x$
    $x - y = -4$

4. $(x - 2)^2 + (y - 3)^2 = 4$
    $x + y + 3 = 0$

5. $(x - 2)^2 + (y - 3)^2 = 4$
    $x + y = 4$

6. $xy = 1$
    $x + y = 2$

Hint: Recall Article 4–5 for the graph of this quadratic equation.

For each of the Problems 7 through 10, find $A \cap B$ if

7. $A = \{(x, y)|y^2 + 2xy - 3x^2 + 7 = 0\}$,
    $B = \{(x, y)|x - 3y + 1 = 0\}$

8. $A = \{(x, y)|x^2 + y^2 - 2x = 1\}$
    $B = \{(x, y)|2x + y - 5 = 0\}$

9. $A = \{(x, y)|3xy + 6x = 4y\}$
    $B = \{(x, y)|2y - 3x - 4 = 0\}$

10. $A = \{(x, y)|4x^2 + 3xy - 2y^2 - x - y + 1 = 0\}$
    $B = \{(x, y)|x - 2y + 3 = 0\}$

11. The circle $x^2 + y^2 = a^2$ and the straight line $y = mx + b$ will intersect in two points, be tangent, or not intersect, depending upon whether the solutions of this system of equations are real and distinct, real and equal, or imaginary. Find the value of b in terms of a and m so that the straight line will be tangent to the circle.

12. Find the dimensions of a rectangle if its diagonal is 17 inches and its perimeter is 46 inches.

13. The product of a two-digit number and the number obtained by reversing its digits is 736. If the difference of the two numbers is 9, find the numbers.

14. A and B, working together, can complete a certain job in $7\frac{1}{2}$ hours. Working alone, A would take 8 hours longer than B to do the job. How long would it take each working alone?

15. The sum of two numbers is 11, while the sum of their reciprocals is $\frac{11}{28}$. Find the numbers.

REVIEW PROBLEMS

In Problems 1 through 6, determine all the values of x for which each of the following will be (a) positive, (b) negative, (c) zero.

1. $\dfrac{-2x(x^2 + 5)^2 - 4x(5 - x)(x^2 + 5)}{(x^2 + 5)^3}$

2. $\dfrac{x}{3\sqrt{300^2 + x^2}} - \dfrac{1}{5}$ if $0 < x < 600$

3. $3x\,\dfrac{-2}{2\sqrt{9 - 2x}} + 3\sqrt{9 - 2x}$ 　　　　**4.** $15x^5 + 10x^3 - 6x$

5. $x(x - 1)^2(x - 2)^3$ 　　　　　　**6.** $-32(x^2 + 4)^{-2} + 128x^2(4 + x^2)^{-3}$

7. Solve the equation $\dfrac{x^2}{(1 - x^2)^{3/2}} + \dfrac{2}{(1 - x^2)^{1/2}} = 0$.

8. Find the value of z if $\frac{2}{3}\sqrt{2}x^{-1/3} + \frac{1}{2}xy^{-1/2}z - y^{1/2} = 0$, $x = 16$, and $y = 5$.

9. Find the value of w in terms of x and y if

$$\tfrac{2}{3}x^{-1/3} + \tfrac{2}{3}y^{-1/3}z = 0 \quad \text{and} \quad -\tfrac{2}{9}x^{-4/3} - \tfrac{2}{9}x^{4/3}z^2 + \tfrac{2}{3}y^{-1/3}w = 0.$$

10. If $M = \{(x, y)|y^2 = 4(x - 2)\}$ and $N = \{(x, y)|5y^2 = 8(x + 4)\}$, find $M \cap N$.

11. If $A = \{(x, y)|x^2 = 4y\}$ and $B = \{(x, y)|x^2 + 4 = 8y\}$, find $A \cap B$.

12. If $f(n) = \dfrac{n - 1}{2n - 1}$, then $f(n + 1)$ is equal to

　a) $\dfrac{n + 1}{2n + 1}$ 　　　　b) $\dfrac{n + 1}{2n + 2}$ 　　　　c) $\dfrac{n}{2n + 1}$

　d) $\dfrac{n}{2n}$ 　　　　　　e) none of these

13. If $f(x) = \sqrt{x}$, then $\dfrac{f(x + h) - f(x)}{h}$, where $h \neq 0$, is equal to

　a) $\dfrac{\sqrt{h}}{h}$ 　　b) $\dfrac{1}{\sqrt{x + h} + \sqrt{x}}$ 　　c) 1 　　　d) none of these

14. If $f(n) = -\frac{3}{2}(n^2 + 9)^{-3}$, find the value of $f(4) - f(-1)$.

15. If $f(x) = \dfrac{x^2}{(2x - 1)^{2/3}}$, show that $f\left(\dfrac{n + 1}{2}\right) = \frac{1}{4}(n^{4/3} + 2n^{1/3} + n^{-2/3})$.

16. If $f(x) = -6x^{1/3} + 8\sqrt[3]{4}x^{4/3} - \frac{18}{5}x^{5/3}$, find the value of $f(27) - f(8)$.

17. Graph the set $A \cap B \cap C$ if

$$A = \{(x, y)|2x + y - 6 > 0\},$$
$$B = \{(x, y)|x - 2y + 2 < 0\},$$
$$C = \{(x, y)|y - 4 < 0\}.$$

*18. Graph the set $A \cap B$ if

$$A = \{(x, y)|x + y - 7 < 0 \text{ and } 2x + y - 6 > 0\},$$
$$B = \{(x, y)|x - 2y + 2 < 0 \text{ and } y - 4 < 0\}.$$

19. Graph the function f given by the expression

$$f = \left\{(x, y)|y = \begin{cases} -1 & \text{for } x < 0 \\ 1 & \text{for } 0 < x \end{cases}\right\}.$$

a) Give the domain and range of f.

b) How does f compare to $\left\{(x, y)|y = \dfrac{|x|}{x}\right\}$?

20. Graph the function g given by the expression.

$$g = \left\{(x, y)|y = \begin{cases} \dfrac{x - 2}{x^2 - 4} & \text{for } x \neq 2 \\ 1 & \text{for } x = 2 \end{cases}\right\}.$$

Is this graph that of a straight line?

21. Show that $\left|x - \dfrac{4}{7}\right| < \dfrac{3}{7}$ if and only if $\left|\dfrac{1}{x} - 4\right| < 3$.

22. The graphs of the two functions f and g are shown in Fig. 6-8. Solve the following two equations graphically for x.

a) $f(x) = g(1)$ b) $g(x) = f(2)$

23. Show that the point $P(x, y)$ is equidistant from the point $(3, 0)$ and the y-axis if and only if $y^2 - 6x + 9 = 0$.

24. Explain why the graph of the equation $[y - f(x)][y - g(x)] = 0$ is the union of the graphs of f and of g.

25. In a similar way, how would you describe the graph of the equation

a) $[y - f(x)]^2 + [y - g(x)]^2 = 0$ in terms of the graphs of f and of g?

b) $[y - f(x)] + k[y - g(x)] = 0$ in terms of the graphs of f and of g?

---

* Problems of this type are of importance in modern mathematical social science studies, especially in such fields as game theory and linear programming.

CHAPTER 7

MATRICES AND DETERMINANTS

In mathematics it is frequently convenient to consider rectangular arrays of numbers such as

$$\begin{bmatrix} 1 & 2 & -3 \\ 0 & -1 & 4 \end{bmatrix} \quad \text{or} \quad \begin{bmatrix} 3 \\ 2 \\ -8 \end{bmatrix}.$$

Such an array is called a *matrix*. The numbers 1, 2, −3, and so on, are called the *elements* or *entries* of the matrix. The horizontal lines of numbers are called *rows*, while the vertical lines of numbers are called *columns*. In general, if a rectangular array has *m* rows and *n* columns, we call it an *m* by *n* matrix. The number of rows is always stated first, followed by the number of columns, so that in the examples above, the first is a 2 by 3 matrix, while the second is 3 by 1.

7–1 BASIC PROPERTIES OF MATRICES

We shall use capital letters to denote matrices, and shall enclose the actual matrix in square brackets.* For example,

$$A = \begin{bmatrix} 3 & 2 & -1 \\ 1 & 2 & 4 \end{bmatrix}, \quad \text{or} \quad B = \begin{bmatrix} 0 & 2 \\ 1 & 3 \\ 5 & -2 \end{bmatrix}.$$

Clearly, we would not wish to say that $A = B$. To determine whether two matrices are equal we make the following definition.

Definition 7–1. Two matrices A and B are equal if and only if

1) the two rectangular arrays have the same number of rows and columns,
2) their corresponding entries are equal.

For example, if

$$A = \begin{bmatrix} 2 & 1 & 3 \\ -1 & 0 & 2 \end{bmatrix}, \quad B = \begin{bmatrix} -1 & 0 & 2 \\ 2 & 1 & 3 \end{bmatrix}, \quad C = \begin{bmatrix} \frac{2}{1} & 3-2 & 3 \\ -\frac{2}{2} & 2\times 0 & \frac{2}{1} \end{bmatrix},$$

then $A \neq B$, $B \neq C$, but $A = C$.

---

* Other notations use parentheses or double vertical bars.

We define the sum of two matrices, if they have the same number of rows and columns.

Definition 7–2. The sum of two matrices A and B, denoted by $A + B$, is the matrix such that each of its entries is the sum of the corresponding entries of A and B.

In the previous example,

$$A + B = \begin{bmatrix} 2 - 1 & 1 + 0 & 3 + 2 \\ -1 + 2 & 0 + 1 & 2 + 3 \end{bmatrix} = \begin{bmatrix} 1 & 1 & 5 \\ 1 & 1 & 5 \end{bmatrix}.$$

With the definition of any operation, we now immediately think of the possibility of an "identity element," or in this case, the identity matrix for the operation of addition.

Definition 7–3. If all of the entries of a matrix are zeros, the matrix is called the zero matrix, and is denoted by O.

Thus the 2 by 3 zero matrix is

$$\begin{bmatrix} 0 & 0 & 0 \\ 0 & 0 & 0 \end{bmatrix},$$

and $A + O = A$ for any matrix A. Furthermore, there is the "inverse matrix" with respect to addition, called the negative of A and denoted by $-A$.

Definition 7–4. Any matrix in which each entry is the negative of the corresponding entry in a given matrix A is called the negative of A.

For example, if

$$A = \begin{bmatrix} 2 & 1 & 3 \\ -1 & 0 & 2 \end{bmatrix}, \quad \text{then} \quad -A = \begin{bmatrix} -2 & -1 & -3 \\ 1 & 0 & -2 \end{bmatrix}.$$

Note that $A + (-A) = O$.

One further definition should be made here, that of the multiplication of a matrix by a scalar (a real number in this book).

Definition 7–5. The product of a scalar k and a matrix A, denoted by kA, is the matrix in which each entry is k times the corresponding entry of A.

Again, if

$$A = \begin{bmatrix} 2 & 1 & 3 \\ -1 & 0 & 2 \end{bmatrix},$$

then

$$2A = \begin{bmatrix} 4 & 2 & 6 \\ -2 & 0 & 4 \end{bmatrix} \quad \text{and} \quad -3A = \begin{bmatrix} -6 & -3 & -9 \\ 3 & 0 & -6 \end{bmatrix}.$$

Note that Definition 7–4 is a special case of 7–5, where $k = -1$. Also, it should be clear that subtraction would be defined as it was for real numbers, namely,

$$A - B = A + (-B).$$

PROBLEMS

Find the values of a, b, c, and d in Problems 1 through 4.

1. $[a \quad b \quad c] = [2 \quad -1 \quad 3]$

2. $\begin{bmatrix} a & b \\ c & a \end{bmatrix} = \begin{bmatrix} -1 & 2 \\ 3 & -4 \end{bmatrix}$

3. $\begin{bmatrix} a+3 & 2b+1 \\ c-3 & 2d-2 \end{bmatrix} = \begin{bmatrix} 2 & 1 \\ -3 & 2 \end{bmatrix}$

4. $\begin{bmatrix} 2a+3 & 2b-2 & c+1 \\ a & 4 & d \end{bmatrix} = \begin{bmatrix} a-5 & b+1 & 2c+3 \\ -8 & 4 & 2d \end{bmatrix}$

In Problems 5 through 10, if

$$A = \begin{bmatrix} 2 & -1 & 3 \\ 0 & 1 & 2 \end{bmatrix} \quad \text{and} \quad B = \begin{bmatrix} -1 & 3 & 0 \\ 2 & -1 & 1 \end{bmatrix},$$

find a 2 by 3 matrix equal to the given expression.

5. $A + B$

6. $2A + 3B$

7. $A - B$

8. $3A - 2B$

9. $A + 2(B - A)$

10. $-3(A + 2B)$

Perform the indicated operations.

11. $\begin{bmatrix} 2 & -1 & x \\ 3 & y & 2 \end{bmatrix} + 3 \begin{bmatrix} x & y & 2 \\ 0 & -1 & 3 \end{bmatrix}$

12. $2 \begin{bmatrix} 3 & -1 \\ a & 3 \\ -4 & 0 \end{bmatrix} + \begin{bmatrix} a & b \\ -b & a \\ a & 5 \end{bmatrix} - \begin{bmatrix} 0 & -3 \\ 2 & b \\ 1 & -3 \end{bmatrix}$

If

$$A_1 = \begin{bmatrix} a_1 & b_1 & c_1 \\ d_1 & e_1 & f_1 \end{bmatrix}, \quad A_2 = \begin{bmatrix} a_2 & b_2 & c_2 \\ d_2 & e_2 & f_2 \end{bmatrix}, \quad \text{and} \quad A_3 = \begin{bmatrix} a_3 & b_3 & c_3 \\ d_3 & e_3 & f_3 \end{bmatrix}$$

are any three 2 by 3 matrices, and k and h are real numbers, show that:

13. Matrix addition is commutative, that is,

$$A_1 + A_2 = A_2 + A_1.$$

14. Matrix addition is associative, that is,

$$(A_1 + A_2) + A_3 = A_1 + (A_2 + A_3).$$

15. $A_1 + A_2$ is a 2 by 3 matrix (closure).

16. If $A_1 + A_2 = A_1 + A_3$, then $A_2 = A_3$.

17. $A_1 + O = A_1$.   **18.** $A_1 + (-A_1) = O$.

19. $k(A_1 + A_2) = kA_1 + kA_2$.   **20.** $(k + h)A_1 = kA_1 + hA_1$.

21. $0A = O$.   **22.** $kO = O$.

Solve the following matrix equations for the matrix X, that is, find the matrix X which satisfies the given equation.

23. $X + \begin{bmatrix} 2 & -3 \\ 0 & 2 \end{bmatrix} = 2 \begin{bmatrix} -1 & 4 \\ 2 & 0 \end{bmatrix}$

Hint: To obtain the result, complete the scalar multiplication on the right, and then add the additive inverse of

$$\begin{bmatrix} 2 & -3 \\ 0 & 2 \end{bmatrix}$$

to each member of the equation.

Solve the matrix equations in Problems 24 through 26.

24. $X - 2 \begin{bmatrix} 4 & -1 \\ 0 & 3 \end{bmatrix} = \begin{bmatrix} 2 & -1 \\ 3 & 0 \end{bmatrix}$ **25.** $2X + 3 \begin{bmatrix} 1 & -2 \\ 2 & 0 \end{bmatrix} = \begin{bmatrix} 5 & 4 \\ 2 & -2 \end{bmatrix}$

26. $2 \begin{bmatrix} 3 & -1 & 2 \\ 2 & 4 & 3 \end{bmatrix} - 2X = \begin{bmatrix} 5 & 0 & 3 \\ -2 & 1 & -1 \end{bmatrix}$

▶ **27.** Consider the matrices

$$\begin{bmatrix} 3 & -1 & 2 \\ 2 & 3 & 0 \end{bmatrix} \quad \text{and} \quad \begin{bmatrix} 3 & 2 \\ -1 & 3 \\ 2 & 0 \end{bmatrix}.$$

The second matrix is called the *transpose* of the first, since it is obtained by interchanging the rows and columns. For any given matrix A, its transpose is denoted by A^T. Is the addition of any matrix A and its transpose A^T always defined? Explain.

28. Show that for any 2 by 3 matrix

a) $-A^T = (-A)^T$ b) $(A^T)^T = A$

Would these properties be true for any matrix?

29. As a result of the discussion in Problem 27, it should be clear that $A + A^T$ is defined if A is a square matrix. If A and B are any 2 by 2 square matrices, show that

$$A^T + B^T = (A + B)^T.$$

30. Under the same conditions as stated in Problem 29, show that

$$A^T + B = (A + B^T)^T.$$

7-2 PRODUCTS OF MATRICES

We now wish to define the product AB of any two matrices, where the number of columns of A is equal to the number of rows of B.

Definition 7–6. The *product* of two matrices A and B is the matrix AB whose entry in the ith row and jth column is the sum of the products formed by multiplying each entry in the ith row of A by the corresponding entry in the jth column of B.

It should be clear from this definition why the number of columns in A must be equal to the number of rows in B.

Example 1. If

$$A = \begin{bmatrix} 3 & 2 & -1 \\ 1 & 2 & 4 \end{bmatrix} \quad \text{and} \quad B = \begin{bmatrix} 0 & 2 \\ 1 & 3 \\ 5 & -2 \end{bmatrix},$$

find AB and BA.

Solution

$$AB = \begin{bmatrix} 3 & 2 & -1 \\ 1 & 2 & 4 \end{bmatrix} \begin{bmatrix} 0 & 2 \\ 1 & 3 \\ 5 & -2 \end{bmatrix}$$

$$= \begin{bmatrix} (3)(0) + (2)(1) + (-1)(5) & (3)(2) + (2)(3) + (-1)(-2) \\ (1)(0) + (2)(1) + (4)(5) & (1)(2) + (2)(3) + (4)(-2) \end{bmatrix}$$

$$= \begin{bmatrix} -3 & 14 \\ 22 & 0 \end{bmatrix}.$$

$$BA = \begin{bmatrix} 0 & 2 \\ 1 & 3 \\ 5 & -2 \end{bmatrix} \begin{bmatrix} 3 & 2 & -1 \\ 1 & 2 & 4 \end{bmatrix}$$

$$= \begin{bmatrix} (0)(3) + (2)(1) & (0)(2) + (2)(2) & (0)(-1) + (2)(4) \\ (1)(3) + (3)(1) & (1)(2) + (3)(2) & (1)(-1) + (3)(4) \\ (5)(3) + (-2)(1) & (5)(2) + (-2)(2) & (5)(-1) + (-2)(4) \end{bmatrix}$$

$$= \begin{bmatrix} 2 & 4 & 8 \\ 6 & 8 & 11 \\ 13 & 6 & -13 \end{bmatrix}.$$

It must be clear from the results of this example that AB is not always equal to BA, that is, matrix multiplication is not commutative.

Also, the product of two matrices AB may not have the same number of rows and columns as either A or B. If, however, the matrices are square, that is, the number of rows equals the number of columns, then the product matrix is also square and the same size, although such multiplication is still not commutative. Any square n by n matrix is said to be of the order n.

The set of all square matrices of the same size has an identity matrix under the operation of multiplication.

Definition 7–7. If A is a square n by n matrix, the matrix whose entries on the main diagonal (that from the upper left to the lower right corner) are 1's and whose other entries are all 0's is called the *identity matrix*, and is denoted by I.

Example 2. If

$$A = \begin{bmatrix} a & b \\ c & d \end{bmatrix}, \quad \text{and} \quad I = \begin{bmatrix} 1 & 0 \\ 0 & 1 \end{bmatrix},$$

show that $AI = A = IA$.

Solution

$$AI = \begin{bmatrix} a & b \\ c & d \end{bmatrix} \begin{bmatrix} 1 & 0 \\ 0 & 1 \end{bmatrix} = \begin{bmatrix} (a)(1) + (b)(0) & (a)(0) + (b)(1) \\ (c)(1) + (d)(0) & (c)(0) + (d)(1) \end{bmatrix}$$

$$= \begin{bmatrix} a & b \\ c & d \end{bmatrix} = A.$$

$$IA = \begin{bmatrix} 1 & 0 \\ 0 & 1 \end{bmatrix} \begin{bmatrix} a & b \\ c & d \end{bmatrix} = \begin{bmatrix} (1)(a) + (0)(c) & (1)(b) + (0)(d) \\ (0)(a) + (1)(c) & (0)(b) + (1)(d) \end{bmatrix}$$

$$= \begin{bmatrix} a & b \\ c & d \end{bmatrix} = A.$$

PROBLEMS

Carry out the indicated matrix multiplication in each of the following problems.

1. $\begin{bmatrix} 1 & 3 \\ 2 & 4 \end{bmatrix} \begin{bmatrix} -1 & 0 \\ 2 & 1 \end{bmatrix}$

2. $\begin{bmatrix} 2 & 3 \\ -1 & 5 \end{bmatrix} \begin{bmatrix} 2 & -1 \\ 0 & 3 \end{bmatrix}$

3. $\begin{bmatrix} 1 & 3 \\ 2 & 5 \end{bmatrix} \begin{bmatrix} -5 & 2 \\ 3 & 1 \end{bmatrix}$

4. $\begin{bmatrix} 0 & 1 \\ 2 & 3 \end{bmatrix} \begin{bmatrix} 7 & 2 \\ 1 & 3 \end{bmatrix}$

5. $\begin{bmatrix} 2 & 1 & 3 \\ -1 & 3 & 0 \\ 4 & 2 & -1 \end{bmatrix} \begin{bmatrix} 1 & 2 & 1 \\ -3 & 0 & 1 \\ 1 & 2 & 3 \end{bmatrix}$

6. $\begin{bmatrix} 1 & 3 & 2 \\ -1 & 0 & 6 \\ 5 & -1 & 4 \end{bmatrix} \begin{bmatrix} -3 & -2 & 1 \\ 2 & 4 & 0 \\ 3 & 5 & 1 \end{bmatrix}$

7. $\begin{bmatrix} 3 \\ -2 \\ 1 \end{bmatrix}$ [2   1   3]

8. $\begin{bmatrix} 1 & 2 \\ 0 & 1 \end{bmatrix} \begin{bmatrix} 2 & -1 & 0 & 3 \\ 0 & 3 & 2 & -1 \end{bmatrix}$

In Problems 9 through 13, if

$$A = \begin{bmatrix} 2 & -1 \\ 0 & 1 \end{bmatrix}, \quad B = \begin{bmatrix} 1 & -1 \\ 2 & 3 \end{bmatrix}, \quad \text{and} \quad C = \begin{bmatrix} -1 & 3 \\ 2 & -1 \end{bmatrix},$$

find a 2 by 2 matrix equal to the expressions given.

9. $A(B + C)$ **10.** $(AB)C$ **11.** $A^T B^T$

12. $(AC)^T$ **13.** $C^T(BA)$

14. Explain how the matrix product

$$\begin{bmatrix} a_1 & b_1 \\ a_2 & b_2 \end{bmatrix} \begin{bmatrix} x \\ y \end{bmatrix}$$

set equal to the matrix $\begin{bmatrix} c_1 \\ c_2 \end{bmatrix}$, is equivalent to

$$a_1 x + b_1 y = c_1, \qquad a_2 x + b_2 y = c_2.$$

Recall Equation (6–25).

15. Write the set of equations

$$x + 2y = 4,$$
$$3x - 2y = -12,$$

in the form of a matrix equation, and solve the pair for the matrix $\begin{bmatrix} x \\ y \end{bmatrix}$.

16. Solve the matrix equation

$$\begin{bmatrix} 4 & 3 \\ 2 & -5 \end{bmatrix} X = \begin{bmatrix} 27 \\ -19 \end{bmatrix}, \qquad \text{where } X = \begin{bmatrix} x \\ y \end{bmatrix}.$$

17. Solve the matrix equation

$$\begin{bmatrix} 3 & -4 \\ 9 & 2 \end{bmatrix} X = \begin{bmatrix} -4 \\ 9 \end{bmatrix}, \qquad \text{where } X = \begin{bmatrix} x \\ y \end{bmatrix}.$$

18. Show whether the matrix equation

$$\begin{bmatrix} 3 & 1 \\ -2 & 0 \end{bmatrix} X = \begin{bmatrix} 4 & 1 \\ -5 & 2 \end{bmatrix} \qquad \text{has} \qquad X = \begin{bmatrix} 5 & -2 \\ -7 & 8 \end{bmatrix}$$

for a solution.

19. Does

$$X = \begin{bmatrix} \frac{5}{2} & -1 \\ -\frac{7}{2} & 4 \end{bmatrix}$$

satisfy the equation in Problem 18?

20. Does

$$X = \begin{bmatrix} 2 & 3 \\ -1 & 4 \end{bmatrix}$$

satisfy

$$\begin{bmatrix} 1 & 0 \\ 0 & -1 \end{bmatrix} X = \begin{bmatrix} 0 & 0 \\ 0 & 0 \end{bmatrix} ?$$

21. If we let $XX = X^2$, does

$$X = \begin{bmatrix} 3 & 1 \\ -2 & 0 \end{bmatrix}$$

satisfy

$$X^2 - 3X + 2I = O?$$

If A, B, and C are any 2 by 2 matrices, prove the statements given in Problems 22 through 25.

22. $(AB)C = A(BC)$ **23.** $A(B + C) = AB + AC$

24. $AO = OA = O$ **25.** $(AB)^T = B^T A^T$

26. Prove that the product of two matrices may be the zero matrix, although neither of them is zero. Let

$$A = \begin{bmatrix} 1 & 2 \\ 2 & 4 \end{bmatrix} \quad \text{and} \quad B = \begin{bmatrix} -4 & 6 \\ 2 & -3 \end{bmatrix}.$$

27. Prove that the square of a matrix may be the zero matrix, even when the matrix itself is not zero. *Hint:* Consider

$$\begin{bmatrix} 1 & 1 \\ -1 & -1 \end{bmatrix}.$$

28. Let

$$A = \begin{bmatrix} 1 & 3 \\ 2 & 5 \end{bmatrix} \quad \text{and} \quad B = \begin{bmatrix} -5 & 3 \\ 2 & -1 \end{bmatrix}.$$

Show that $AB = I$. In such a case, each of these matrices is called the multiplicative inverse of the other. See the next section.

29. Show that $AB = I$ if

$$A = \begin{bmatrix} 3 & 4 \\ 2 & 3 \end{bmatrix} \quad \text{and} \quad B = \begin{bmatrix} 3 & -4 \\ -2 & 3 \end{bmatrix}.$$

30. Any matrix A such that $AA^T = I$ is called an *orthogonal matrix*. Show that each of the following matrices is orthogonal.

a) $\begin{bmatrix} \dfrac{1}{2} & \dfrac{\sqrt{3}}{2} \\[2mm] -\dfrac{\sqrt{3}}{2} & \dfrac{1}{2} \end{bmatrix}$, b) $\begin{bmatrix} \dfrac{1}{\sqrt{2}} & -\dfrac{1}{\sqrt{2}} \\[2mm] \dfrac{1}{\sqrt{2}} & \dfrac{1}{\sqrt{2}} \end{bmatrix}$, c) $\begin{bmatrix} \sin\phi & \cos\phi \\ -\cos\phi & \sin\phi \end{bmatrix}$,

where ϕ is any angle.

31. Let

$$A = \begin{bmatrix} a & b \\ c & d \end{bmatrix}.$$

Show that if A is orthogonal, then (1) $a^2 + b^2 = 1$, (2) $c^2 + d^2 = 1$, (3) $ac + bd = 0$.

32. State and prove the converse of the statement made in Problem 31.

7-3 THE INVERSE OF A MATRIX

In Problems 24 and 25 of the last section, we noticed that both matrices A and B had an inverse. We wish to define the inverse of a general n by n matrix, and find what conditions are sufficient for its existence.

> **Definition 7-8.** The multiplicative inverse of an n by n matrix A is an n by n matrix denoted by A^{-1} where
> $$AA^{-1} = I, \tag{7-1}$$
> the n by n identity matrix.

For example, if A is the matrix

$$\begin{bmatrix} 1 & 3 \\ 2 & 5 \end{bmatrix}, \quad \text{then} \quad A^{-1} = \begin{bmatrix} -5 & 3 \\ 2 & -1 \end{bmatrix}$$

since

$$AA^{-1} = \begin{bmatrix} 1 & 0 \\ 0 & 1 \end{bmatrix}.$$

But does this type of inverse of any square matrix always exist? We recall that the real number zero has no multiplicative inverse.

Suppose that

$$A = \begin{bmatrix} a & b \\ c & d \end{bmatrix}.$$

If A has a multiplicative inverse,

$$A^{-1} = \begin{bmatrix} x & y \\ z & w \end{bmatrix}, \quad \text{then} \quad AA^{-1} = \begin{bmatrix} a & b \\ c & d \end{bmatrix}\begin{bmatrix} x & y \\ z & w \end{bmatrix} = \begin{bmatrix} 1 & 0 \\ 0 & 1 \end{bmatrix},$$

or, if we make use of Definition 7–6, this is equivalent to

$$ax + bz = 1, \qquad cx + dz = 0, \tag{7–2}$$

$$ay + bw = 0, \qquad cy + dw = 1. \tag{7–3}$$

If we eliminate z and then, in a similar fashion x, from Eqs. (7–2) we obtain

$$(ad - bc)x = d \quad \text{and} \quad (ad - bc)z = -c. \tag{7–4}$$

If we follow the same method for the two equations in (7–3), we also get

$$(ad - bc)y = -b \quad \text{and} \quad (ad - bc)w = a. \tag{7–5}$$

If these equations are solved for x, y, z, and w (which can be done if $ad - bc \neq 0$), we have

$$x = \frac{d}{ad - bc}, \qquad z = \frac{-c}{ad - bc}, \tag{7–6}$$

and

$$y = \frac{-b}{ad - bc}, \qquad w = \frac{a}{ad - bc}. \tag{7–7}$$

This common denominator, $ad - bc$, will be discussed in a more general way in the next sections. It is a functional value of the square matrix A, denoted by $\delta(A)$, and called delta of A or the determinant of A. Clearly, if $\delta(A) \neq 0$, that is, if A is nonsingular,*

$$A^{-1} = \begin{bmatrix} x & y \\ z & w \end{bmatrix} = \frac{1}{\delta(A)} \begin{bmatrix} d & -b \\ -c & a \end{bmatrix}, \tag{7–8}$$

a solution of Eq. (7–1). In fact, the inverse A^{-1}, is unique as a result of the method by which this inverse was obtained. We have thus proved the following theorem:

Theorem 7–1. For any square matrix A, its inverse A^{-1} exists and is unique if $\delta(A) \neq 0$.

The converse is also true, namely, for any square matrix A, if its inverse A^{-1} exists, then $\delta(A) \neq 0$. Stated† in an equivalent form we have

Theorem 7–2. If for any square matrix A, $\delta(A) = 0$, then A^{-1} does not exist.

Proof. As in the case of Theorem 7–1, we shall prove this theorem for the 2 by 2 matrix,

$$A = \begin{bmatrix} a & b \\ c & d \end{bmatrix}.$$

---

* If $\delta(A) = 0$, A is said to be singular.
† We recall in logic that $p \Rightarrow q$ is equivalent to not $q \Rightarrow$ not p.

Let us suppose A^{-1} exists and is equal to

$$\begin{bmatrix} x & y \\ z & w \end{bmatrix}.$$

We wish to arrive at a contradiction. Since $\delta(A) = 0$ and as a result of Equations (7–4) and (7–5),

$$A = \begin{bmatrix} 0 & 0 \\ 0 & 0 \end{bmatrix}, \quad \text{so that} \quad AA^{-1} = \begin{bmatrix} 0 & 0 \\ 0 & 0 \end{bmatrix}\begin{bmatrix} x & y \\ z & w \end{bmatrix} = O.$$

This clearly contradicts the fact that $AA^{-1} = I$, and the proof is complete.

If the inverse of any 2 by 2 matrix A exists, it can be found by using Equation (7–8).

Example. Find A^{-1} if

$$A = \begin{bmatrix} 2 & -1 \\ 7 & 4 \end{bmatrix}.$$

Solution. We recall that $\delta(A) = ad - bc$, which in this case is $2(4) - (-1)(7) = 15$, since $a = 2$, $b = -1$, $c = 7$, and $d = 4$. As a result, by Eq. (7–8) we have

$$A^{-1} = \frac{1}{15}\begin{bmatrix} 4 & 1 \\ -7 & 2 \end{bmatrix} = \begin{bmatrix} \frac{4}{15} & \frac{1}{15} \\ -\frac{7}{15} & \frac{2}{15} \end{bmatrix}.$$

Let us check this result.

$$AA^{-1} = \begin{bmatrix} 2 & -1 \\ 7 & 4 \end{bmatrix}\begin{bmatrix} \frac{4}{15} & \frac{1}{15} \\ -\frac{7}{15} & \frac{2}{15} \end{bmatrix} = \begin{bmatrix} \frac{8}{15} + \frac{7}{15} & \frac{2}{15} - \frac{2}{15} \\ \frac{28}{15} - \frac{28}{15} & \frac{7}{15} + \frac{8}{15} \end{bmatrix} = \begin{bmatrix} 1 & 0 \\ 0 & 1 \end{bmatrix}.$$

PROBLEMS

In Problems 1 through 8 find the inverse for the given matrix, if it exists.

1. $\begin{bmatrix} 5 & 3 \\ 8 & 5 \end{bmatrix}$　　2. $\begin{bmatrix} 3 & 4 \\ 2 & 3 \end{bmatrix}$　　3. $\begin{bmatrix} 3 & 4 \\ 6 & 8 \end{bmatrix}$　　4. $\begin{bmatrix} 2 & -3 \\ -6 & 9 \end{bmatrix}$

5. $\begin{bmatrix} 5 & 3 \\ 2 & -2 \end{bmatrix}$　　6. $\begin{bmatrix} 7 & -2 \\ -3 & -1 \end{bmatrix}$　　7. $\begin{bmatrix} 3 & 1 \\ 5 & 2 \end{bmatrix}$　　8. $\begin{bmatrix} 7 & -10 \\ 5 & -7 \end{bmatrix}$

9. Show that $I^{-1} = I$, where I is the second order matrix identity.

10. For any orthogonal matrix A, what is the relation between A^{-1} and A^T? Recall Problem 30 in the last section.

11. In Problems 14 through 17 of the last section, we found a method for solving matrix equations of the form $AX = B$ under certain conditions. If, as in the case of real numbers, we multiply on the left each member of this matrix equation by A^{-1}, assuming that it exists, and recall that $A^{-1}A = I$, and $IX = X$, we obtain the solution $X = A^{-1}B$. This gives us an alternative method. Solve the matrix equation

$$\begin{bmatrix} 1 & 2 \\ 3 & -2 \end{bmatrix} \begin{bmatrix} x \\ y \end{bmatrix} = \begin{bmatrix} 4 \\ -12 \end{bmatrix}$$

by this method. *Hint:* If we let

$$A = \begin{bmatrix} 1 & 2 \\ 3 & -2 \end{bmatrix},$$

we find

$$A^{-1} = \begin{bmatrix} \frac{1}{4} & \frac{1}{4} \\ \frac{3}{8} & -\frac{1}{8} \end{bmatrix},$$

so that

$$X = \begin{bmatrix} \frac{1}{4} & \frac{1}{4} \\ \frac{3}{8} & -\frac{1}{8} \end{bmatrix} \begin{bmatrix} 4 \\ -12 \end{bmatrix} = \begin{bmatrix} -2 \\ 3 \end{bmatrix}.$$

12. Solve the matrix equation

$$\begin{bmatrix} 4 & 3 \\ 2 & -5 \end{bmatrix} X = \begin{bmatrix} 27 \\ -19 \end{bmatrix},$$

where

$$X = \begin{bmatrix} x \\ y \end{bmatrix}.$$

13. Solve the matrix equation

$$\begin{bmatrix} 3 & -4 \\ 9 & 2 \end{bmatrix} X = \begin{bmatrix} -4 \\ 9 \end{bmatrix},$$

where

$$X = \begin{bmatrix} x \\ y \end{bmatrix}.$$

14. Let A be the 3 by 3 matrix

$$\begin{bmatrix} a_1 & b_1 & c_1 \\ a_2 & b_2 & c_2 \\ a_3 & b_3 & c_3 \end{bmatrix}.$$

Assume there exists an inverse A^{-1} such that $AA^{-1} = I$, the identity 3 by 3 matrix. Show that there are nine equations which must be solved to find A^{-1}, and explain how these equations are obtained.

15. Show that Eqs. (6–27) can be written in the matrix form of an equation $AX = B$, and tell how many rows and columns each matrix has.

In Problems 16 through 18 let

$$A = \begin{bmatrix} a_1 & b_1 \\ a_2 & b_2 \end{bmatrix} \quad \text{and} \quad B = \begin{bmatrix} c_1 & d_1 \\ c_2 & d_2 \end{bmatrix},$$

and assume the inverse of each exists. Show that

16. $(A^T)^{-1} = (A^{-1})^T$ 　　　　　　　　　　　　　 **17.** $\delta(AB) = \delta(A)\,\delta(B)$

18. $(AB)^{-1} = B^{-1}A^{-1}$

19. Show that if

$$A = \begin{bmatrix} a_1 & b_1 \\ a_2 & b_2 \end{bmatrix} \quad \text{and} \quad I = \begin{bmatrix} 1 & 0 \\ 0 & 1 \end{bmatrix},$$

then

$$\delta(A - xI) = x^2 - (a_1 + b_2)x + \delta(A).$$

This expression is called the *characteristic polynomial* (quadratic in this case) of A.

20. If the characteristic polynomial is set equal to zero, we have the *characteristic equation* of A. The roots of this equation are called *characteristic roots*. Find the characteristic roots of

a) $\begin{bmatrix} 2 & -1 \\ 0 & 4 \end{bmatrix}$ 　　　　　　　　　　 b) $\begin{bmatrix} -3 & 6 \\ 6 & 2 \end{bmatrix}$

7–4 DETERMINANTS OF ORDERS TWO AND THREE

In finding the multiplicative inverse of a 2 by 2 square matrix in the last section, we found the expression $\delta(A) = ad - bc$, a significant one. With each square matrix of any order, we associate a real number called the *determinant* of that matrix. More specifically, we define a function δ, where the elements of the domain are square matrices and the range is the set of real numbers R. For the square matrix of order 2, this functional value was defined to be the product of the elements in the upper left and lower right corners minus the product of the elements in the lower left and upper right, so that we have the following definition.

Definition 7–9. The function δ, whose domain is the square matrix

$$A = \begin{bmatrix} a_1 & b_1 \\ a_2 & b_2 \end{bmatrix},$$

where a_1, a_2, b_1, and b_2 are real numbers, is the determinant of the matrix A Its functional value is $a_1b_2 - a_2b_1$, and symbolized

$$\delta(A) = \begin{vmatrix} a_1 & b_1 \\ a_2 & b_2 \end{vmatrix} = a_1b_2 - a_2b_1, \tag{7–9}$$

Illustration

a) If

$$A = \begin{bmatrix} 3 & 2 \\ 5 & 4 \end{bmatrix},$$

$$\delta(A) = \begin{vmatrix} 3 & 2 \\ 5 & 4 \end{vmatrix} = (12) - (10) = 2,$$

b) If

$$B = \begin{bmatrix} -1 & -4 \\ 2 & -3 \end{bmatrix},$$

$$\delta(B) = \begin{vmatrix} -1 & -4 \\ 2 & -3 \end{vmatrix} = (-1)(-3) - 2(-4) = 11.$$

PROBLEMS

Evaluate the determinants in Problems 1 through 6.

1. $\begin{vmatrix} 3 & 4 \\ 5 & 6 \end{vmatrix}$
    2. $\begin{vmatrix} 6 & -1 \\ 3 & -2 \end{vmatrix}$
    3. $\begin{vmatrix} -2 & 3 \\ -5 & 6 \end{vmatrix}$

4. $\begin{vmatrix} 8 & 0 \\ 1 & 2 \end{vmatrix}$
    5. $\begin{vmatrix} a & b \\ -b & a \end{vmatrix}$
    6. $\begin{vmatrix} c & d \\ d & c \end{vmatrix}$

▶ 7. From Example 3, Article 6–10, show that the solution of the system of equations

$$a_1 x + b_1 y = c_1, \qquad a_2 x + b_2 y = c_2$$

may be written in terms of determinants as

$$x = \frac{\begin{vmatrix} c_1 & b_1 \\ c_2 & b_2 \end{vmatrix}}{\begin{vmatrix} a_1 & b_1 \\ a_2 & b_2 \end{vmatrix}}, \qquad y = \frac{\begin{vmatrix} a_1 & c_1 \\ a_2 & c_2 \end{vmatrix}}{\begin{vmatrix} a_1 & b_1 \\ a_2 & b_2 \end{vmatrix}}. \qquad (7\text{–}10)$$

8. Using Eqs. (7–10), solve Problems 1, 3, 5 of Article 6–10.

9. Using Eqs. (7–10), solve Problems 2, 4, 6 of Article 6–10.

10. Solve for x:

$$\begin{vmatrix} 3 & 2 \\ x & 4 \end{vmatrix} = 0.$$

11. Solve for x:

$$\begin{vmatrix} 2x & 3 \\ -5 & -4 \end{vmatrix} = 7x.$$

12. Prove the identity

$$\begin{vmatrix} x - 2 & 3 \\ x - 2 & 5 \end{vmatrix} \equiv 2(x - 2).$$

13. Prove the identity

$$\begin{vmatrix} a - b & 0 \\ 1 & c - d \end{vmatrix} \equiv (a - b)(c - d).$$

14. For what values of x is $\begin{vmatrix} x & 5 \\ 125 & x \end{vmatrix} > 0$?

15. What can be said about the nature of the roots of

$$ax^2 + bx + c = 0$$

if

$$\begin{vmatrix} b & 4a \\ c & b \end{vmatrix} > 0, \qquad = 0, \qquad < 0?$$

Let us now consider the square matrix of order three,

$$M = \begin{bmatrix} a_1 & b_1 & c_1 \\ a_2 & b_2 & c_2 \\ a_3 & b_3 & c_3 \end{bmatrix}. \tag{7–11}$$

For each element in such a matrix there exists a matrix of order 2, obtained by deleting the row and column in which the element lies. The second order determinant associated with the matrix obtained in this way is called the *minor* of the element under consideration. For example, denoting the matrix whose determinant is the minor of any element by the corresponding capital letter, we have

$$\delta(A_1) = \begin{vmatrix} b_2 & c_2 \\ b_3 & c_3 \end{vmatrix}, \qquad \delta(B_3) = \begin{vmatrix} a_1 & c_1 \\ a_2 & c_2 \end{vmatrix}, \qquad \delta(C_2) = \begin{vmatrix} a_1 & b_1 \\ a_3 & b_3 \end{vmatrix}.$$

We now define the determinant of the third order matrix in Eq. (7–11) by

$$\delta(M) = \begin{vmatrix} a_1 & b_1 & c_1 \\ a_2 & b_2 & c_2 \\ a_3 & b_3 & c_3 \end{vmatrix} = a_1\,\delta(A_1) - b_1\,\delta(B_1) + c_1\,\delta(C_1). \tag{7–12}$$

Example 1. Find the determinant of the matrix

$$\begin{bmatrix} 2 & -1 & 3 \\ 3 & -2 & 1 \\ 4 & -3 & 2 \end{bmatrix}.$$

Solution

$$\begin{vmatrix} 2 & -1 & 3 \\ 3 & -2 & 1 \\ 4 & -3 & 2 \end{vmatrix} = 2 \begin{vmatrix} -2 & 1 \\ -3 & 2 \end{vmatrix} - (-1) \begin{vmatrix} 3 & 1 \\ 4 & 2 \end{vmatrix} + 3 \begin{vmatrix} 3 & -2 \\ 4 & -3 \end{vmatrix}$$

$$= 2(-4 + 3) + 1(6 - 4) + 3(-9 + 8)$$

$$= -2 + 2 - 3$$

$$= -3.$$

Example 2. Express $\delta(M)$, Eq. (7–12), in terms of the elements only.

Solution

$$\delta(M) = \begin{vmatrix} a_1 & b_1 & c_1 \\ a_2 & b_2 & c_2 \\ a_3 & b_3 & c_3 \end{vmatrix} = a_1 \begin{vmatrix} b_2 & c_2 \\ b_3 & c_3 \end{vmatrix} - b_1 \begin{vmatrix} a_2 & c_2 \\ a_3 & c_3 \end{vmatrix} + c_1 \begin{vmatrix} a_2 & b_2 \\ a_3 & b_3 \end{vmatrix}$$

$$= a_1(b_2 c_3 - b_3 c_2) - b_1(a_2 c_3 - a_3 c_2) + c_1(a_2 b_3 - a_3 b_2)$$

$$= a_1 b_2 c_3 + a_2 b_3 c_1 + a_3 b_1 c_2 - a_1 b_3 c_2 - a_2 b_1 c_3 - a_3 b_2 c_1. \qquad (7\text{–}13)$$

PROBLEMS

Evaluate each of the determinants in Problems 1 through 4.

1. $\begin{vmatrix} 1 & 2 & 3 \\ -2 & -1 & -2 \\ 3 & 1 & 4 \end{vmatrix}$ 2. $\begin{vmatrix} -1 & 2 & -3 \\ 2 & -1 & -4 \\ 3 & -2 & 1 \end{vmatrix}$ 3. $\begin{vmatrix} 2 & 1 & 3 \\ -1 & 4 & 7 \\ 4 & 2 & 6 \end{vmatrix}$ 4. $\begin{vmatrix} 1 & -1 & 1 \\ 4 & 2 & 10 \\ 2 & 2 & 6 \end{vmatrix}$

Verify the following, using the value in Eq. (7–13).

▶ 5. $\delta(M) = -a_2 \, \delta(A_2) + b_2 \, \delta(B_2) - c_2 \, \delta(C_2)$

▶ 6. $\delta(M) = a_3 \, \delta(A_3) - b_3 \, \delta(B_3) + c_3 \, \delta(C_3)$

7. $\delta(M) = a_1 \, \delta(A_1) - a_2 \, \delta(A_2) + a_3 \, \delta(A_3)$

8. $\delta(M) = -b_1 \, \delta(B_1) + b_2 \, \delta(B_2) - b_3 \, \delta(B_3)$

9. $\delta(M) = c_1 \, \delta(C_1) - c_2 \, \delta(C_2) + c_3 \, \delta(C_3)$

    Note: The third order determinant $\delta(M)$ could have been defined equally well by the equation given in Problems 5, 6, 7, 8, or 9. The definition (Eq. 7–12) gives the expansion of $\delta(M)$ by minors according to the elements of the first row. Problems 5 and 6 give the expansion by minors according to the elements of the second and third rows, respectively. Problems 7, 8, and 9 give the expansion by minors according to columns.

10. Using the results of Problems 5 through 9, and Eq. (7–12), prove the following statement: The determinant of order three may be expressed as the sum of three products formed by multiplying each element of any row (or column) by its minor, where each such product has assigned to it a plus or minus sign, depending upon whether the sum of the number of the row and the number of the column in which each element is located is even or odd.

11. Evaluate Problems 1 through 4 by expansion by minors according to some row or column other than the first.

▶ 12. Show that

$$\begin{vmatrix} x_1 & y_1 & 1 \\ x_2 & y_2 & 1 \\ x_3 & y_3 & 1 \end{vmatrix} = \begin{vmatrix} x_1 & y_1 \\ x_2 & y_2 \end{vmatrix} - \begin{vmatrix} x_1 & y_1 \\ x_3 & y_3 \end{vmatrix} + \begin{vmatrix} x_2 & y_2 \\ x_3 & y_3 \end{vmatrix}.$$

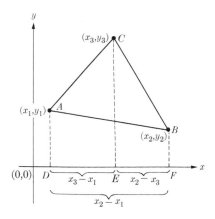

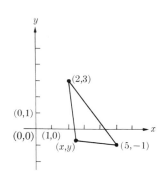

Figure 7–1   **Figure 7–2**

▶ **13.** Using Fig. 7–1 and recalling that the area of a trapezoid is $\frac{1}{2}(b_1 + b_2)h$, where b_1 and b_2 are its bases and h its altitude, show that the area K of the triangle ABC in terms of the coordinates of its vertices is

$$K = \text{area of } ADEC + CEFB - ADFB$$

$$= \tfrac{1}{2} \begin{vmatrix} x_1 & y_1 & 1 \\ x_2 & y_2 & 1 \\ x_3 & y_3 & 1 \end{vmatrix}. \quad \textit{Hint: Use Problem 12.} \qquad (7\text{–}14)$$

14. Find the area of the triangle whose vertices are the points

a) $(2, 3)$, $(5, 4)$, and $(4, 7)$ b) $(-4, 2)$, $(-2, -3)$, and $(3, -1)$

15. Find the area of the triangle the coordinates of whose vertices are (x, y), $(2, 3)$, and $(5, -1)$. (See Fig. 7–2.)

▶ **16.** The condition that the area of the triangle described in Problem 15 is equal to zero is equivalent to the fact that the point (x, y) lies on the line through $(2, 3)$ and $(5, -1)$. Using this fact, find the equation of the straight line through $(2, 3)$ and $(5, -1)$.

17. Find the equation of the straight line through $(-2, -4)$ and $(3, 5)$, using the method of this section.

18. Two nonparallel straight lines in the plane always intersect in one point. The condition that three such lines,

$$a_1x + b_1y = c_1, \qquad a_2x + b_2y = c_2, \qquad a_3x + b_3y = c_3,$$

pass through the same point is that the determinant of the matrix

$$\begin{bmatrix} a_1 & b_1 & c_1 \\ a_2 & b_2 & c_2 \\ a_3 & b_3 & c_3 \end{bmatrix}$$

is equal to zero. Assuming that such is the case, show that the three straight lines

$$x - 2y = -3, \qquad 3x - y = 1, \qquad 5x - 2y = 1$$

pass through the same point.

19. Show that the system of equations $3x - 2y + 11 = 0$, $x - y + 5 = 0$, $2x + y = 2$ has a common solution, and find it.

20. Find the value of x if

a) $\begin{vmatrix} 1 & 2 & 5 \\ 1 & x & 5 \\ 3 & -1 & 2 \end{vmatrix} = 0,$

b) $\begin{vmatrix} 1 & 2 & -3 \\ 1 & x & -3 \\ 1 & 4 & -x \end{vmatrix} = 0.$

7-5 DETERMINANTS OF ORDER n

As might be expected, there exist determinants of any finite order. To consider them and their general properties, it will be convenient to use a different notation for the matrix and its elements. Let us denote the matrix by M and any element by the symbol a_{ij} (read "a sub i-j"), where i denotes the number of the row and j the number of the column in which the particular element appears. The notation used here was introduced by the English mathematician A. Cayley (1821–1895). According to this notation, Eq. (7–13) is written

$$\delta(M) = \begin{vmatrix} a_{11} & a_{12} & a_{13} \\ a_{21} & a_{22} & a_{23} \\ a_{31} & a_{32} & a_{33} \end{vmatrix}$$

$$= a_{11}(a_{22}a_{33} - a_{23}a_{32}) - a_{12}(a_{21}a_{33} - a_{23}a_{31}) + a_{13}(a_{21}a_{32} - a_{22}a_{31})$$

$$= a_{11}a_{22}a_{33} + a_{12}a_{23}a_{31} + a_{13}a_{21}a_{32} - a_{11}a_{23}a_{32} - a_{12}a_{21}a_{33} - a_{13}a_{22}a_{31}. \qquad (7\text{--}15)$$

It should be clear from this expression that each of the six products consists of one and only one element from each row and each column. Each of these products has been ordered by placing the first subscripts in natural numerical order. With the exception of the first term, the second subscripts are not in natural order. Let us consider the number of *inversions* of the second subscripts, that is, the number of times a greater integer precedes a smaller one.

	Second subscripts			Number of inversions
	1	2	3	0
Positive products	2	3	1	2
	3	1	2	2
	1	3	2	1
Negative products	2	1	3	1
	3	2	1	3

From this table, we see that the positive products have an even number of inversions, while the negative products have an odd number. Thus the correct sign for any term can be expressed $(-1)^k$, where k is the number of inversions. It is by means of a direct generalization of this study that we define the nth order determinant of the n square matrix.

Definition 7–10. The function δ whose domain is the set of all square n by n matrices,

$$M = \begin{bmatrix} a_{11} & a_{12} & a_{13} & \cdots & a_{1n} \\ a_{21} & a_{22} & a_{23} & \cdots & a_{2n} \\ a_{31} & a_{32} & a_{33} & \cdots & a_{3n} \\ \vdots & & & & \\ a_{n1} & a_{n2} & a_{n3} & \cdots & a_{nn} \end{bmatrix}, \tag{7-16}$$

where the a_{ij} are real numbers, is the determinant of this matrix. Its functional value, denoted by $\delta(M)$, is equal to the algebraic sum of all possible products formed by taking one and only one element from each row and each column. The sign of each product is chosen as $(-1)^k$, where k is the number of inversions of the second subscripts when the factors are so arranged that their first subscripts are in natural numerical order.

In any possible product of n elements with the first subscripts in natural order, the second subscript in the first element may be any one of n numbers, the subscript for the second element any one of the remaining $n - 1$ numbers, and so on, so that there are $n!* = n(n - 1)(n - 2) \cdots 2 \cdot 1$ terms in the expansion of $\delta(M)$. For example, we recall that there are $3! = 6$ terms in the expansion of the third order determinant. There are $4! = 24$ in the fourth, and $5! = 120$ terms in the expansion of the fifth order determinant. Because of the large number of terms in the expansion of a determinant, our definition is clearly not a convenient way to find the value of the determinant. Before we consider a practical method of evaluation, we shall prove some of the elementary properties of determinants.

Theorem 7–3. If the corresponding rows and columns of a matrix are interchanged, its determinant remains unchanged.

For example,

$$\begin{vmatrix} a_{11} & a_{12} & a_{13} \\ a_{21} & a_{22} & a_{23} \\ a_{31} & a_{32} & a_{33} \end{vmatrix} = \begin{vmatrix} a_{11} & a_{21} & a_{31} \\ a_{12} & a_{22} & a_{32} \\ a_{13} & a_{23} & a_{33} \end{vmatrix}.$$

Proof. We recall that for each element our notation indicated the row by the first subscript, and the column by the second subscript. If we now consider the determinant associated with a new matrix M' whose rows and columns are respectively the corresponding columns and rows of M, every term of $\delta(M')$ will again have

---

* The symbol $n!$ (read "factorial n") denotes the product of the positive integers from 1 to n. Specifically, $1! = 1$, $2! = 2$, $3! = 6$, and so on. This symbol will be used in later chapters.

one element from each row and each column. If the second subscripts are placed in their natural numerical order, the number of inversions of the first subscripts will determine the sign of any particular term. Thus the interchange of rows and columns serves only to change the notation, and the result for each term is the same. Consequently, $\delta(M')$ is identical to $\delta(M)$.

As a direct result of Theorem 7–3, in any further property of determinants the words "row" and "column" may be interchanged throughout.

Theorem 7–4. If any two columns (rows) of a matrix are interchanged, the sign of the associated determinant is changed.

Proof. Let us first consider the interchange of two adjacent columns. In the expansion of the new determinant, the first subscripts will remain the same, but the second subscripts—those representing the columns—will be interchanged, and as a result the number of inversions in each term will be increased or decreased by one. Thus the sign of every term, and consequently the value of the determinants, will be changed.

Now suppose we wish to interchange the j and k columns (where for convenience $j < k$) and there are m columns between them. This may be done by moving the jth column to the position just to the left of the kth column (m interchanges), interchanging these two adjacent columns (1 interchange), and moving the kth column back to the original position of the jth column (m interchanges). Since the total number of interchanges, $2m + 1$, is odd, and each requires a change in sign, we again have our required result.

Theorem 7–5. If two columns (rows) of a matrix are identical, its determinant is zero.

Proof. If $\delta(M)$ is the value of the determinant, with the two identical columns interchanged, the value becomes $-\delta(M)$, by Theorem 7–4. But since the two columns were identical, the determinant has not changed. Thus, $\delta(M) = -\delta(M)$, that is $\delta(M) = 0$.

Theorem 7–6. If each element of a column (row) in a matrix is multiplied by the same number m, the value of its determinant is multiplied by m.

For example,

$$\begin{vmatrix} a_{11} & ma_{12} & a_{13} \\ a_{21} & ma_{22} & a_{23} \\ a_{31} & ma_{32} & a_{33} \end{vmatrix} = m \begin{vmatrix} a_{11} & a_{12} & a_{13} \\ a_{21} & a_{22} & a_{23} \\ a_{31} & a_{32} & a_{33} \end{vmatrix}.$$

Proof. This property follows directly from the definition. If each element of a column is multiplied by m, each term in the expansion of the determinant will have m as a factor.

As a direct result of Theorem 7–6, we have the following corollary.

Corollary 7–6. Any quantity that is a factor of each element in a column of a matrix (row) is actually a factor of the expansion of the determinant.

Theorem 7-7. If three matrices M_1, M_2, and M_3 have corresponding elements equal except for one column (row) in which the elements of M_1 are the sums of the corresponding elements of M_2 and M_3, then $\delta(M_1) = \delta(M_2) + \delta(M_3)$.

For example,

$$
\begin{vmatrix} a_{11} + a'_{11} & a_{12} & a_{13} \\ a_{21} + a'_{21} & a_{22} & a_{23} \\ a_{31} + a'_{31} & a_{32} & a_{33} \end{vmatrix} = \begin{vmatrix} a_{11} & a_{12} & a_{13} \\ a_{21} & a_{22} & a_{23} \\ a_{31} & a_{32} & a_{33} \end{vmatrix} + \begin{vmatrix} a'_{11} & a_{12} & a_{13} \\ a'_{21} & a_{22} & a_{23} \\ a'_{31} & a_{32} & a_{33} \end{vmatrix}.
$$

Proof. Every term in the expansion of $\delta(M_1)$ contains one and only one of these sums, each of which may be expressed as two terms. The expansions of $\delta(M_2)$ and $\delta(M_3)$ are the direct result.

Theorem 7-8. If each element of any column (row) of a matrix is multiplied by the same number m and added to the corresponding element of another column, the associated determinant remains unchanged.

For example,

$$
\begin{vmatrix} a_{11} & a_{12} & a_{13} \\ a_{21} & a_{22} & a_{23} \\ a_{31} & a_{32} & a_{33} \end{vmatrix} = \begin{vmatrix} a_{11} + ma_{13} & a_{12} & a_{13} \\ a_{21} + ma_{23} & a_{22} & a_{23} \\ a_{31} + ma_{33} & a_{32} & a_{33} \end{vmatrix}.
$$

Proof. This follows directly by using Theorems 7-7, 7-6, and 7-5 in considering the determinant on the right.

Many of these properties will be useful in the evaluation of the nth order determinant. Methods for such evaluation will be given in the next article.

PROBLEMS

1. Explain why the following two determinants are equal. Verify this fact by actual evaluation.

$$
\begin{vmatrix} 2 & 4 & 1 \\ 3 & 2 & -1 \\ -1 & 3 & 2 \end{vmatrix} \qquad \begin{vmatrix} 2 & 3 & -1 \\ 4 & 2 & 3 \\ 1 & -1 & 2 \end{vmatrix}
$$

2. Show by actual expansion that the sign of the determinant

$$
\begin{vmatrix} 3 & -1 & 2 \\ 2 & 4 & 5 \\ -1 & 3 & 2 \end{vmatrix}
$$

is changed if the first and third row are interchanged.

Without evaluating, state why each of the determinants in Problems 3 and 4 has the value zero. Check by evaluating.

3. $\begin{vmatrix} 2 & -3 & 2 \\ 1 & 2 & 1 \\ 6 & 4 & 6 \end{vmatrix}$

4. $\begin{vmatrix} 3 & 1 & -2 \\ 2 & 7 & 3 \\ 6 & 2 & -4 \end{vmatrix}$

5. Evaluate the following determinant by factoring out the common terms from any row or column and then expanding. Check by expanding directly.

$$\begin{vmatrix} 3 & 3 & 5 \\ 6 & 16 & 8 \\ -12 & 6 & 10 \end{vmatrix}$$

6. Use Theorem 7–7 to express the sum of the two determinants as a single determinant. Check the work by evaluating all three.

$$\begin{vmatrix} 3 & 1 & -2 \\ 2 & 3 & 5 \\ -1 & 4 & 3 \end{vmatrix} + \begin{vmatrix} -2 & 1 & -2 \\ -1 & 3 & 5 \\ 2 & 4 & 3 \end{vmatrix}$$

7. In the following matrix, multiply each of the elements in the second row by 3, and form a new matrix by adding these results to the corresponding elements of the first row. Show by direct expansion of the determinant of the new matrix that the value of the determinant of the original matrix is unchanged.

$$\begin{bmatrix} 2 & 5 & -6 \\ -1 & 2 & 4 \\ 3 & 1 & 5 \end{bmatrix}$$

8. In the matrix of Problem 7, multiply each of the elements in the third column by 2 and subtract the products from the corresponding elements in the first column, forming a new matrix. Show by direct evaluation that the values of the associated determinants are unchanged.

9. Determine the roots of the equation

$$\begin{vmatrix} 1 & 1 & 1 \\ x & a & b \\ x^2 & a^2 & b^2 \end{vmatrix} = 0 \qquad (a \neq b).$$

Hint: If $x = a$, the first two columns are equal.

10. Determine the roots of the equation

$$\begin{vmatrix} 1 & a & a^2 & a^3 \\ 1 & b & b^2 & b^3 \\ 1 & c & c^2 & c^3 \\ 1 & x & x^2 & x^3 \end{vmatrix} = 0 \quad (a \neq b \neq c \neq a).$$

11. Find the roots of the equation

$$\begin{vmatrix} 3 & 1 & 9 \\ 2x & 2 & 6 \\ x^2 & 3 & 3 \end{vmatrix} = 0$$

by using Theorems 7–5 and 7–6, and check by expanding the determinant.

12. Prove that

$$2 \begin{vmatrix} a_1 & b_1 & c_1 \\ a_2 & b_2 & c_2 \\ a_3 & b_3 & c_3 \end{vmatrix} = \begin{vmatrix} b_1 + c_1 & c_1 + a_1 & a_1 + b_1 \\ b_2 + c_2 & c_2 + a_2 & a_2 + b_2 \\ b_3 + c_3 & c_3 + a_3 & a_3 + b_3 \end{vmatrix}.$$

7–6 EXPANSION OF A DETERMINANT BY MINORS

The statement in Problem 10 of the second set of problems in Article 7–4 may be considered the method for the expansion of a third order determinant by minors. The method holds true in general. The *minor* of an element of a square matrix of order n is the determinant of the $(n - 1)$st order matrix obtained by deleting the row and column in which this element lies. The minor of a_{ij} will be denoted by $\delta(A_{ij})$ where A_{ij} is the appropriate $(n - 1)$st order matrix. We wish to prove the following theorem for the determinant $\delta(M)$ of the nth order matrix given in Eq. (7–16).

> **Theorem 7–9.** The determinant, $\delta(M)$ of any matrix M, is the algebraic sum of the products obtained by multiplying each element of a column (row) of the matrix M by its minor. The sign of each such product is $(-1)^{i+j}$, where the element is in the ith row and jth column.

For example,

$$\begin{vmatrix} a_{11} & a_{12} & a_{13} & a_{14} \\ a_{21} & a_{22} & a_{23} & a_{24} \\ a_{31} & a_{32} & a_{33} & a_{34} \\ a_{41} & a_{42} & a_{43} & a_{44} \end{vmatrix} = -a_{12} \begin{vmatrix} a_{21} & a_{23} & a_{24} \\ a_{31} & a_{33} & a_{34} \\ a_{41} & a_{43} & a_{44} \end{vmatrix} + a_{22} \begin{vmatrix} a_{11} & a_{13} & a_{14} \\ a_{31} & a_{33} & a_{34} \\ a_{41} & a_{43} & a_{44} \end{vmatrix}$$

$$- a_{32} \begin{vmatrix} a_{11} & a_{13} & a_{14} \\ a_{21} & a_{23} & a_{24} \\ a_{41} & a_{43} & a_{44} \end{vmatrix} + a_{42} \begin{vmatrix} a_{11} & a_{13} & a_{14} \\ a_{21} & a_{23} & a_{24} \\ a_{31} & a_{33} & a_{34} \end{vmatrix}$$

is the expansion of the fourth order determinant by the second column.

Proof. The theorem is proved by noting two facts. Consider first the product $a_{11} \delta(A_{11})$. In this product, consisting of all the terms with a_{11} as a factor, all the signs of each term are correct, since the number of inversions in A_{11} is not changed by prefixing a_{11}.

Now consider any element a_{ij}. It may be moved to the original position of a_{11} by first moving the ith row to the first row, requiring $i - 1$ interchanges of rows, and then moving the jth column to the position of the first column, requiring an additional $j - 1$ interchange of columns. This process will produce $i - 1 + j - 1 = i + j - 2$ changes in sign. If M' is the new matrix, and $\delta(M')$ its determinant, the relation between $\delta(M')$ and $\delta(M)$ is expressed by

$$\delta(M') = (-1)^{i+j-2} \delta(M) = (-1)^{i+j} \delta(M).$$

Thus the terms of the expansion with a_{ij} as a factor are $(-1)^{i+j} a_{ij} \delta(A_{ij})$, where $\delta(A_{ij})$ is the original minor of a_{ij} in M. Thus $\delta(M)$ may be expanded by means of any column (row) as indicated in the theorem.

We are now prepared to evaluate any determinant. In the following examples, note the use of the foregoing theorems.

Example 1. Find the value of the determinant

$$\delta(M) = \begin{vmatrix} -4 & 2 & 5 & 6 \\ 2 & 1 & 0 & 3 \\ 7 & 2 & -3 & 2 \\ 4 & -1 & 7 & 5 \end{vmatrix}.$$

Solution. Since $a_{23} = 0$, it will simplify the work to expand by either the second row or third column. Since the elements in the third column are larger than the second row, we shall choose the second row. Thus,

$$\delta(M) = -2 \begin{vmatrix} 2 & 5 & 6 \\ 2 & -3 & 2 \\ -1 & 7 & 5 \end{vmatrix} + 1 \begin{vmatrix} -4 & 5 & 6 \\ 7 & -3 & 2 \\ 4 & 7 & 5 \end{vmatrix} + 3 \begin{vmatrix} -4 & 2 & 5 \\ 7 & 2 & -3 \\ 4 & -1 & 7 \end{vmatrix}.$$

Expanding each of the third order determinants, we get

$$\begin{vmatrix} 2 & 5 & 6 \\ 2 & -3 & 2 \\ -1 & 7 & 5 \end{vmatrix} = 2(-15 - 14) - 5(10 + 2) + 6(14 - 3)$$
$$= -58 - 60 + 66 = -52,$$

$$\begin{vmatrix} -4 & 5 & 6 \\ 7 & -3 & 2 \\ 4 & 7 & 5 \end{vmatrix} = -4(-15 - 14) - 5(35 - 8) + 6(49 + 12)$$
$$= 116 - 135 + 366 = 347,$$

$$\begin{vmatrix} -4 & 2 & 5 \\ 7 & 2 & -3 \\ 4 & -1 & 7 \end{vmatrix} = -4(14 - 3) - 2(49 + 12) + 5(-7 - 8)$$
$$= -44 - 122 - 75 = -241.$$

Using these values, we have

$$\delta(M) = -2(-52) + 347 + 3(-241) = -272.$$

We note in this example that the work was shortened by the fact that one of the elements was zero. By making use of Theorem 7–8, we may introduce other zeros and shorten the work still further. Let us consider another example.

Example 2. Find the value of the determinant

$$\delta(M) = \begin{vmatrix} 3 & -2 & -1 & 2 \\ 4 & 1 & 2 & -3 \\ -9 & -5 & 7 & -8 \\ 1 & 5 & 3 & -2 \end{vmatrix}.$$

Solution. We look for an element equal to 1 or −1, and work with the row or column containing the ±1. Let us select the −1 in the first row. By using Theorem 7–8, we are able to introduce zeros in the first row. In turn we (1) multiply the elements of the third column by 3 and add the products to the corresponding elements of the first column, (2) multiply the elements of the third column by −2 and add the products to the corresponding elements of the second column, and (3) multiply the elements of the third column by 2 and add the products to the corresponding elements of the fourth column. Therefore,

$$\delta(M) = \begin{vmatrix} 0 & 0 & -1 & 0 \\ 10 & -3 & 2 & 1 \\ 12 & -19 & 7 & 6 \\ 10 & -1 & 3 & 4 \end{vmatrix}.$$

Now, expanding by the first row as in Example 1, we have

$$\delta(M) = -1 \begin{vmatrix} 10 & -3 & 1 \\ 12 & -19 & 6 \\ 10 & -1 & 4 \end{vmatrix}.$$

We may again introduce zeros to simplify the work. In this third order matrix, (1) multiply the elements of the first row by −6 and add the products to the corresponding elements of the second row, (2) multiply the elements of the first row by −4 and add the products to the corresponding elements of the third row. This results in

$$\delta(M) = -1 \begin{vmatrix} 10 & -3 & 1 \\ -48 & -1 & 0 \\ -30 & 11 & 0 \end{vmatrix},$$

which, expanded by the last column, gives

$$\delta(M) = -1\{1[(-48)(11) - (-30)(-1)]\}$$
$$= -1(-528 - 30) = 558.$$

If there is no element equal to 1 or -1 in any column or row, we are usually able to introduce such an element by using Theorem 7–8 and continuing as above. Although the introduction of a 1 is not necessary, the process eliminates the possibilities of fractions if there were none initially.

PROBLEMS

Evaluate the determinants of each of the following matrices.

1.
$$\begin{bmatrix} 1 & -2 & 2 & -3 \\ 0 & 5 & 0 & -2 \\ 2 & 4 & -6 & 2 \\ 3 & -4 & 1 & -2 \end{bmatrix}$$

2.
$$\begin{bmatrix} 2 & 4 & 3 & -5 \\ 3 & 0 & 2 & -1 \\ -? & 3 & 1 & 6 \\ 1 & -4 & 2 & 8 \end{bmatrix}$$

3.
$$\begin{bmatrix} 4 & 2 & 4 & 8 \\ 7 & 5 & 2 & 4 \\ -7 & 2 & 3 & -8 \\ 6 & 4 & 5 & 6 \end{bmatrix}$$

4.
$$\begin{bmatrix} 3 & 2 & -1 & 4 \\ 4 & -3 & 5 & -2 \\ 6 & -1 & 4 & 7 \\ 5 & -2 & 8 & 3 \end{bmatrix}$$

5.
$$\begin{bmatrix} 3 & -1 & 2 & 6 \\ 2 & 3 & 5 & 4 \\ 4 & -2 & 2 & 7 \\ -3 & 2 & -1 & -3 \end{bmatrix}$$

6.
$$\begin{bmatrix} 1 & 1 & 1 & 1 \\ 1 & 2 & 3 & 4 \\ 1 & 3 & 6 & 10 \\ 1 & 4 & 10 & 20 \end{bmatrix}$$

7-7 SOLUTION OF A SYSTEM OF LINEAR EQUATIONS BY DETERMINANTS

In Articles 6–10 and 6–11 we discussed the solution of systems of linear equations in two and three unknowns. Systems of linear equations involving any number of unknowns, with the proper number of equations, may be expressed in terms of matrices. Recall Problem 14, Article 7–2. In considering the general case with n linear equations in n unknowns, we have

$$a_{11}x_1 + a_{12}x_2 + \cdots + a_{1n}x_n = k_1,$$
$$a_{21}x_1 + a_{22}x_2 + \cdots + a_{2n}x_n = k_2, \qquad (7\text{-}17)$$
$$\vdots$$
$$a_{n1}x_1 + a_{n2}x_2 + \cdots + a_{nn}x_n = k_n.$$

This, of course, may be written

$$\begin{bmatrix} a_{11} & a_{12} & \cdots & a_{1n} \\ a_{21} & a_{22} & \cdots & a_{2n} \\ \vdots & & & \\ a_{n1} & a_{n2} & \cdots & a_{nn} \end{bmatrix} \begin{bmatrix} x_1 \\ x_2 \\ \vdots \\ x_n \end{bmatrix} = \begin{bmatrix} k_1 \\ k_2 \\ \vdots \\ k_n \end{bmatrix}, \qquad \text{or more briefly} \qquad MX = K,$$

where the expressions for the matrices M, X, and K are understood. We are able to prove a theorem which is known as Cramer's Rule, in honor of the Swiss mathematician Gabriel Cramer (1704–1752).

Theorem 7–10. If M is the matrix of the coefficients of the unknowns, the product of $\delta(M)$ and any one of the unknowns is equal to the determinant $\delta(M_i)$, obtained from $\delta(M)$ by substituting the constant terms in place of the coefficients of that unknown in M and leaving the other elements unchanged.

Proof. Since

$$M = \begin{bmatrix} a_{11} & a_{12} & \cdots & a_{1n} \\ a_{21} & a_{22} & \cdots & a_{2n} \\ \vdots & & & \\ a_{n1} & a_{n2} & \cdots & a_{nn} \end{bmatrix},$$

by Theorem 7–6,

$$x_1\,\delta(M) = \begin{vmatrix} a_{11}x_1 & a_{12} & \cdots & a_{1n} \\ a_{21}x_1 & a_{22} & \cdots & a_{2n} \\ \vdots & & & \\ a_{n1}x_1 & a_{n2} & \cdots & a_{nn} \end{vmatrix}.$$

If we now multiply each element of the second column by x_2, of the third by x_3, and so on, and add all these products to the corresponding elements in the first column, we have, by Theorem 7–8,

$$x_1\,\delta(M) = \begin{vmatrix} a_{11}x_1 + a_{12}x_2 + \cdots + a_{1n}x_n & a_{12} & \cdots & a_{1n} \\ a_{21}x_1 + a_{22}x_2 + \cdots + a_{2n}x_n & a_{22} & \cdots & a_{2n} \\ \vdots & & & \\ a_{n1}x_1 + a_{n2}x_2 + \cdots + a_{nn}x_n & a_{n2} & \cdots & a_{nn} \end{vmatrix}$$

$$= \begin{vmatrix} k_1 & a_{12} & \cdots & a_{1n} \\ k_2 & a_{22} & \cdots & a_{2n} \\ \vdots & & & \\ k_n & a_{n2} & \cdots & a_{nn} \end{vmatrix} = \delta(M_1).$$

In this way, we find

$$\begin{aligned} x_1\,\delta(M) &= \delta(M_1), \\ x_2\,\delta(M) &= \delta(M_2), \\ &\vdots \\ x_n\,\delta(M) &= \delta(M_n), \end{aligned} \qquad (7\text{–}18)$$

where M_i is obtained from M by substituting $k_1, k_2, \ldots, k_n$ for the elements $a_{1i}, a_{2i}, \ldots, a_{ni}$ of the ith column of M.

If $\delta(M) \neq 0,$* the unique solution of Eqs. (7–17) is obtained from Eqs. (7–18) by division:

$$x_1 = \frac{\delta(M_1)}{\delta(M)}, \qquad x_2 = \frac{\delta(M_2)}{\delta(M)}, \qquad \cdots, \qquad x_n = \frac{\delta(M_n)}{\delta(M)}. \qquad (7\text{–}19)$$

It is clear that this set of values satisfies the system given in Eqs. (7–17), and therefore is a solution. For example, the first equation is satisfied, since

$$k_1 \, \delta(M) - a_{11} \, \delta(M_1) - a_{12} \, \delta(M_2) - \cdots - a_{1n} \, \delta(M_n)$$

is the expansion of

$$\begin{vmatrix} k_1 & a_{11} & a_{12} & \cdots & a_{1n} \\ k_1 & a_{11} & a_{12} & \cdots & a_{1n} \\ k_2 & a_{21} & a_{22} & \cdots & a_{2n} \\ \vdots & & & & \\ k_n & a_{n1} & a_{n2} & \cdots & a_{nn} \end{vmatrix} \qquad (7\text{–}20)$$

hy the first row. Dut this determinant is zero, since the first two rows are identical. The other equations are similarly satisfied.

PROBLEMS

1 through 4. Solve the systems of equations given in Problems 1, 3, 5, and 7 of Article 6‑11 by the method of this article.

5 through 8. Solve the systems of equations given in Problems 2, 4, 6, and 8 of Article 6–11 by the method of this article.

Solve the following systems of equations by determinants.

9. $x + y + z + w = -4$
   $x + 2y + 3z + 4w = 0$
   $x + 3y + 6z + 10w = 9$
   $x + 4y + 10z + 20w = 24$

10. $x + 2y - z = 8$
    $y + 3z - w = 3$
    $z + 4w - x = -20$
    $w + 5x - y = 9$

Express each of the matrix equations in Problems 11 and 12 in terms of four linear cquations in x, y, z, and w, and solve.

11. $$\begin{bmatrix} 1 & -2 & 1 & -1 \\ 2 & -1 & -1 & 1 \\ 1 & 0 & -2 & 1 \\ 1 & 3 & -1 & 0 \end{bmatrix} \begin{bmatrix} x \\ y \\ z \\ w \end{bmatrix} = \begin{bmatrix} -7 \\ 4 \\ 6 \\ 8 \end{bmatrix}$$

---

* If $\delta(M) = 0$, solutions may or may not exist. A complete discussion is beyond the scope of this book.

12.

$$\begin{bmatrix} 3 & -2 & 1 & -4 \\ 1 & 2 & 0 & -1 \\ 0 & 2 & -3 & 2 \\ 1 & 0 & -2 & 1 \end{bmatrix} \begin{bmatrix} x \\ y \\ z \\ w \end{bmatrix} + \begin{bmatrix} 3 \\ 4 \\ 7 \\ 4 \end{bmatrix} = \begin{bmatrix} 0 \\ 0 \\ 0 \\ 0 \end{bmatrix}$$

13. One of the well-known methods (used in numerical analysis with high-speed computing machines) of finding the nth degree expression* which passes through $n + 1$ distinct points makes use of determinants. Explain why the determinant,

$$\begin{vmatrix} f(x) & 1 & x & x^2 \\ f(x_1) & 1 & x_1 & x_1^2 \\ f(x_2) & 1 & x_2 & x_2^2 \\ f(x_3) & 1 & x_3 & x_3^2 \end{vmatrix},$$

set equal to zero, can be considered as the defining equation of the function f, where the expression for $f(x)$ is second degree and is satisfied by the coordinates of three points. *Hint:* If $x = x_1$, $f(x) = f(x_1)$, so that the first two rows are identical, and so on.

14. Explain Problem 16, Article 7–4, in the light of Problem 13 above.

15. By expanding the determinant, simplify the expression,

$$\begin{vmatrix} f(x) & 1 & x & x^2 \\ 1 & 1 & 1 & 1 \\ 2 & 1 & 2 & 4 \\ 11 & 1 & -1 & 1 \end{vmatrix} = 0,$$

and thus find the specific quadratic function of the form $f(x) = ax^2 + bx + c$ which passes through $(1, 1)$, $(2, 2)$, and $(-1, 11)$.

---

* Here we mean an nth degree polynomial, which will be discussed in the next chapter. [See Eq. (8–1). Recall the definition in Article 3–3.]

CHAPTER 8

POLYNOMIAL FUNCTIONS

In Chapter 6 we considered the first and second degree functions. We wish to generalize this type of function.

Definition 8–1. The function f, defined by the equation in the form

$$f(x) = a_0 x^n + a_1 x^{n-1} + a_2 x^{n-2} + \cdots a_n,$$

and written

$$f = \{(x, y) | y = a_0 x^n + a_1 x^{n-1} + a_2 x^{n-2} | \cdots u_n \}, \qquad (8\text{–}1)$$

where $a_0 \neq 0$, n is a positive integer, and $a_i (i = 1, 2, 3, \ldots n)$ are constants, is called a *rational integral function* or a *polynomial function of the nth degree in x.*

The expression for $f(x)$ is called a *polynomial.* (Compare the definition in Article 3–3.) Unless otherwise stated, f will denote such a function in this chapter.

8–1 CERTAIN THEOREMS

There are several theorems of considerable importance in the study of the polynomial function which must now be established, not only to facilitate graphing the function but also to help solve polynomial equations.

Theorem 8–1 (The Remainder Theorem). If a polynomial $f(x)$ is divided by $x - r$, where r is any constant, until a constant remainder independent of x is obtained, this remainder is equal to $f(r)$.

Proof. Let $q(x)$ denote the quotient when $f(x)$ is divided by $x - r$, and let R denote the constant remainder. Then $f(x)$ may be expressed [recall Eqs. (3–8) and (3–9) of Article 3–3] by the identity

$$f(x) \equiv (x - r) \cdot q(x) + R, \qquad (8\text{–}2)$$

where clearly $q(x)$ is of degree $n - 1$, since we assume $f(x)$ is of degree n. Since this identity is true for all values of x, it is true for $x = r$. Therefore,

$$f(r) = (r - r) \cdot q(r) + R = 0 \cdot q(r) + R$$

or

$$f(r) = R. \qquad (8\text{–}3)$$

Illustration 1. Let $f(x) = 5x^3 - 14x + 3$, and $r = 2$. Then, as was shown in Example 3, Article 3–3, $R = 15$. By substituting $r = 2$ for x in $f(x)$, we have $f(2) = 5(2)^3 - 14(2) + 3 = 40 - 28 + 3 = 15$, which is in accord with the Remainder Theorem.

Because of this theorem, the method of synthetic division described in Article 3–3 is most useful in finding the value of $f(x)$ for different values of x. It has advantages over direct substitution that are especially evident either when n is large or when r is other than a small integer.

Until quite recently this method was the only one used for evaluating polynomials. Today, however, it is important that the reader be aware of the changes which the computer viewpoint brings to elementary analysis and, in fact, observe and learn certain of these changes. One of the changes is the use of the iterative method in modern computing, and this iterative method is easily illustrated by another method for evaluating a polynomial.

Let us find the value of

$$f(x) = 5x^3 - 8x^2 + 6x + 4 \text{ at } x = 2.$$

Let the first approximation, called $f_0(2)$, to our result be 5, that is,

$$f_0(2) = 5.$$

Multiply $f_0(2)$ by 2, add -8, and call $f_1(2)$, that is,

$$f_1(2) = 5(2) - 8.$$

Multiply $f_1(2)$ by 2, add 6, and call $f_2(2)$, that is,

$$f_2(2) = [5(2) - 8]2 + 6 = 5(2)^2 - 8(2) + 6.$$

Multiply $f_2(2)$ by 2, add 4, and obtain $f(2)$, that is,

$$f(2) = [5(2)^2 - 8(2) + 6]2 + 4 = 5(2)^3 - 8(2)^3 + 6(2) + 4.$$

The result, of course is $5(2)^3 - 8(2)^2 + 6(2) + 4 = 24$, which should be checked by synthetic division, but the importance of this method is the iterative process. At each step, exactly the same process is repeated. It is for this reason that the computation is easy for a computing machine as well as the program writer.

Theorem 8–2 (*The Factor Theorem*). If $f(r) = R$ is zero, that is, r is a zero of $f(x)$, then $(x - r)$ is a factor of $f(x)$.

Proof. Since r is a zero of $f(x)$, that is $R = 0$, we have

$$f(x) \equiv (x - r) \cdot q(x) + 0.$$

Thus $(x - r)$ is a factor.

Theorem 8–3 (*Converse of the Factor Theorem*). If $(x - r)$ is a factor of $f(x)$, then $f(r) = R = 0$, and r is a zero of $f(x)$.

Proof. Since $x - r$ is a factor of $f(x)$,

$$f(x) \equiv (x - r) \cdot q(x),$$

where $q(x)$ is the quotient of $f(x)/(x - r)$. Therefore,

$$f(r) = (r - r) \cdot q(r) = 0 \cdot q(r) = 0,$$

which states that r is a zero of $f(x)$.

Illustration 2. The quantity $x - 3$ is a factor of $f(x) \equiv x^3 - 27$, since

$$f(3) = (3)^3 - 27 = 0.$$

Illustration 3. The functional equation $f(x) = x^3 - 6x^2 + 3x + 10$ is exactly divisible by $x - 2$, since $f(2) = 0$. The fact that $f(2) = 0$ is shown by synthetic division.

$$
\begin{array}{rrrr|r}
1 & -6 & 3 & 10 & \underline{2} \\
  & 2 & -8 & -10 & \\
\hline
1 & -4 & -5 & 0 &
\end{array}
$$

PROBLEMS

By using synthetic division, find the remainder, and check by direct substitution, when

1. $3x^2 - 2x - 4$ is divided by $x - 3$
2. $x^3 + 4x - 7$ is divided by $x - 3$
3. $x^3 - 2x^2 + 9$ is divided by $x + 2$
4. $x^4 - 2x^3 - 3x^2 - 4x - 8$ is divided by (a) $x - 2$, (b) $x + 1$
5. $2x^4 - 3x^3 - 20x^2 - 6$ is divided by (a) $x - 4$, (b) $x + 3$
6. $x^3 + 3x^2 - 2x - 5$ is divided by (a) $x + 2$, (b) $x + 3$

By using the Factor Theorem, determine whether the first quantity is a factor of the second in Problems 7 through 12.

7. $x - 2$, $x^4 + 3x^3 - 5x^2 + 2x - 24$
8. $x + 3$, $x^3 - 4x^2 - 18x + 9$
9. $x - 3$, $x^4 - 5x^3 + 8x^2 + 15x - 2$
10. $x - 5$, $x^3 + 2x^2 - 25x - 50$
11. $2x + 3$, $2x^4 + 5x^3 + 3x^2 + 8x + 12$
12. $3x + 1$, $9x^3 + 6x^2 + 4x + 2$
13. Show that $x - y$ is a factor of $x^5 - y^5$, $x^6 - y^6$, $x^7 - y^7$, and $x^8 - y^8$.

By using synthetic division, find the quotient in each case.

14. Show that $x + y$ is a factor of $x^5 + y^5$ and $x^7 + y^7$. By using synthetic division, find the quotient in each case.

Find the value of each of the polynomials at the specified value by the iterative process illustrated above. Write out each approximation.

15. $x^3 - 8x^2 + 6x + 4$ at $x = 3$

16. $x^4 - 4x^3 + x^2 - 3x + 8$ at $x = 5$

17. $x^4 + 5x^3 + 3x^2 + 8x - 4$ at $x = -4$

18. $x^3 + 5x^2 - 6x - 9$ at $x = -\frac{3}{2}$

19. Outline a proof for the fact that $f(c) = a_0 c^n + a_1 c^{n-1} + a_2 c^{n-2} + \cdots + a_{n-1}c + a_n$ is the correct value of $f(x)$ given in Eq. (8–1) at $x = c$, if the iterative process is used.

20. Explain why such an iterative process would not be used to evaluate a product.

One of the more important theorems in connection with the zeros of a polynomial function may be expressed in terms of synthetic division.

Theorem 8–4. In the synthetic division of

$$f(x) = a_0 x^n + a_1 x^{n-1} + a_2 x^{n-2} + \cdots + a_{n-1}x + a_n \quad by \quad x - r,$$

where $a_0 > 0$,

1. if $r > 0$ and all the numbers in the third row are positive, then r is an upper bound for the positive zeros of $f(x)$.
2. if $r < 0$ and the signs of the numbers in the third row alternate in sign, then r is a lower bound for the negative zeros of $f(x)$.

Proof. Because of the process of synthetic division, in either (1) or (2) a numerical increase in r will numerically increase all the numbers in the third row except the first. Thus, if r were to be increased numerically, the final number in the third row would be numerically increased, so that the remainder would never be zero for any numerical increase in r.

Example. Find an upper and lower bound for the zeros of

$$f(x) = x^4 + 3x^3 - 9x^2 + 3x - 10.$$

Solution. By using synthetic division, we have

$$
\begin{array}{rrrrr|r}
1 & 3 & -9 & 3 & -10 & 3 \\
  & 3 & 18 & 27 & 90 & \\
\hline
1 & 6 & 9 & 30 & 80 &
\end{array}
$$

Since all the numbers in the third row are positive, 3 is an upper bound for the zeros of $f(x)$.
    Again,

$$
\begin{array}{rrrrr|r}
1 & 3 & -9 & 3 & -10 & -6 \\
  & -6 & 18 & -54 & 306 & \\
\hline
1 & -3 & 9 & -51 & 296 &
\end{array}
$$

Since the signs in the third row alternate, there is no zero less than -6.
    The next theorem, unfortunately, has no elementary proof but, because of its importance, will be assumed.

Theorem 8–5 (*Fundamental Theorem of Algebra*). Every polynomial function whose defining equation is

$$f(x) = a_0x^n + a_1x^{n-1} + a_2x^{n-2} + \cdots + a_{n-1}x + a_n,$$

$n \geq 1$, $a_0 \neq 0$, has at least one (real or imaginary)* zero.

This theorem was first proved by the German mathematician Karl Friedrich Gauss, at the age of 22. It enables us to prove a theorem on the number of zeros of a polynomial function.

Theorem 8–6. Every polynomial function whose defining equation is

$$f(x) = a_0x^n + a_1x^{n-1} + a_2x^{n-2} + \cdots + a_{n-1}x + a_n \qquad (a_0 \neq 0)$$

has exactly n zeros.

Proof. Since, by Theorem 8–5, $f(x)$ has at least one zero, r_1, Theorem 8–2 implies that $(x - r_1)$ is a factor of $f(x)$. Thus,

$$f(x) \equiv (x - r_1) \cdot q_1(x), \tag{8–4}$$

where $q_1(x)$ is the quotient of $f(x)$ by $(x - r_1)$. Again, $q_1(x)$ has a zero r_2, so that

$$q_1(x) \equiv (x - r_2) \cdot q_2(x),$$

where $q_2(x)$ is the quotient of $q_1(x)$ by $(x - r_2)$. Therefore, we may write

$$f(x) \equiv (x - r_1) \cdot (x - r_2) \cdot q_2(x). \tag{8–5}$$

Since we know that each new quotient is of one degree less than the preceding quotient, we can continue the process until we finally have

$$f(x) \equiv (x - r_1)(x - r_2) \cdots (x - r_n) \cdot q_n(x), \tag{8–6}$$

where, since there are n factors $(x - r_i)$, $q_n(x)$ must be the constant a_0; hence

$$f(x) \equiv a_0(x - r_1)(x - r_2) \cdots (x - r_n), \tag{8–7}$$

where each r_i is a zero of $f(x)$.

Let r be any number. Since Eq. (8–7) is an identity, it is true for all values of x. Thus,

$$f(r) \equiv a_0(r - r_1)(r - r_2) \cdots (r - r_n).$$

If $r \neq r_i$ for any i, none of the factors $(r - r_i)$ is zero. Since $a_0 \neq 0$, $f(r) \neq 0$, and r is not a zero of $f(x)$. Therefore there are *exactly n zeros*, and the theorem is proved.

Illustration 4. The function $(x - 3)^2(x - 1)(x + 2)^3$ is a polynomial of the sixth degree. Its six zeros are 3, 3, 1, -2, -2, -2. Note that any zero which occurs m times is considered as m zeros.

---

* Imaginary numbers are discussed in some detail in Chapter 13.

PROBLEMS

Find by inspection the zeros of each of the following functions, and give the multiplicity of each.

1. $(x - 2)(x - 3)^2(x + 4)^3$

2. $(x + 1)^4(x - 2)^5$

3. $(x + 7)(2x - 3)^3$

4. $(x^2 - 4x + 4)(x^2 + 3x - 10)$

5. $(3x + 5)(x^2 - 6x + 9)^2$

Find an upper bound and a lower bound for the zeros of the following functions.

6. $x^3 - 3x^2 - 2x + 15$

7. $x^3 + 2x^2 - 7x - 8$

8. $x^4 - 2x^3 - 7x^2 + 10x + 10$

9. $x^4 - x^3 - x^2 - 2x - 6$

10. $x^4 - 4x^3 + x^2 + 6x + 2$

11. $x^4 - 5x^2 + 6x - 9$

12. $x^3 - 8x + 5$

13. $x^3 + 16x - 29$

14. $x^5 + 5x^2 - 7$

15. $x^5 - 3x^3 + 24$

8–2 GRAPHING OF POLYNOMIAL FUNCTIONS

One of the methods of finding the real zeros of a function was mentioned in connection with the graphs in Article 5–2. It is quite possible to use this method for any polynomial function. Since, by using synthetic division, we can easily obtain the values of the function for any value of the variable, a table of values can be constructed and the graph may be sketched. Care must be taken in joining the plotted points. We recall that the real zeros of a function f are the abscissas of the points where the graph of $y = f(x)$ crosses or touches the x-axis.

Example 1. Draw the graph of $y = f(x) = x^4 - 2x^3 - 7x^2 + 10x + 10$, and verify that it has one real zero between -3 and -2, one between -1 and 0, and two between 2 and 3.

Solution. First construct the table of values shown below. For any arbitrary x, the corresponding value of the function is found by synthetic division. Usually it is wise to use all integral values of x between an upper and lower bound. (Why?) In addition, fractional values may be necessary to ascertain the shape of the curve. The values from the table have been plotted as points and the graph drawn in Fig. 8–1. Note that the scales on the two axes are conveniently *not* the same. From the figure it is clear that the zeros are located as suggested in the statement of the example.

x	-3	-2	-1	0	1	2	$2\frac{1}{2}$	3	4
y	52	-6	-4	10	12	2	$-\frac{15}{16}$	4	66

In Example 1 the fourth degree function has four real zeros. This is not always the case, for some of the zeros may be imaginary. An imaginary zero of a function cannot be approximated from its graph.

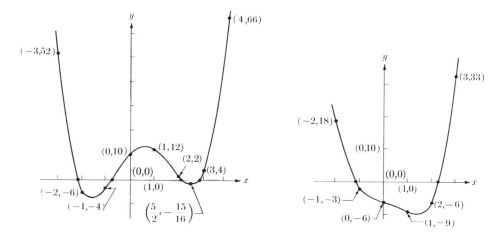

Figure 8–1   **Figure 8–2**

Example 2. Draw the graph of the function whose defining equation is

$$y = f(x) = x^4 - x^3 - x^2 - 2x - 6,$$

and approximate its real zeros.

Solution. Again the table of values is constructed, the points are plotted, and the graph is drawn (Fig. 8–2).

x	-2	-1	0	1	2	3
y	18	-3	-6	-9	-6	33

Although the function is of the fourth degree, its graph crosses the x-axis only twice. These two real zeros are between -2 and -1, and between 2 and 3, while the other two are imaginary.

There is, unfortunately, no simple method for approximating the imaginary zeros of a general polynomial function.

PROBLEMS

Draw the graphs of the function defined by each of the following equations, and thus verify the statement given in Problems 1 through 4.

1. $f(x) = x^3 - x^2 - 2x + 1$ has one zero between -2 and -1, 0 and 1, and 1 and 2.

2. $f(x) = x^3 - 3x + 1$ has one zero between -2 and -1, 0 and 1, and 1 and 2.

3. $f(x) = x^4 - 2x^2 + 12x - 17$ has one zero between -3 and -2, and one between 1 and 2.

4. $f(x) = x^4 - 4x^3 + x^2 + 6x + 2$ has two zeros between 2 and 3, and two between -1 and 0.

Draw the graphs of the following functional equations, showing the approximate location of all the real zeros.

5. $f(x) = x^4 - 20x^2 + 48x - 32$ 6. $f(x) = x^3 + x^2 - 3x - 4$

7. $f(x) = 4x^3 + 8x^2 - 11x + 3$ 8. $f(x) = x^4 - 2x^3 + 3x^2 + x + 6$

9. $f(x) = x^5 - 3x^3 + 9x^2 - 8x + 11$ 10. $f(x) = -x^4 + 2x^2 + 8x + 3$

11. $f(x) = x^3 - 4x^2 + x + 1$ 12. $f(x) = x^4 + 2x^3 + x^2 - 1$

13. $f(x) = x^3 + 5x^2 + 13x + 19$ 14. $f(x) = 2x^3 - 3x^2 + 4x - 6$

15. $f(x) = x^4 - 6x^2 + 8x - 2$

8–3 GENERAL REMARKS ON ZEROS AND ROOTS

We recall that the zeros of any function are identical with the roots of the equation formed by equating the function to zero. Consequently, all our previous remarks about the zeros of the polynomial function apply also to the roots of the associated equation.

In Chapter 6 we found specific methods for solving any polynomial equation

$$a_0x^n + a_1x^{n-1} + a_2x^{n-2} + \cdots + a_{n-1}x + a_n = 0 \quad (a_0 \neq 0)$$

when $n = 1$ (linear equation) and $n = 2$ (quadratic equation). There are also formulas for solving this type of equation when $n = 3$ and 4, but these are beyond the scope of this book. Tartaglia was the first to obtain formulas for the solution of the general cubic equation. These were published in 1545 by Cardan and are known as *Cardan's formulas*. Shortly thereafter Ferrari obtained formulas for the solution of the general quartic or fourth degree equation. For equations when $n \geq 5$, it has been proved that, in general, no algebraic formulas for the roots in terms of the coefficients exist. Many attempts were made to obtain general formulas, but finally, in 1824, N. H. Abel (1802–1829), a Norwegian, proved that in the general case no such formulas exist. Later, E. Galois (1811–1832), a Frenchman, was able to show that such formulas did exist under certain conditions.

It is comparatively simple, however, to find all the rational roots of a polynomial equation and approximate any irrational roots. Imaginary roots will be discussed briefly in Chapter 13.

8–4 RATIONAL ROOTS

With regard to the rational roots of an equation with integral coefficients, we have the following theorem.

Theorem 8–7. If the rational number p/q, a fraction in lowest terms, is a root of the equation

$$a_0x^n + a_1x^{n-1} + a_2x^{n-2} + \cdots + a_{n-1}x + a_n = 0, \quad (8\text{–}8)$$

where a_i $(i = 0, 1, 2, \ldots, n)$ are integral coefficients, then p is an exact divisor of a_n and q is an exact divisor of a_0.

Proof. Since p/q is a root of Eq. (8–8), we have

$$a_0 \left(\frac{p}{q}\right)^n + a_1 \left(\frac{p}{q}\right)^{n-1} + a_2 \left(\frac{p}{q}\right)^{n-2} + \cdots + a_{n-1} \left(\frac{p}{q}\right) + a_n = 0.$$

Multiplying each term of this equation by q^n, we get

$$a_0 p^n + a_1 p^{n-1} q + a_2 p^{n-2} q^2 + \cdots + a_{n-1} pq^{n-1} + a_n q^n = 0. \qquad (8–9)$$

If we transpose $a_n q^n$ to the right side and divide both members by p,

$$a_0 p^{n-1} + a_1 p^{n-2} q + a_2 p^{n-3} q^2 + \cdots + a_{n-1} q^{n-1} = \frac{-a_n q^n}{p}.$$

Since each a_i, p, and q is an integer, the left member, and therefore the right member, is an integer. Also, p and q have no common factor, so that p does not divide q^n. Thus p is an exact divisor of a_n.

If, in Eq. (8–9), we take the term $a_0 p^n$ to the opposite side of the equation and divide both members by q, we get

$$a_1 p^{n-1} + a_2 p^{n-2} q + \cdots + a_{n-1} pq^{n-2} + a_n q^{n-1} = \frac{-a_0 p^n}{q}.$$

By the same type of argument, we have the fact that q is an exact divisor of a_0. A direct corollary of this is clearly the following theorem.

Theorem 8–8. Any rational root of the equation

$$x^n + a_1 x^{n-1} + a_2 x^{n-2} + \cdots + a_{n-1} x + a_n = 0, \qquad (8–10)$$

where each a_i is an integral coefficient, must be an integer which is an exact divisor of the constant term a_n.

We are now prepared to find all the rational roots of any polynomial equation of the type given by Eq. (8–8).

Example 1. Solve the equation

$$x^4 - x^3 - 7x^2 - 14x - 24 = 0$$

by first finding the rational roots.

Solution. In examining the equation for possible rational roots, we find by Theorem 8–8 that they are ± 1, ± 2, ± 3, ± 4, ± 6, ± 8, ± 12, and ± 24. By synthetic division we find that 1, 2, and 3 are not roots. For $x = 4$,

1	−1	−7	−14	−24	4
	4	12	20	24	
1	3	5	6	0	

Putting this result in algebraic form (Eq. 3–9), we get

$$x^4 - x^3 - 7x^2 - 14x - 24 \equiv (x^3 + 3x^2 + 5x + 6)(x - 4).$$

Since $x - 4$ is a factor of the original equation, $x = 4$ is one root, and our problem reduces to finding the roots of the depressed equation $x^3 + 3x^2 + 5x + 6 = 0$. Since all the signs in this equation are plus, there are no positive roots. (Why?) By using synthetic division, we find -1 is not a root but $x = -2$ is a root.

$$
\begin{array}{rrrr|r}
1 & 3 & 5 & 6 & \underline{-2} \\
 & -2 & -2 & -6 & \\
\hline
1 & 1 & 3 & 0 &
\end{array}
$$

The new depressed equation is $x^2 + x + 3 = 0$. Solving this by the quadratic formula (Eq. 6–10), we have $x = (-1 \pm \sqrt{-11})/2$, so that our complete solution is

$$
x = 4, \qquad -2, \qquad \frac{-1 \pm \sqrt{-11}}{2},
$$

with the last two roots imaginary.

Example 2. Solve for the exact roots of

$$
4x^5 - 16x^4 + 17x^3 - 19x^2 + 13x - 3 = 0.
$$

Solution. Since the signs of the terms alternate, this equation has no negative roots. (Why?) Its possible rational roots are $1, 3, \frac{1}{2}, \frac{3}{2}, \frac{1}{4}$, and $\frac{3}{4}$.

By using synthetic division, we find that 1 is not a root but $\frac{1}{2}$ is.

$$
\begin{array}{rrrrrr|r}
4 & -16 & 17 & -19 & 13 & -3 & \tfrac{1}{2} \\
 & 2 & -7 & 5 & -7 & 3 & \\
\hline
4 & -14 & 10 & -14 & 6 & 0 &
\end{array}
$$

Since the depressed equation has a common factor of 2 in each term, it may be divided out, reducing to $2x^4 - 7x^3 + 5x^2 - 7x + 3 = 0$. Again we find that $\frac{1}{2}$ is a root, so that it is a double root of the original equation.

$$
\begin{array}{rrrrr|r}
2 & -7 & 5 & -7 & 3 & \tfrac{1}{2} \\
 & 1 & -3 & 1 & -3 & \\
\hline
2 & -6 & 2 & -6 & 0 &
\end{array}
$$

Again, factoring out the common 2, we find that the new depressed equation becomes $x^3 - 3x^2 + x - 3 = 0$. The only possible remaining rational root is the integer 3. (Why?)

$$
\begin{array}{rrrr|r}
1 & -3 & 1 & -3 & 3 \\
 & 3 & 0 & 3 & \\
\hline
1 & 0 & 1 & 0 &
\end{array}
$$

We see that 3 is a root, and the solution of the depressed equation $x^2 + 1 = 0$ gives the final two imaginary roots $\pm\sqrt{-1}$. Thus the complete solution is $x = \frac{1}{2}, \frac{1}{2}, 3, \pm\sqrt{-1}$.

PROBLEMS

Find the exact roots of the following equations.

1. $2x^3 - 3x^2 - 11x + 6 = 0$

2. $x^3 - 6x^2 + 11x - 6 = 0$

3. $x^4 - 16x^3 + 86x^2 - 176x + 105 = 0$

4. $x^3 + x^2 - 24x + 36 = 0$

5. $x^4 - x^3 - 19x^2 + 49x - 30 = 0$

6. $x^4 - 4x^3 + 4x - 1 = 0$

7. $4x^4 + 8x^3 - 7x^2 - 21x - 9 = 0$

8. $2x^4 + 5x^3 - 11x^2 - 20x + 12 = 0$

9. $x^4 - 4x^3 + 6x^2 - 4x + 1 = 0$

10. $10x^4 - 13x^3 + 17x^2 - 26x - 6 = 0$

11. $8x^5 - 12x^4 + 14x^3 - 13x^2 + 6x - 1 = 0$

12. $12x^3 - 52x^2 + 61x - 15 = 0$

13. $2x^4 + x^3 - 2x^2 - 4x \quad 3 \quad 0$

14. $x^4 - 9x^3 + 25x^2 - 27x + 10 = 0$

15. $x^4 - 14x^3 + 71x^2 - 154x + 120 = 0$

16. $x^4 - 6x^3 - x^2 + 34x + 8 = 0$

17. $x^4 - 5x^3 - 3x^2 + 17x - 10 = 0$

18. $x^2 - 2 = 0$. What does this say concerning the rational nature of $\sqrt{2}$?

19. Prove that $\sqrt{3}$ is irrational.

20. Prove that $\sqrt[3]{5}$ is irrational.

8–5 IRRATIONAL ROOTS

There are several well-known approximation methods* for solving polynomial equations for irrational roots. We shall consider the most elementary method. In Article 8–2 we noticed that any simple root of $f(x) = 0$ could theoretically be isolated. If the function is relatively simple, this can be done with little work. If $f(a)$ and $f(b)$ are opposite in sign, there is at least one value of x between a and b where $f(x) = 0$. It is this basic idea that will be used in the following example.

Example 1. Find the approximate value of the largest positive root of

$$x^3 - x^2 - 3x + 1 = 0.$$

---

* Methods such as Graeffe's, Horner's, or Newton's appear in most books on the theory of equations. With the advent of high-speed computing machines, Newton's method has become most important. Rather than assuming a straight line between two points on the curve, it makes use of one point and estimates where the approximating tangent to the curve at that point crosses the x-axis. Its simplicity is in the repetitive nature of the process, which can be used for any type of reasonably well-behaved function, whether polynomial or not.

Solution. **By** first plotting the graph of the function

$$y = x^3 - x^2 - 3x + 1,$$

as shown in Fig. 8–3, we see that the root which we wish to approximate is between 2 and 3. If we divide this interval into ten equal parts and successively use synthetic division for the values $x = 2.1, 2.2, 2.3, \ldots, 2.9, 3$, we find $f(2.1) = -0.45$, while $f(2.2) = 0.21$, so that the root lies between 2.1 and 2.2. If we repeat this process for the values 2.11, 2.12, 2.13, $\ldots$, 2.19, 2.2, we find

$$f(2.17) = -0.0006, \qquad f(2.18) = 0.0678.$$

We are thus led to believe that $x = 2.17$ represents the root correct to two decimal places. In fact, $f(2.171) = 0.00621$, which indicates that $x = 2.170$ is correct to three decimal places. This process may, of course, be continued indefinitely.

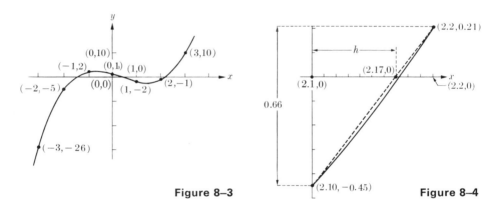

Figure 8–3   Figure 8–4

The amount of work involved in approximating such a root may be greatly reduced by the method of *linear interpolation*. We found that the root in question lay between 2.1 and 2.2. This section of the curve appears in Fig. 8–4, with the location of the two points whose abscissas are 2.1 and 2.2. If we assume that the curve approximates a straight line between the two points, by similar triangles

$$\frac{h}{0.45} = \frac{0.1}{0.66},$$

so that $h = 0.07$ approximately. Therefore, a good estimate for x is $2.1 + 0.07 = 2.17$. We now evaluate $f(2.17)$ and find it negative. From the way in which the curve is drawn, we realize that the root in question is greater than 2.17. By evaluating $f(2.18)$, we isolate this root without trying all the other eight possible values. This method of linear interpolation can be carried out for each new decimal, until the desired accuracy is obtained.

The beauty of this method is its simplicity. Moreover, it can be used to approximate any real root, provided the graph of the function actually crosses the x-axis, rather than merely being tangent to it.

PROBLEMS

Plot the graphs of each of the functions associated with the following equations and find, accurately to two decimals, the value of the indicated real roots.

1. $x^3 - 3x^2 - x + 2 = 0$ (the least positive)
2. $x^3 + 3x^2 - 6x - 3 = 0$ (the greatest positive)
3. $x^3 - x^2 - 2x + 1 = 0$ (the least positive)
4. $x^3 - 3x + 1 = 0$ (the three real roots)
5. $x^3 - 7x + 7 = 0$ (the two roots between 1 and 2)
6. $x^4 - x^3 + 2x^2 - 3x - 3 = 0$ (all)
7. $x^4 - 2x^3 + x^2 - 1 = 0$ (all)
8. $x^4 - 4x^3 - 4x + 12 = 0$ (all)

Find accurately to three decimals the indicated principal roots.

9. $\sqrt[3]{6}$ 10. $\sqrt[3]{15}$ 11. $\sqrt[4]{2}$ 12. $\sqrt[5]{-9}$

13. Recall that $\delta(A - xI)$ was defined as the characteristic polynomial of the 2 by 2 matrix in Problem 19, Article 7–3. If this is generalized for any third order matrix what degree will the polynomial be? Give your reasoning.

14. If $\delta(A - xI)$ is set equal to zero, we again have a characteristic equation. Find the characteristic equation for each of the following matrices.

a) $\begin{bmatrix} 2 & -1 & 3 \\ 1 & -2 & 0 \\ 3 & 1 & 1 \end{bmatrix}$ b) $\begin{bmatrix} 1 & 2 & -3 \\ 0 & -2 & 4 \\ 1 & -3 & 1 \end{bmatrix}$

15. Find all the real characteristic roots of the matrices given in Problem 14, correct to two decimal places.

CHAPTER 9

INVERSE FUNCTIONS

In the last few chapters we have discussed rather specific types of functions. Under certain conditions the relation between functions becomes important. One of these relations will be especially useful for us in further discussions.

9–1 INVERSE FUNCTIONS

If f is the function

$$f:x \rightarrow \frac{12 - 3x}{4}, \qquad (9-1)$$

where both its domain and range is R, we have the defining equation $f(x) = (12 - 3x)/4$. If, in addition, the function g is defined

$$g:x \rightarrow \frac{12 - 4x}{3}, \qquad (9-2)$$

where again this function has R for its domain and range, we can consider both $f[g(x)]$, and $g[f(x)]$. Specifically, since $g(x) = (12 - 4x)/3$ for all x, by $f[g(x)]$ we mean the functional value of f for $(12 - 4x)/3$, that is,

$$f\left(\frac{12 - 4x}{3}\right).$$

We have

$$f\left(\frac{12 - 4x}{3}\right) = \frac{12 - 3[(12 - 4x)/3]}{4} = \frac{12 - (12 - 4x)}{4} = x,$$

so that

$$f[g(x)] = x \qquad (9-3)$$

for all x in the domain of g. In a similar way we can show that

$$g[f(x)] = x \qquad (9-4)$$

for all x in the domain of f. Two functions of this type are *inverses* of each other.

Another rather simple example we might mention is the function f where $f:x \rightarrow 1/x$, for all $x \in R$, where $x \neq 0$. This function is its own inverse, since $f[f(x)] = 1/(1/x) = x$, for all $x \neq 0$.

The idea of inverse functions can be stated in general.

Definition 9–1. If f and g are two functions which are so related that

$$f[g(x)] = x*$$

for every x in the domain of g and

$$g[f(x)] = x$$

for every x in the domain of f, then f and g are called *inverses* of each other. *Each function f and g has an inverse, and each function is the other's inverse.*

Although each of the two functions in the examples we mentioned at the beginning of this section has an inverse, this is not always the case. Consider the function

$$f:x \to \frac{x^2 - 1}{x}, \tag{9–5}$$

which is defined for all $x \in R$, $x \neq 0$. The function f does not have an inverse function. Let us prove this by assuming that f's inverse exists and is equal to g. If g is the inverse of f, we know that $g[f(x)] - x$ for all x in the domain of f. If $x = 1$, we have $g[f(1)] = g(0)$. Moreover, if $x = -1$, we have $g[f(-1)] = g(0)$. Therefore, $g[f(1)] = g[f(-1)]$. But since we have assumed g is the inverse of f, by definition $g[f(1)] = 1$, and $g[f(-1)] = -1$, so that $1 = -1$. Our assumption leads to a contradiction, so that no inverse function exists for this function f.

The reason for this difficulty should be clear if we examine the function f more closely. If we solve the defining equation $f(x) = (x^2 - 1)/x$ for x, we find, by clearing fractions, that $xf(x) = x^2 - 1$, or $x^2 - xf(x) - 1 = 0$. This equation is quadratic in x, so that

$$x = \frac{f(x) \pm \sqrt{[f(x)]^2 + 4}}{2}. \tag{9–6}$$

Thus, for any particular value of $f(x)$, two different values of x correspond. For example, if $f(x) = 0$ (the case we considered above) $x = 1$ or -1. In other words, the function f maps both 1 and -1 into the same value in the range of f. No function which maps two distinct elements into the same element can have an inverse function. We state this as a theorem.

Theorem 9–1. If the function f has an inverse, then, for any two elements x_1 and x_2 in the domain of f, where $x_1 \neq x_2$, $f(x_1) \neq f(x_2)$.

Proof. Let us assume the theorem is not true. Then we have $x_1 \neq x_2$, but $f(x_1) = f(x_2)$. Since the inverse exists, let us call it g and we have $g[f(x_1)] = g[f(x_2)]$. But since g is the inverse of f, $g[f(x_1)] = x_1$ and $g[f(x_2)] = x_2$, so that $x_1 = x_2$. Since this contradicts the fact that $x_1 \neq x_2$, our assumption was false, and the theorem is proved.

---

* Note that this could be stated: $f \circ g$ is the identity function for every x in the domain of g, and so on.

Recall from Article 1–1 the definition of a one-to-one correspondence for sets (Definition 1–1). We have shown that if f has an inverse the function is one-to-one, that is, each distinct element in the domain is mapped by the function into a distinct element in the range. The converse of this theorem is also true.

Theorem 9–2. If the function f is one-to-one, then f has an inverse.

Proof. For any y in the range of f, there exists one and only one x in f's domain such that $y = f(x)$. If this element x is associated with the element y, a function g is defined which maps y into x, namely, $g:y \rightarrow x$, so that $x = g(y)$ where the domain of g is the range of f (and the range of g is the domain of f). Thus $f[g(y)] = f(x) = y$ and $g[f(x)] = g(y) = x$. But this was precisely the definition of the fact that g is the inverse of f (and f the inverse of g).

Let us denote the inverse (if it exists) of any function f, by f^{-1} (read "f inverse" or "the inverse of f").

We have not only proved Theorem 9–2, but have shown that

$$f[f^{-1}(x)] = x \quad \text{and} \quad f^{-1}[f(x)] = x, \tag{9–7}$$

whenever the inverse exists. Moreover, the inverse of f, f^{-1} will exist if and only if the function f is one-to-one.

If we think of f as defined by a set of ordered pairs and consider the inverse function f^{-1}, we are led to a most helpful consequence. Recall that f may be defined (Definition 5–2),

$$\{(x, y) | y = f(x)\}. \tag{9–8}$$

Since this set of ordered pairs defines a function, no two of the ordered pairs have the same first element, and, moreover, if we assume f^{-1} exists (the function f is one-to-one), no two of the ordered pairs have the same second element. Therefore, if x is in the domain of f and $y = f(x)$, then, $x = f^{-1}(y)$, or the function f^{-1} may be defined as the set of ordered pairs where the numbers in the ordered pairs defining f are merely interchanged. That is, f^{-1} may be defined as the set

$$\{(y, x) | x = f^{-1}(y)\}. \tag{9–9}$$

For example, if f is defined $f:x \rightarrow (12 - 3x)/4$, so that $f(x) = y = (12 - 3x)/4$, we may solve this equation $y = (12 - 3x)/4$ for x, obtain $x = (12 - 4y)/3$, and interchanging the x and y, have $y = (12 - 4x)/3$. Thus, $f^{-1}:x \rightarrow (12 - 4x)/3$. In general, if $y = f(x)$ is the defining equation for any function which has an inverse, its inverse may be obtained by interchanging the numbers x and y, so that $x = f(y)$, and then solving for y. The range of f will be the domain for f^{-1}, and the domain of f will be the range for f^{-1}. Certain difficulties may arise from this method,* and *care must be taken in choosing the domains and ranges of each function to guarantee that f is one-to-one.*

---

* We may not be able to solve algebraically for y, as in the case $x = y - \sin y$.

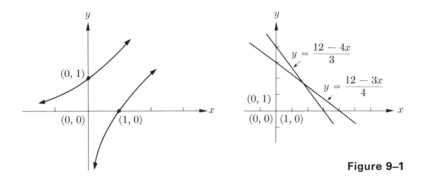

Figure 9–1

In the illustrations tabulated below, note that the domain and range of each function must be limited.

	$y = f(x)$		$y = f^{-1}(x)$	
a)	$y = \dfrac{12 - 3x}{4}$	$(-\infty < x < \infty)*$	$y = \dfrac{12 - 4x}{3}$	$(-\infty < x < \infty)$
b)	$y = \dfrac{1}{x}$	$(x \neq 0)$	$y = \dfrac{1}{x}$	$(x \neq 0)$
c)	$y = \dfrac{x^2 - 1}{x}$	$(0 < x)$	$y = \dfrac{x + \sqrt{x^2 + 4}}{2}$	$(-\infty < x < \infty)$
		$(x < 0)$	$y = \dfrac{x - \sqrt{x^2 + 4}}{2}$	$(-\infty < x < \infty)$
d)	$y = \sqrt{1 - x^2}$	$(0 \le x \le 1)$	$y = \sqrt{1 - x^2}$	$(0 \le x \le 1)$
		$(-1 \le x \le 0)$	$y = -\sqrt{1 - x^2}$	$(0 \le x \le 1)$
	$y = -\sqrt{1 - x^2}$	$(0 \le x \le 1)$	$y = \sqrt{1 - x^2}$	$(-1 \le x \le 0)$
		$(-1 \le x \le 0)$	$y = -\sqrt{1 - x^2}$	$(-1 \le x \le 0)$

The graphs of $f(x)$ and $f^{-1}(x)$ for illustrations (a) and the first function in (c) are shown in Fig. 9–1. Note that the curves for $y = f(x)$ and $y = f^{-1}(x)$ are symmetric with respect to the line $y = x$. Would you expect this always to be the case? Examine the graphs of the other functions in the illustrations.

PROBLEMS

Find the inverse of each of the functions defined by the following equations (Problems 1 through 11) if the inverse exists. If the inverse does not exist for the largest possible domain, limit the domain so that the inverse will exist. In each case, give the domain and range of both the function and its inverse.

---

* The notation $-\infty < x < \infty$ means all finite real values of x, both positive and negative.

1. $y = 5x - 6$

2. $y = x^2$

3. $y = x^2 - 4x$

4. $y = \dfrac{x}{x - 3}$

5. $y = \dfrac{x^2 - 1}{x^2}$

6. $y = \dfrac{x^2 - 1}{x}$

7. $y = x^n$

8. $y = x^{2n} + 2x^n + 1$

9. $y = \sqrt{x^2 - 4}$

10. $y = \dfrac{-3\sqrt{25 - x^2}}{5}$

11. $y = \dfrac{x}{x^2 - 1}$

12. Explain why a line parallel to the x-axis or y-axis will intersect the graph of a function once at most if the function has an inverse.

13. A function f, defined for all x where $a \le x \le b$, is said to be *increasing* over this domain if $f(x_1) < f(x_2)$ whenever $x_1 < x_2$. Show that if f is increasing, f^{-1} exists.

14. We noticed that if (a, b) is any point on the graph of f, that (b, a) is a point on the graph of f^{-1}. Describe the relation between these two points relative to the graph of the straight line whose equation is $y = x$. This property is useful in sketching the graph of f^{-1} if the graph of f is known.

9-2 GRAPHING OF CERTAIN RELATIONS

If we consider the set of ordered pairs

$$\{(x, y) \mid xy - x^2 + 1 = 0\}, \tag{9-10}$$

we may consider this set as a function $f : x \to y$, since for any value of x except zero, the equation sets up a unique corresponding value of y. We can see this is true, for if we solve $xy - x^2 + 1 = 0$ for y, we have $y = (x^2 - 1)/x$. However, if we solve the equation for x, we obtain $x = (y \pm \sqrt{y^2 + 4})/2$, so that we cannot consider the equation $xy - x^2 + 1 = 0$ as defining a function which maps $y \to x$, but merely a relation. Such relations, defined by similar equations, however, may be graphed. The graph of the set defined by Eq. 9-10 is shown in Fig. 9-2. Notice that when $x = 0$, y is not defined. This graph represents a *hyperbola*. In plotting the graphs of such equations, it is frequently helpful to use the expression for y, in terms of x, and for x, in terms of y, although they may not necessarily define a function.

Of special interest in this discussion is the quadratic equation given as part of Eq. 6-28; if $b = 0$, $a, c \ne 0$, and $a \ne c$. Any such equation,

$$ax^2 + cy^2 + dx + ey + f = 0 \tag{9-11}$$

represents an ellipse if a and c have the same sign. If a and c are opposite in sign, the equation represents a hyperbola. In either case the curve has its axis parallel to either the x- or y-axis.

Example 1. Sketch the graph of the ellipse

$$9x^2 + 4y^2 + 18x - 16y - 11 = 0.$$

Solution. If we complete the square (Article 6-3) in both x and y, it is easier to solve for either x or y in terms of the other. Since we have

$$9(x^2 + 2x + \quad) + 4(y^2 - 4y + \quad) = 11,$$

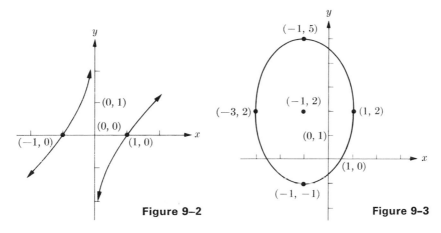

Figure 9-2   Figure 9-3

we must add 1 in the first parenthesis and 4 in the second in order to complete the squares. Since this is equivalent to adding 9 and 16 (why?), the equation reduces to

$$9(x + 1)^2 + 4(y - 2)^2 = 36. \tag{9-12}$$

If we now solve for y, we get $2(y - 2) = \pm\sqrt{36 - 9(x + 1)^2}$, or

$$y = 2 \pm \tfrac{3}{2}\sqrt{4 - (x + 1)^2}. \tag{9-13}$$

If we solve for x, we have $3(x + 1) = \pm\sqrt{36 - 4(y - 2)^2}$, or

$$x = -1 \pm \tfrac{2}{3}\sqrt{9 - (y - 2)^2}. \tag{9-14}$$

From these two equations it should be clear that if $x = -1$, $y = -1$ or 5, and if $y = 2$, $x = -3$ or 1. In addition the coordinates of any point on the curve must satisfy the condition $-3 \le x \le 1$, and $-1 \le y \le 5$. The coordinates of additional points on the curve may be obtained from either (9-13) or (9-14). The graph of this equation which represents an ellipse appears in Fig. 9-3.

If a and c in Eq. (9-11) are values which are opposite in sign, the curve represents a hyperbola whose axis is parallel to one of the coordinate axes. The method of graphing such a curve is similar to that in Example 1.

Example 2. Sketch the graph of the curve whose equation is

$$8x^2 - 9y^2 - 48x - 18y + 135 = 0.$$

Solution. If we complete the square as before, we have

$$9(y + 1)^2 = 8(x - 3)^2 + 72.$$

Thus, if we solve for x in terms of y,

$$x = 3 \pm \frac{3}{\sqrt{8}}\sqrt{(y + 1)^2 - 8},$$

or, if we solve for y in terms of x,

$$y = -1 \pm \frac{\sqrt{8}}{3}\sqrt{(x - 3)^2 + 9}.$$

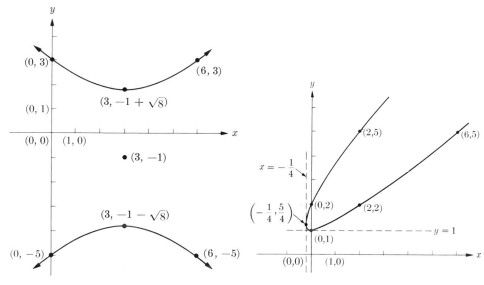

Figure 9–4   Figure 9–5

Note that x can be any value but that $y \leq -1 - \sqrt{8}$ or $y \geq -1 + \sqrt{8}$. With the aid of this knowledge, and a few specific values of pairs of coordinates, the graph of the curve is easily sketched. See Fig. 9–4.

Let us consider one further example.

Example 3. Sketch the graph of the relation expressed by the equation

$$x^2 - 2xy + y^2 + 2x - 3y + 2 = 0.$$

Solution. By using the quadratic formula to solve for x in terms of y, we find

$$x = y - 1 \pm \sqrt{y - 1}.$$

From this expression we may tabulate a few values, noticing that for each y, there are two corresponding values for x. For example, when $y = 2$, $x = 2$ or 0. When $y = 1$, $x = 0$ is a double root and the curve is tangent to $y = 1$ at this point. Moreover, when $y < 1$, the values of x are imaginary, so that the curve lies only where $y \geq 1$.

Solving for y in terms of x, we find

$$y = \frac{2x + 3 \pm \sqrt{4x + 1}}{2}.$$

Again, we can easily find sets of values which satisfy the equation. In addition, the curve lies only where $x \geq -\frac{1}{4}$ and is tangent to the line $x = -\frac{1}{4}$ at $y = \frac{5}{4}$. The resulting curve, shown in Fig. 9–5, is a parabola, although its equation is not as simple as those considered in Article 6–3.

Systems of equations such as that considered in Example 2, Article 6–12, can now be solved graphically.

PROBLEMS

Sketch the graph of the relations expressed by each of the equations 1 through 20.

1. $16x^2 + 25y^2 - 400 = 0$ **2.** $x^2 - y^2 - 1 = 0$

3. $xy = 1$ **4.** $x - 2 = \dfrac{1}{y-3}$

5. $4x^2 + 4y^2 - 12x - 10y + 5 = 0$ **6.** $2xy + 4y - 6x = 0$

7. $x^2 + y^2 - 2x + 6y + 6 = 0$ **8.** $x^2 - 4y^2 + 6x + 8y + 1 = 0$

9. $4x^2 + 9y^2 - 24x + 36y + 36 = 0$ **10.** $x^2 - y^2 - 4x + 4y - 1 = 0$

11. $4x^2 + y^2 + 16x - 10y + 37 = 0$ **12.** $2y^2 + 4y - 8x + 18 = 0$

13. $9x^2 - 4y^2 + 36x + 8y - 4 = 0$ **14.** $x^2 + 4y^2 - 10x - 40y + 109 = 0$

15. $9x^2 - 4y^2 - 54x + 8y + 113 = 0$ **16.** $12x^2 + 16y^2 - 12x - 9 = 0$

17. $x^2 + 2xy + y^2 - 2x - 2y = 1$ **18.** $x^2 + xy + y^2 - 3y - 3 = 0$

19. Solve graphically Example 2, Article 6–12.

20. Solve graphically Problems 7, 9, Article 6–12.

21. Solve graphically Problems 8, 10, Article 6–12.

REVIEW PROBLEMS

1. Find $A \cap B$ if $A = \{(x, y) | y^2 = -4(x - 1)\}$ and $B = \{(x, y) | y^2 = -2(x - 2)\}$.

2. Find the values of k so that the straight line $y = 2x + k$ will be tangent to the circle $x^2 + y^2 = 16$.

3. The expression $1 + x + x^2 + \cdots + x^n$ (where $x \neq 1$) is identical to

a) $\dfrac{1 - x^{n+1}}{1 - x}$ b) x^{n+1} c) $\dfrac{1}{1 - x}$ d) $(1 + x)^n$

4. Find numbers A, B, C, D, and E so that

$$4x^2 - 9y^2 - 24x + 18y + 27 \equiv A(x - B)^2 + C(y + D)^2 + E$$

is an identity in x.

5. Determine A, B, and C so that $(18t)^2 + (27t^2 - 3)^2 \equiv A(Bt^2 + C)^2$ is an identity in t.

6. In order to obtain an inverse of a 3 by 3 nonsingular matrix using the method outlined in Article 7–3, how many equations in how many variables must be solved? Outline a method of finding the inverse of a given 3 by 3 matrix, but do not carry out the details.

7. Find the characteristic polynomial for the matrix

$$\begin{bmatrix} 1 & -2 & 2 & -3 \\ 0 & 5 & 0 & -2 \\ 2 & 4 & -1 & 2 \\ 3 & -4 & 1 & -2 \end{bmatrix}.$$

8. Find the characteristic polynomial for the matrix

$$\begin{bmatrix} 2 & -4 & 2 & 1 \\ 0 & 1 & 3 & -4 \\ 0 & 0 & -1 & 5 \\ 0 & 0 & 0 & 3 \end{bmatrix}.$$

From this example can you draw any generalization?

9. Recall the iterative process discussed in Article 8–1 in connection with the value of a polynomial for a specific value. Another such example is considered here. If $f_1 = \sqrt{2}$, and $f_{n+1} = \sqrt{2f_n}$ for each integer $n > 1$, write out the first three terms, and note that, again, we have an iterative process. Can you estimate the value "approached by f_n as n gets larger and larger?" *Hint:* If there is a finite value, f_n and f_{n+1} approximate this value. Square $f_{n+1} = \sqrt{2f_n}$ and solve.

10. Follow the same procedure for the set defined by $f_1 = \sqrt{2}$, $f_{n+1} = \sqrt{2 - f_n}$. Again estimate the value "approached by f_n as n gets larger and larger." A computing machine could compute a good approximation to this value quite simply and easily.

Each of the equations in Problems 11 through 14 defines a function. Find the defining equation of the inverse for each and state whether it is a function or relation.

11. a) $y = \frac{1}{2}(x - 4)$ b) $y = \dfrac{x}{x^2 - 9}$

12. a) $y = \dfrac{3x}{x - 4}$ b) $y = \dfrac{3x^2}{x - 4}$

13. a) $y = \sqrt{x - 5}$ b) $y = |x|$

14. $x^2 + y + 4x = 12$

15. Sketch the graph of the relation R, where

$$R = \{(x, y) | 2x^2 + 3xy - 2y^2 - 5 = 0\}.$$

16. Sketch the graph of the relation S, where

$$S = \{(x, y) | x^2 + 2xy + y^2 - 2x - 2y = 0\}.$$

17. Sketch the graph of the relation

$$B = \{(x, y) | x^{13} + (2y)^{13} = 52\}.$$

Hint: This is called the "Bridge Card Equation!"

18. Recall that $n! = 1 \cdot 2 \cdot 3 \cdots (n - 1) \cdot n$. Show that

a) $\dfrac{(n + 4)(n + 3)!}{(n + 4)!} = 1$ b) $\dfrac{(2n + 2)!}{(2n - 1)!2n} = 2(n + 1)(2n + 1)$

19. Write the first four terms in the expansion $[1 - (1/x)]^{10}$.

20. Use an appropriate binomial expansion to approximate $(0.99)^{20}$ correct to two decimal places.

CHAPTER 10

PERMUTATIONS, COMBINATIONS, AND THE BINOMIAL THEOREM

Frequently we are asked to find the number of ways a set of objects may be arranged under certain conditions. How many ways can eight people be seated at a table? How many different license plates are possible if each consists of three numbers and two letters, and so on? Answers to these questions and many more important and complicated ones are possible by a process sometimes called *sophisticated counting*. Although an extensive treatment is impossible here, certain elementary aspects of the subject will be discussed, since it is so useful in mathematics and other natural and social sciences.

10–1 THE FUNDAMENTAL PRINCIPLE

We shall begin by considering a simple example. Let us find how many numbers of two different digits can be formed from the four integers 1, 2, 3, and 4 if no digit is repeated. Any one of the four may be chosen for the tens digit of the number. With each particular choice of this type, there will remain three integers from which to choose the units digit. Thus, for each of the four choices, there are three more choices, making a total of $4 \cdot 3$ or 12 numbers in all. We have then

$$
\begin{aligned}
&12, 13, 14, \text{ (1 for the tens digit),} \\
&21, 23, 24, \text{ (2 for the tens digit),} \\
&31, 32, 34, \text{ (3 for the tens digit),} \\
&41, 42, 43, \text{ (4 for the tens digit)}
\end{aligned}
\qquad (10\text{–}1)
$$

as the possible two-digit numbers.

This example can be illustrated (Fig. 10–1) by a simple tree diagram. If repetitions are permitted, the result is $4 \cdot 4 = 16$ possible two-digit numbers instead of 12.

A slightly more complicated problem would be to find how many numbers of three different digits could be formed with the same integers 1, 2, 3, and 4. Each of the 12 numbers listed in Eq. (10–1) can be regarded as representing the hundreds and tens digits. Since two of the four integers have already been selected in each case, the possibility for the new units digit must be one of the two remaining integers. For example, with the first number 41, we may have 2 or 3, forming the numbers 412 or 413. We therefore have $(4 \cdot 3) \cdot 2$ or 24 numbers, each containing three digits, which can be formed from the given integers.

A tree diagram in this case would be similar to that in Fig. 10–1, but in addition, at the ends of each of the last branches there would be two additional branches. Similarly, if repetitions are permitted in this case the result would be $4 \cdot 4 \cdot 4 = 64$.

These examples have illustrated a fundamental principle.

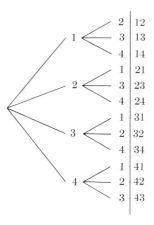

Figure 10–1

> **Fundamental Principle.** If one thing can be done independently in n_1 different ways, and if a second thing can be done independently in n_2 different ways, and a third thing can be done independently in n_3 different ways, and so on (for any finite number of things), then the total number of ways in which all the things may be done in the stated order is $n_1 n_2 n_3 \cdots$.

Example 1. How many of the two-digit numbers in Eq. (10–1) are odd?

Solution. In order for any of these numbers to be odd, its last digit must be a 1 or 3. For each of these two possibilities there are three choices for the first digit, so that there are $2 \cdot 3$ or 6 of these two-digit numbers that are odd. Check the example and note that this is the case.

Although the order of choosing the number of possibilities for any particular position is arbitrary, it is frequently wise to perform any special operation first, as in the case of the choice of the units digit in Example 1.

Example 2. How many different committees consisting of one Democrat and one Republican can be formed from seven Democrats and four Republicans?

Solution. The Democrat can be chosen in any one of seven ways, and independently, the Republican can be chosen in any one of four ways. Thus, by the fundamental principle, the total number of different possible committees is $7 \cdot 4 = 28$.

Example 3. If two cubical dice are thrown, in how many ways can they fall?

Solution. Since each cube has six faces, each may fall independently any one of six different ways. Consequently, there are $6 \cdot 6 = 36$ possible ways for them to fall.

Example 4. In a certain election, there are three candidates for president, four for vice-president, five for secretary, but only two for treasurer. In how many different ways may the election turn out?

Solution. With each of the three possibilities for president, there are four for vice-president. With each of these ($4 \cdot 3 = 12$) possibilities, there are five possibilities for secretary, and so on. Thus the total number of different possible election results is $4(3)(5)(2) = 120$.

PROBLEMS

1. A nickel and a dime are tossed on a table. In how many ways can they fall?

2. If all questions are answered in a true-false quiz of ten questions, how many ways are there of answering the entire quiz?

3. How many numbers of three different digits less than 500 can be formed from the integers 1, 2, 3, 4, 5, 6, 7?

4. If there are 12 milers entered in a race, in how many ways can first, second, and third place be awarded?

5. There are five main roads between the cities A and B, and four between B and C. In how many ways can a person drive from A to C and return, going through B on both trips, without driving on the same road twice?

6. How many numbers of at most three different digits can be formed from the integers 1, 2, 3, 4, 5, 6?

7. How many numbers of at least three different digits can be formed from the integers 1, 2, 3, 4, 5, 6?

8. A tennis club consists of 12 boys and 9 girls. How many mixed doubles teams (one boy and one girl) are possible? In how many ways can a mixed doubles match be arranged?

9. A freshman student must take a modern language, a natural science, a social science, and English. If there are four possible different modern languages, five natural sciences, three social sciences, but each student must take the same English course, in how many different ways can he select his course of study?

10. In selecting an ace, king, queen, and jack from an ordinary deck of 52 cards, how many ways may we choose if
   a) they must be of different suits,
   b) they may or may not be of different suits,
   c) they must be of the same suit,
   d) they must be in a particular suit?

11. If there are eight outside doors in a dormitory, in how many ways can a student enter one and
   a) leave by a different door,
   b) leave by any door?

12. A baseball stadium has four entrance gates and nine exits. In how many ways may two men enter together, but leave by different exits?

10-2 PERMUTATIONS

We wish to define what is meant by a *permutation*.

Definition 10-1. Each different arrangement or ordered set of objects is called a *permutation of those objects*.

For example, the numbers 423 and 234 consist of the same digits, but they are different numbers, since they are different order arrangements of the digits 2, 3, and 4. In general, if we have n objects and arrange r of them (where $r \leq n$)

in a definite order, such an arrangement is called a permutation of n objects taken r at a time.

An expression for the total number of permutations of n objects taken r at a time is easily established by using the fundamental principle of Article 10–1. This expression, which is a functional value of the integers n and r, will be denoted by $P(n, r)$.*

> **Theorem 10–1.** The total number of permutations of n objects taken r at a time $P(n, r)$, is given by the expression,

$$P(n, r) = n(n - 1)(n - 2) \cdots (n - r + 1). \tag{10–2}$$

Proof. The possible number of arrangements of n things taken r at a time is equivalent to the number of ways of choosing from n different things to fill r positions. There are n choices for the first position, then $n - 1$ choices for the second position, $n - 2$ choices for the third, and so on. The rth position can be filled with any of the $n - (r - 1) = n - r + 1$ remaining things, so that the r positions can be filled in $n(n - 1)(n - 2) \cdots (n - r + 1)$ ways. Thus,

$$P(n, r) = n(n - 1)(n - 2) \cdots (n - r + 1).$$

If we are interested in the permutation of n things taken n (or all) at a time, we note that $r = n$ in Eq. (10–2), and we have

$$P(n, r) = n(n - 1)(n - 2) \cdots 3 \cdot 2 \cdot 1 = n!. \tag{10–3}$$

By multiplying the numerator and denominator of the right member of Eq. (10–2) by $(n - r)!$, we obtain an alternative formula for $P(n, r)$,

$$P(n, r) = \frac{n(n - 1)(n - 2) \cdots (n - r + 1)(n - r)!}{(n - r)!}$$

or

$$P(n, r) = \frac{n!}{(n - r)!} \cdot \tag{10–4}\dagger$$

Example 1. Find the number of permutations of the four integers 1, 2, 3, and 4 taken two at a time.

Solution. Since we wish to find the number of permutations of four things taken two at a time,

$$P(4, 2) = 4 \cdot 3 = 12.$$

These twelve arrangements are listed in Article 10–1.

Example 2. If four persons enter a bus in which there are ten vacant seats, how many ways are there for the four to be seated?

---

* The symbol $_nP_r$ is also frequently used.
† Factorial zero, 0!, is by definition equal to 1.

Solution. Since this represents the arrangement of ten seats taken four at a time,

$$P(10, 4) = 10 \cdot 9 \cdot 8 \cdot 7 = 5040.$$

Example 3. In how many ways may five books be arranged on a shelf?

Solution. This represents the permutation of five things taken five at a time. Thus,

$$P(5, 5) = 5! = 120.$$

Although the number of permutations of the eight letters of the word "readings" is clearly 8!, the number of such permutations of the letters of "gargling" is somewhat less, since three of the letters are alike. An example will illustrate the next theorem.

Example 4. Find the number of permutations of the eight letters of "gargling."

Solution. Considering all the letters different, we would have P, the required number of permutations, equal to 8!. This might be done by giving each of the g's a different subscript, such as g_1, g_2, and g_3. Actually, however, the three g's could be permuted among themselves in 3! ways. In fact, for each distinct arrangement of the other letters, this would be the case. Thus $3! \, P = 8!$, or

$$P = \frac{8!}{3!}.$$

The proof of the following general theorem parallels the reasoning in Example 4 and is left as an exercise.

> **Theorem 10–2.** If P represents the number of different permutations of n things taken all at a time, when p are of one kind, q are of another kind, r of a third kind, and so on, then
>
> $$P = \frac{n!}{p!\,q!\,r! \ldots}. \tag{10–5}$$

Example 5. How many permutations are there of the 11 letters in "Mississippi" taken all together?

Solution. Since there are four s's, four i's, and two p's, we have

$$P = \frac{11!}{4!4!2!} = 34,650.$$

PROBLEMS

1. How many numbers of three different digits each can be formed from the digits 1, 2, 3, 4, 5, 6, 7, 8, 9?

2. How many numbers of three different digits each less than 700 can be formed from the digits in Problem 1?

3. How many numbers of at most three different digits each can be formed from the digits in Problem 1?

4. In how many ways can a class elect a president, vice-president, secretary, and treasurer from a class of 100 students?

5. In how many ways can four boys and three girls be seated in a row containing seven seats

    a) if they may sit anywhere,
    b) if the boys and girls must alternate?

6. In how many ways can four boys and four girls be seated in a row containing eight seats

    a) if they may sit anywhere,
    b) if the boys and girls must alternate?

7. A baseball manager insists on having his best hitter bat fourth and the pitcher bat last. In such circumstances, how many batting orders are possible?

8. In how many ways can eight people be seated in a row of eight seats if two people insist on sitting next to each other?

9. A language teacher wants to keep books of the same language together on his shelf. If he has 12 spaces for 5 French, 4 Italian, and 3 German books, in how many ways can they be placed on his shelf?

10. In how many ways can eight people be seated around a table?

11. In how many ways can eight people be seated around a table if two people insist on sitting next to each other?

12. How many license plates can be made using any two letters for the first two places and any of the numbers 0 through 9 for the last three?

13. Do Problem 12, with the condition that no letter or number be repeated.

14. How many permutations are there of the letters of the word

    a) "algebra,"   b) "college?"

15. How many permutations are there of the letters of the word "Tennessee?"

16. In how many ways can four red beads, five white beads, and three blue beads be arranged in a row?

17. In how many ways can seven different colored beads be made into a bracelet?

18. Show that $P(n + 1, r) \equiv (n + 1)P(n, r - 1)$.

19. Solve the equation $P(n, 5) = 20P(n, 3)$ for n.

20. Find the value of $P(5, 1) + P(5, 2) + P(5, 3) + P(5, 4) + P(5, 5)$.

10–3 COMBINATIONS

In contrast to a permutation, which is a certain ordered arrangement of different objects, a *combination* is a set or collection of objects in no particular order. Thus, by the combinations of n different objects taken r at a time ($r \leq n$), we mean all the possible selections of r different objects from the n objects, with no regard to order or arrangement. This total number of combinations is designated $C(n, r)$,* since it is again a functional value of n and r.

---

* The symbols $_nC_r$ and $\binom{n}{r}$ are also frequently used. We have chosen $C(n, r)$ since this notation is consistent with that for a functional value. It also may be typed more readily, an added advantage in computing machine language.

The difference between permutations and combinations, and an important one, is order or arrangement. The following theorem will clarify the distinction.

Theorem 10–3. The total number of combinations of n objects taken r at a time, $C(n, r)$, is given by the expression

$$C(n, r) = \frac{n!}{(n - r)!r!}. \tag{10–6}$$

Proof. For any one of the $C(n, r)$ combinations, consisting of r different objects, these r objects may be rearranged by permuting them in $r!$ different ways. Thus, for each combination, there will be $r!$ permutations, so that for all the $C(n, r)$ possible combinations, there will be $C(n, r)r!$ different permutations. Since these are all possible permutations of n objects taken r at a time, we have

$$C(n, r)r! = P(n, r),$$

or

$$C(n, r) = \frac{P(n, r)}{r!}. \tag{10–7}$$

If we now substitute the expression (Eq. 10–4) for $P(n, r)$, we get,

$$C(n, r) = \frac{n!}{(n - r)!r!}. \tag{10–6}$$

An immediate important result of this equation is that

$$C(n, r) = C(n, n - r). \tag{10–8}$$

This, of course, may be used to reduce the amount of computation involved, if n is relatively large, and $r \leq n$, but also large. (See Example 1.)

Example 1. Compute $C(15, 12)$.

Solution. By using Eq. (10–7), the expression most frequently used in problems,

$$C(15, 12) = \frac{15 \cdot 14 \cdot 13 \cdot 12 \cdot 11 \cdot 10 \cdot 9 \cdot 8 \cdot 7 \cdot 6 \cdot 5 \cdot 4}{1 \cdot 2 \cdot 3 \cdot 4 \cdot 5 \cdot 6 \cdot 7 \cdot 8 \cdot 9 \cdot 10 \cdot 11 \cdot 12}$$

$$= \frac{15 \cdot 14 \cdot 13}{1 \cdot 2 \cdot 3} = C(15, 3),$$

so that $C(15, 12) = 455$.

Example 2. In a class of 15 boys and 10 girls, in how many ways may a committee made up of 3 boys and 2 girls be selected?

Solution. Since order has nothing to do with membership on the committee, the boys may be selected in $C(15, 3)$ ways, while the girls may be selected in $C(10, 2)$

ways. By the fundamental principle, we have

$$C(15, 3) \cdot C(10, 2) = \frac{15 \cdot 14 \cdot 13}{1 \cdot 2 \cdot 3} \cdot \frac{10 \cdot 9}{1 \cdot 2} = 20,475.$$

Example 3. On a certain examination, the student must answer 8 out of the 12 questions, including exactly 5 of the first 6. In how many ways may he write the examination?

Solution. Since five of the first six must be answered, this may be done in $C(6, 5)$ ways. Having now answered five questions, he must answer three of the remaining six. This may be done in $C(6, 3)$ ways. Therefore the number of ways in which he can write the examination is given by

$$C(6, 5) \cdot C(6, 3) = 120.$$

Frequently we wish to find the total number of combinations of n things taken 1, 2, 3, . . . , or n at a time.

Example 4. How many different sums of money can be made from a penny, a nickel, a dime, and a quarter?

Solution. Since there are four coins, the number of different amounts of money is

$$C(4, 1) + C(4, 2) + C(4, 3) + C(4, 4) = 15.$$

There will be a simpler method for this computation suggested in the next article. (See Problem 29, Article 10–4.)

PROBLEMS

1. Find the value of
   a) $C(7, 4)$ b) $C(10, 2)$ c) $C(21, 19)$

2. Find the value of
   $$C(8, 3) + C(8, 4) + C(8, 5) + C(8, 6) + C(8, 7) + C(8, 8)$$

3. In how many ways may a committee of 4 be chosen from a group of 25?

4. From a group of 25 Democrats and 18 Republicans, how many committees consisting of 3 Democrats and 2 Republicans are possible?

5. From the group in Problem 4, if one of two specific Democrats is to be chairman, how many committees are possible with the same balance of Democrats and Republicans as previously stated?

6. How many football games are played if each of the nine football teams in a certain conference plays each of the other teams in that conference once?

7. On a college baseball squad, there are three catchers, five pitchers, seven infielders, and seven outfielders. How many different baseball nines can be formed?

8. In how many ways can a bridge hand of 13 cards be chosen from a deck of 52 cards?

9. In how many ways can a person get a bridge hand consisting of only aces or face cards?

10. In how many ways can a person get a bridge hand which consists of cards seven or lower?

11. In how many ways can a person get a bridge hand consisting of two aces, one king, one queen, three jacks, and the six other cards ten or less?

12. From four red balls, five white balls, and six blue balls, how many selections consisting of five balls can be made if two are to be red, one white, and two blue?

13. Without considering special cases,

a) how many straight lines are determined by nine points?
b) how many circles are determined by nine points?

14. How many triangles are determined by nine points no three of which lie on the same straight line?

15. How many tetrahedrons are determined by nine points no four of which lie in the same plane?

16. From a group of 15 people, how many committees can be formed consisting of two, three, or four people?

17. In how many ways may a college president's wife invite

a) two,   b) three,   c) two or more,

of eight faculty wives to a tea?

18. How many different sums of money can be formed from a penny, nickel, dime, quarter, and half dollar if at least two coins are used?

19. Solve for n the equation $C(n + 2, 4) = 6C(n, 2)$.

▶ **20.** Prove $C(n, r) + C(n, r - 1) \equiv C(n + 1, r)$.

n \ r	0	1	2	3	4	5	6
0	1						
1	1	1					
2	1	2	1				
3	1	3	3	1			
4	1	4	6	4	1		
5	1	5	10	10	5	1	
6	1	6	15	20	15	6	1

▶ **21.** Examine the numbers listed in the table above. It represents $C(n, r)$ where the values for r are listed horizontally, and n vertically. For example, $C(4, 3) = 4$, since we go across the row corresponding to $n = 4$ and down the column corresponding to $r = 3$. In the space where this row and column intersect we have the number 4. Notice that the equation $C(n + 1, r) \equiv C(n, r) + C(n, r - 1)$ satisfies the entries.

22. The equation $C(n + 1, r) \equiv C(n, r) + C(n, r - 1)$ is called Pascal's Rule. Pascal (1623–1662) was one of the men in the seventeenth century to study this array of numbers in the table above in connection with his study of games of chance. The numbers in this array are called Pascal's Triangle. By using the equation, extend the table with n and r continuing to 10, and assuming $C(n, 0)$ and $C(n, n) = 1$.

23. Prove the relation

$$C(n, r+1) = \frac{n-r}{r+1} C(n, r), \quad \text{for } 0 \le r < n.$$

By means of this formula, Pascal's Triangle can be constructed. Use it to find the numbers corresponding to $n = 7$, assuming $C(7, 0) = 1$.

24. Prove the relation $rC(n, r) = nC(n-1, r-1)$.

10–4 THE BINOMIAL THEOREM

Relative to the ideas we have considered in this chapter is an important theorem in algebra. We learned in Chapter 3 the method of multiplying polynomials. By such multiplication we find,

$$(a+b)^1 = a + b,$$
$$(a+b)^2 = a^2 + 2ab + b^2,$$
$$(a+b)^3 = a^3 + 3a^2b + 3ab^2 + b^3,$$

and

$$(a+b)^4 = a^4 + 4a^3b + 6a^2b^2 + 4ab^3 + b^4.$$

If we examine these products, we immediately notice two things. (1) The coefficients are the same as those that appear in the table of Problem 21 in Article 10–3. (2) Each of the coefficients can be expressed in terms of the functional value $C(n, r)$. For example,

$$(a+b)^4 = C(4, 0)a^4 + C(4, 1)a^3b + C(4, 2)a^2b^2 + C(4, 3)ab^3 + C(4, 4)b^4.$$

From these two observations we would expect a similar expression for the expansion of $(a+b)^n$, where n is any positive integer. This, in fact, is the case, and is called the binomial theorem.

Theorem 10–4 (*The Binomial Theorem*). For any positive integer n,

$$(a+b)^n = C(n, 0)a^n + C(n, 1)a^{n-1}b + C(n, 2)a^{n-2}b^2$$
$$+ \cdots + C(n, r)a^{n-r}b^r + \cdots + C(n, n)b^n. \tag{10–9}$$

Proof. For any positive integer n, $(a+b)^n$ is the product of n equal factors, that is,

$$(a+b)^n = \underbrace{(a+b)(a+b)(a+b) + \cdots + (a+b)}_{n \text{ factors}}. \tag{10–10}$$

In carrying out this multiplication, we choose either a or b from each of the n factors and multiply these n letters together. If we form all products by considering every possible choice of either a or b from each factor independently, and add these products together, we have $(a+b)^n$. Specifically, we get a^n by choosing the a from each of the n factors. We get $a^{n-1}b$ terms by choosing a from all but one factor and b from that one, and so on. In general, for any r where $0 \le r \le n$, we get $a^{n-r}b^r$ terms by choosing a from $n-r$ factors, and b from the other r

factors. Let us focus our attention on choosing b from the r factors, and how many different possible choices of the r factors exist. Since, for such a term, we choose r factors from n choices, there are precisely $C(n, r)$ such terms, $a^{n-r}b^r$. Thus, $C(n, r)a^{n-r}b^r$ appears in the expansion. But, because of the range of r, we have the sum of all such terms with r from 0 to n, inclusive, which is precisely the statement of the theorem.

In Fig. 10–2, a tree diagram illustrates the set of possible products for $(a + b)^3$. If we start at point 0, any path through the tree to the right-hand edge represents one of the products in the identity. Notice that there is one a^3, three a^2b products, three ab^2 products, and one b^3, so that there are eight products in all, as there should be.

It is because of this theorem that $C(n, r)$, the combination of n objects taken r at a time, is often referred to as a binomial coefficient.

We immediately note the following properties of the expansion (Eq. 10–9) for any positive integer n.

1. The number of terms in any identity is $n + 1$.

2. The first term in the identity is a^n.

3. The exponent of a decreases by one and that of b increases by one from any term to the next term, so that the sum of the exponents of a and b in any term is n.

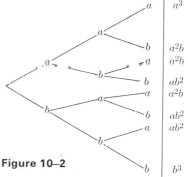

Figure 10–2

4. For the first and last, the second and next to last, the third and third from the last, and so forth, terms of the identity, the coefficients are the same. [Recall Eq. (10–8).]

These properties will be helpful in any use that is made of the theorem. In addition, it is important to note that the rth term in the expansion is

$$C(n, r - 1)a^{n-r+1}b^{r-1} = \frac{n(n - 1)(n - 2) \cdots (n - r + 2)}{(r - 1)!} a^{n-r+1}b^{r-1}.$$

$$(10\text{–}11)$$

Example 1. Expand $(a + 2b)^6$ by the binomial theorem and simplify the result.

Solution. With a the first term and $2b$ the second in the binomial to be expanded, we have

$$(a + 2b)^6 \equiv a^6 + 6a^5(2b) + \frac{6 \cdot 5}{2!} a^4(2b)^2 + \frac{6 \cdot 5 \cdot 4}{3!} a^3(2b)^3$$

$$+ \frac{6 \cdot 5 \cdot 4 \cdot 3}{4!} a^2(2b)^4 + 6a(2b)^5 + (2b)^6$$

$$\equiv a^6 + 12a^5b + 60a^4b^2 + 160a^3b^3$$

$$+ 240a^2b^4 + 192ab^5 + 64b^6.$$

Example 2. Find the first four terms of the expansion of $(x^3 - 3y^2)^{12}$.

Solution. Here $a = x^3$ and $b = -3y^2$. Thus,

$$(x^3 - 3y^2)^{12} \equiv (x^3)^{12} + 12(x^3)^{11}(-3y^2) + \frac{12 \cdot 11}{2!}(x^3)^{10}(-3y^2)^2$$
$$+ \frac{12 \cdot 11 \cdot 10}{3!}(x^3)^9(-3y^2)^3 + \cdots$$
$$\equiv x^{36} - 36x^{33}y^2 + 594x^{30}y^4 - 5940x^{27}y^6 + \cdots$$

Note from the method of this example that when the first term of the binomial is plus and the second minus, the signs in the expansion alternate.

The general term (Eq. 10–11) is of use in many problems involving a specific term.

Example 3. Find the sixth term in the expansion of $[(1/2a) - 3]^{16}$.

Solution. In this example the first term is $1/2a$, and the second is -3, $n = 16$, and $r = 6$. If we substitute in Eq. (10–11), the sixth term is

$$\frac{16 \cdot 15 \cdot 14 \cdot 13 \cdot 12}{2 \cdot 3 \cdot 4 \cdot 5}\left(\frac{1}{2a}\right)^{11}(-3)^5 = -\frac{66339}{128a^{11}}.$$

PROBLEMS

Expand each of the following by the binomial theorem, and simplify if necessary.

1. $(a + b)^7$

2. $(xy - 2)^4$

3. $(2x + y^2)^5$

4. $\left(a^2 - \dfrac{x}{2}\right)^6$

5. $(5x - y^2)^4$

6. $(x^{-1} + 2y^{-2})^6$

7. $(x^{1/3} + y^{1/3})^6$

8. $(x^{2/3} - y^{2/3})^5$

9. $(x^{2/5} - 3y^{-2})^5$

10. $(ax^{1/2} - by^{1/3})^6$

Write and simplify the first four terms of the expansions for the following.

11. $\left(\dfrac{x^2}{2} + \dfrac{2}{y^2}\right)^{12}$

12. $(x^{1/3} - y^{1/3})^9$

13. $(x^{1/3} - y^{-1/3})^{11}$

14. $(x^{-2/3} + 2y^{2/3})^8$

15. $(1 + x)^k$

▶ 16. $(1 + k)^{1/k}$

Hint: Assume that the binomial theorem holds for $n = 1/k$.

Write and simplify the indicated term in the expansions of the following.

17. Seventh term of $(2x - y)^{12}$

18. Ninth term of $\left(2 + \dfrac{x}{4}\right)^{15}$

19. Middle term of $(y^2 - \frac{1}{2})^8$

20. Middle term of $\left(2 + \dfrac{3}{x}\right)^{10}$

21. Term involving x^7 of $(2x - 3)^{10}$

22. Term involving x^3 of $(5 - 2x)^6$

23. Term involving x^5 of $\left(x + \dfrac{1}{2x}\right)^7$

24. Term involving $\dfrac{x^2}{y^2}$ of $\left(\dfrac{x}{y} - \dfrac{y^2}{2x^2}\right)^8$

25. Prove that the $(r + 1)$st term of Eq. (10–9) is

$$\frac{n(n - 1)(n - 2) \cdots (n - r + 1)}{r!} a^{n-r} b^r.$$

26. Solve $C(n, 4) = 35$ for the positive integer n.

27. Prove that

$$2^n = (1 + 1)^n = 1 + C(n, 1) + C(n, 2) + C(n, 3) + \cdots + C(n, n).$$

28. Check the statement in Problem 27 for $n = 5$.

29. Solve Problem 18, Article 10 3 using Problem 27.

30. If n is even, prove

$$C(n, 0) + C(n, 2) + \cdots + C(n, n) = C(n, 1) + C(n_1 3) + \cdots + C(n, n - 1).$$

10–5 THE EXPANSION OF $(1 + x)^n$

Applying the binomial theorem to $(1 + x)^n$, we have

$$(1 + x)^n = 1 + nx + \frac{n(n - 1)}{2!} x^2$$

$$+ \frac{n(n - 1)(n - 2)}{3!} x^3 + \cdots$$

$$+ \frac{n(n - 1) \cdots (n - r + 2)}{(r - 1)!} x^{r-1} + \cdots, \qquad (10\text{–}12)$$

which contains $n + 1$ terms and is valid for all positive integers n. If n were any real number other than a positive integer, the expansion in Eq. (10–12) would not terminate. The question naturally arises: under what conditions would this relation still be valid?

Although the proof is beyond the scope of this book, it can be shown that a finite number of terms of the right member of Eq. (10–12) approximates $(1 + x)^n$, for any value of n which is not a positive integer if $|x| < 1$. It should be clear that the more terms that are considered, the closer the approximation will be, since the size of each term will normally be less in magnitude than the preceding one.

Example 1. Find the value of $(1.02)^{-4}$ correct to four significant figures.

Solution. We expand $(1.02)^{-4}$ by the relationship of Eq. (10–12).

$$
\begin{aligned}
(1.02)^{-4} &= (1 + 0.02)^{-4} \\
&= 1^{-4} + (-4) \cdot 1^{-5}(0.02) \\
&\quad + \frac{(-4)(-5)}{2!} \cdot 1^{-6}(0.02)^2 \\
&\quad + \frac{(-4)(-5)(-6)}{3!} \cdot 1^{-7}(0.02)^3 \\
&\quad + \frac{(-4)(-5)(-6)(-7)}{4!} \cdot 1^{-8}(0.02)^4 + \cdots \\
&= 1 - 0.08 + 0.004 - 0.00016 + 0.0000056 + \cdots \\
&= 0.9238456.
\end{aligned}
$$

We must consider a sufficient number of terms to guarantee the required accuracy. Since the last term above has a zero in the fifth decimal place, and each successive term is decreasing rapidly in size, no additional terms will affect our result, that is,

$$(1.02)^{-4} = 0.9238, \text{ correct to four significant figures.}$$

One of the more interesting results of the expansion of Eq. (10–12) occurs when $n = \frac{1}{2}$. We have

$$
\begin{aligned}
(1 + x)^{1/2} &= 1 + \frac{1}{2}x + \frac{\frac{1}{2}(-\frac{1}{2})}{2!}x^2 + \frac{\frac{1}{2}(-\frac{1}{2})(-\frac{3}{2})}{3!}x^3 + \cdots \\
&= 1 + \frac{x}{2} - \frac{x^2}{8} + \frac{x^3}{16} + \cdots \tag{10–13}
\end{aligned}
$$

In Fig. 10–3, we see the graph of $y = (1 + x)^{1/2}$, above it, the graph of $y = 1 + x/2$ (the approximation by two terms) and below it, the graph of $y = 1 + (x/2) - (x^2/8)$ (the approximation by three terms). Note how closely the two curves approximate the actual expansion. This is especially true for values of x near zero. For example, if $x = 0.21$, we have the exact value $y = (1 + 0.21)^{1/2} = \sqrt{1.21} = 1.1$. The approximations are

$$y \approx 1 + \frac{0.21}{2} = 1.105,^*$$

and

$$y \approx 1 + \frac{0.21}{2} - \frac{(0.21)^2}{8} = 1.09949.$$

This same formula may be used to find square roots for values not near zero if care is taken to reduce the problem to a similar form.

---

*The symbol $\approx$ is introduced to denote *approximately equal to*.

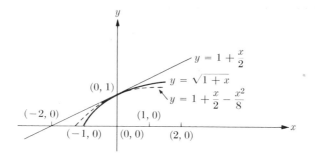

Figure 10–3

Example 2. Find the value of $\sqrt{15}$ correct to four significant figures.

Solution. We use the relationship of Eq. (10–13).

$$\sqrt{15} = \sqrt{16 - 1} = (16 - 1)^{1/2} = [16(1 - \tfrac{1}{16})]^{1/2} = 4(1 - \tfrac{1}{16})^{1/2}$$

$$= 4\left[1 + \frac{1}{2}\cdot\left(-\frac{1}{16}\right) + \frac{\frac{1}{2}(-\frac{1}{2})}{2!}\left(-\frac{1}{16}\right)^2\right.$$

$$\left. + \frac{\frac{1}{2}(-\frac{1}{2})(-\frac{3}{2})}{3!}\left(-\frac{1}{16}\right)^3 + \cdots\right]$$

$$= 4[1 - \tfrac{1}{32} - \tfrac{1}{2048} - \tfrac{1}{65536} - \cdots]$$

$$= 4[1 - 0.03125 - 0.000488 - 0.000015 - \cdots]$$

$$= 3.8730, \text{ correct to four significant figures.}$$

By using the linear approximation, we obtain a good approximation with little work involved:

$$\sqrt{15} = \sqrt{16 - 1} = 4[1 - \tfrac{1}{16}]^{1/2} \approx 4[1 - \tfrac{1}{32}] = 3.875.$$

PROBLEMS

Write out the first four terms of each of the expansions for the following expressions.

1. $\dfrac{1}{1 + x} = (1 + x)^{-1}$ **2.** $\sqrt{1 + x}$

3. $\dfrac{1}{\sqrt{1 - x}}$ ▶ **4.** $(1 + x)^{1/x}$

Compute each of the following to four significant figures.

     5. $(1.01)^{-2}$ **6.** $(1.03)^{-5}$ **7.** $\sqrt[4]{1.02}$ **8.** $\sqrt{1.05}$

     9. $\sqrt{33}$ **10.** $\sqrt[4]{17}$ **11.** $\sqrt[3]{120}$ **12.** $(1.01)^{10}$

     13. Use the appropriate linear approximation for Problems 9, 10, and 11 to find the value.

CHAPTER 11

MATHEMATICAL INDUCTION

11–1 MATHEMATICAL INDUCTION

One of the most important methods of proof in mathematics is that of mathematical induction. The name is unfortunate, for we are likely to associate the word induction with inductive reasoning, by which a conclusion is drawn from a large number of special cases. No certain conclusion can be reached by the inductive logical process. Actually, mathematical induction is deductive in nature, for it leads to a firm conclusion. Since it will be a convenient method of proof for several important results that appear in our work, we shall consider the method in some detail. It is usually employed in proving the validity of a statement involving all positive integral values of n.

Let us illustrate this method of proof. Assume that we have an ordinary ladder with an indefinite number of steps and that we wish to prove that we can climb to any designated step. We can do this if we know two things:

a) we can climb to the first step

b) if we are on any step, we can climb to the next higher step.

Because of (a) we know that we can get on the first step. With this knowledge and the fact stated in (b), we know we can get on the second step. Again, with this knowledge and the general fact stated in (b), we know we can get on the third step, etc.

One of the methods of finding a square root on an ordinary computing or adding machine is based on the fact that the sum of n odd integers is equal to n^2. Specifically,

$$1 = 1 = 1^2,$$
$$1 + 3 = 4 = 2^2,$$
$$1 + 3 + 5 = 9 = 3^2,$$
$$1 + 3 + 5 + 7 = 16 = 4^2.$$

This property is true for all integers, and is not difficult to prove.

Example 1. Prove by mathematical induction that for all positive integral values,

$$1 + 3 + 5 + \cdots + (2n - 1) \equiv n^2.$$

Solution. Part (a): *Verification for a specific value.* We have done this for $n = 1$, 2, 3, and 4, although such verification is necessary only for one value.

Part (b): *Induction property.* If the statement is true for $n = k$, where k denotes any value of n, then we wish to prove that it is true for $n = k + 1$. Thus we assume we know this fact for $n = k$, namely,

$$1 + 3 + 5 + \cdots + (2k - 1) \equiv k^2.$$

Adding $2k + 1$ to both members, we have

$$1 + 3 + 5 + \cdots + (2k - 1) + (2k + 1) \equiv k^2 + (2k + 1)$$
$$\equiv (k + 1)^2.$$

This is precisely the equation $1 + 3 + 5 + \cdots + (2n - 1) \equiv n^2$ stated for $n = k + 1$. Thus the proof of Part (b) is complete.

Part (c): *Conclusion.* We know that the equation is true for $n = 1, 2, 3,$ and 4. Since it is true for $n = 4$, and since we have proved the statement in Part (b), we know the original equation is true for $n = 4 + 1 = 5$; since it is true for $n = 5$, it is also true for $n = 6$. We may reason in this manner for all positive integral values of n.

We observe that a proof by mathematical induction consists of three parts.

Part (a): *Verification* of the validity of the statement or theorem for the smallest integral value of n for which the theorem is to hold. (This is analogous to being able to climb to the first step of the ladder.)

Part (b): *Proof of the inductive property.* If the statement or theorem is valid for $n = k$, where k denotes any value of n, then it is valid for $n = k + 1$. (This is analogous to being able to climb from any step of the ladder to the next higher step.)

Part (c): *Conclusion.* The statement or theorem is valid for all integral values of n equal to or greater than that for which it was verified in Part (a).

We know that $x - y$ is a factor of $x - y$, $x^2 - y^2$, and $x^3 - y^3$. Is it a factor of $x^n - y^n$ for any positive integer n?

Example 2. Prove by mathematical induction that $x^n - y^n$ is divisible by $x - y$ for all positive integral values of n.

Solution. Part (a): When $n = 1$, $x^n - y^n$ becomes $x - y$, which is clearly divisible by $x - y$. When $n = 2$, $x^2 - y^2 \equiv (x + y)(x - y)$, which again is divisible by $x - y$.

Part (b): We assume that $x^k - y^k$ is divisible by $x - y$. With this assumption, we must show that $x^{k+1} - y^{k+1}$ is also divisible by $x - y$. If we add and subtract xy^k to $x^{k+1} - y^{k+1}$, we have

$$x^{k+1} - y^{k+1} \equiv x^{k+1} - xy^k + xy^k - y^{k+1}$$
$$\equiv x(x^k - y^k) + y^k(x - y).$$

Since each term of the right member of this identity is divisible by $x - y$, the right and therefore the left member is divisible by $x - y$. This completes Part (b).

Part (c): We know that the theorem is true for $n = 1$ and 2. Since it is true for $n = 2$, by Part (b) it is true for $n = 2 + 1 = 3$. Similar reasoning applies for all positive integral values of n.

The fact that both Parts (a) and (b) are necessary for complete proof must be stressed. Consider the following examples.

Example 3. In Article 1–4 we considered prime numbers. Does the expression $n^2 - n + 11$ represent a prime number for all positive values of n? For $n = 1, 2, 3, 4,$ and 5, we have the prime numbers 11, 13, 17, 23, and 31. Certainly Part (a) is satisfied for our statement. To show that the statement is not valid, however, let $n = 11$, and we have $11^2 - 11 + 11 = 11^2$, which is not a prime number.

Example 4. For even integers, let us assume the nonvalid statement that

$$2 + 4 + 6 + \cdots + 2n = n^2 + n + 1$$

is true when $n = k$. We can then prove the statement's validity, given this basic assumption, for $n = k + 1$. We have

$$2 + 4 + 6 + \cdots + 2k = k^2 + k + 1.$$

Adding $2k + 2$ to both members of the equality, we obtain

$$
\begin{aligned}
2 + 4 + 6 + \cdots + 2k + 2k + 2 &= k^2 + k + 1 + 2k + 2 \\
&= k^2 + 2k + 1 + k + 1 + 1 \\
&= (k + 1)^2 + (k + 1) + 1.
\end{aligned}
$$

Thus, if the statement is valid for $n = k$, it is also valid for $n = k + 1$, and Part (b) has been proved. It is clear, however, that Part (a) and thus the statement itself is not valid, for consider the case where $n = 1, 2,$ or 3. We would have $2 = 3$, $6 = 7$, or $12 = 13$, respectively.

We should emphasize that many proofs by mathematical induction are possible without adding the same quantity to both members of an equation known to be true. (This was the method in Example 1.)

PROBLEMS

By the method of mathematical induction, prove that the following are valid for all positive integral values of n.

1. $1 + 2 + 3 + \cdots + n = \dfrac{n(n + 1)}{2}$

2. $2 + 4 + 6 + \cdots + 2n = n(n + 1)$

3. $4 + 8 + 12 + \cdots + 4n = 2n(n + 1)$

4. $1 + 4 + 7 + \cdots + (3n - 2) = \dfrac{n(3n - 1)}{2}$

5. $1 + 3 + 6 + \cdots \dfrac{n(n+1)}{2} = \dfrac{n(n+1)(n+2)}{6}$

6. $1^2 + 2^2 + 3^2 + \cdots + n^2 = \dfrac{n(n+1)(2n+1)}{6}$

7. $1^2 + 3^2 + 5^2 + \cdots + (2n-1)^2 = \dfrac{n(2n-1)(2n+1)}{3}$

8. $\dfrac{1}{2} + \dfrac{1}{2^2} + \dfrac{1}{2^3} + \cdots + \dfrac{1}{2^n} = 1 - \dfrac{1}{2^n}$

9. $2 + 2^2 + 2^3 + \cdots + 2^n = 2^{n+1} - 2$

10. $1^3 + 2^3 + 3^3 + \cdots + n^3 = \dfrac{n^2(n+1)^2}{4}$

11. $1^3 + 3^3 + 5^3 + \cdots + (2n-1)^3 = n^2(2n^2 - 1)$

12. $\dfrac{1}{1 \cdot 2} + \dfrac{1}{2 \cdot 3} + \dfrac{1}{3 \cdot 4} + \cdots + \dfrac{1}{n(n+1)} = \dfrac{n}{n+1}$

13. $1 \cdot 2 + 2 \cdot 3 + 3 \cdot 4 + \cdots + n(n+1) = \dfrac{n(n+1)(n+2)}{3}$

14. $1 \cdot 2 + 3 \cdot 4 + 5 \cdot 6 + \cdots + (2n-1)(2n) = \dfrac{n(n+1)(4n-1)}{3}$

15. $1 \cdot 2 \cdot 3 + 2 \cdot 3 \cdot 4 + 3 \cdot 4 \cdot 5 + \cdots + n(n+1)(n+2)$
$$= \dfrac{n(n+1)(n+2)(n+3)}{4}$$

▶ **16.** $t_1 + t_1 r + t_1 r^2 + \cdots + t_1 r^{n-1} = \dfrac{t_1 - t_1 r^n}{1 - r}$

▶ **17.** $t_1 + (t_1 + d) + (t_1 + 2d) + \cdots + t_1 + (n-1)d = \dfrac{n[2t_1 + (n-1)d]}{2}$

18. $x^{2n} - y^{2n}$ is divisible by $x - y$

19. $x^{2n-1} + y^{2n-1}$ is divisible by $x + y$

20. $n^3 + 2n$ is divisible by 3

21. If $a > -1$, $(a+1)^n \geq 1 + na$

22. If n is a positive odd integer, $n(n^2 - 1)$ is divisible by 24

23. $10^n + 3 \cdot 4^{n+2} + 5$ is divisible by 9

24. $2n \leq 2^n$

25. $2^{n-1} \leq n!$

11-2 AN ALTERNATIVE PROOF OF THE BINOMIAL THEOREM

It is quite possible to prove the binomial theorem by mathematical induction. The proof is given below and involves a certain facility with algebra. We give it to emphasize the importance of proofs by mathematical induction and to illustrate another important proof by induction, which does not involve the process of adding the same expression to both sides of an equation known to be true.

Theorem 11–1. For any positive integer n,

$$(a + b)^n \equiv a^n + \frac{n}{1} a^{n-1}b + \frac{n(n - 1)}{1 \cdot 2} a^{n-2}b^2$$

$$+ \frac{n(n - 1)(n - 2)}{1 \cdot 2 \cdot 3} a^{n-3}b^3 + \cdots + b^n.$$

(11–1)

Proof. We recall Eq. (10–11), the general expression for the rth term:

$$\frac{n(n - 1)(n - 2) \cdots (n - r + 2)}{(r - 1)!} a^{n-r+1}b^{r-1}.$$

(11–2)

We are now prepared to prove that Eq. (11–1) holds for all positive integral values of n. Since we have verified it for $n = 1, 2, 3,$ and 4 in Article 10–4, we need only to assume that it is valid for $n = k$, that is,

$$(a + b)^k \equiv a^k + ka^{k-1}b + \frac{k(k - 1)}{2!} a^{k-2}b^2 + \cdots$$

$$+ \frac{k(k - 1)(k - 2) \cdots (k - r + 2)}{(r - 1)!} a^{k-r+1}b^{r-1} + \cdots + b^k,$$

(11–3)

and prove from this that it is valid for $n = k + 1$, or

$$(a + b)^{k+1} \equiv a^{k+1} + (k + 1)a^kb + \frac{(k + 1)k}{2!} a^{k-1}b^2 + \cdots$$

$$+ \frac{(k + 1)(k)(k - 1) \cdots (k - r + 3)}{(r - 1)!} a^{k-r+2}b^{r-1} + \cdots$$

$$+ b^{k+1}.$$

(11–4)

If we multiply each member of the identity (11–3) by $(a + b)$, we have

$$(a + b)^{k+1} \equiv a^{k+1} + ka^kb + \cdots$$

$$+ \frac{k(k - 1) \cdots (k - r + 2)}{(r - 1)!} a^{k-r+2}b^{r-1} + \cdots$$

$$+ ab^k + a^kb + \cdots$$

$$+ \frac{k(k - 1) \cdots (k - r + 3)}{(r - 2)!} a^{k-r+2}b^{r-1} + \cdots$$

$$+ kab^k + b^{k+1}.$$

The terms through ab^k represent the right member of Eq. (11–3) multiplied by a, and the remaining terms represent the right member multiplied by b. To obtain the rth term in the result, we have written the rth term in the first half of the right member and the $(r - 1)$st term in the second, thus both contain $a^{k-r+2}b^{r-1}$.

If we simplify the whole right member, the total coefficient of $a^{k-r+2}b^{r-1}$ will be

$$\frac{k(k-1)\cdots(k-r+2)}{(r-1)!} + \frac{k(k-1)\cdots(k-r+3)}{(r-2)!}$$

$$= \frac{k(k-1)\cdots(k-r+3)}{(r-1)!}(k-r+2)$$

$$+ \frac{k(k-1)\cdots(k-r+3)}{(r-1)(r-2)!}(r-1)$$

$$= \frac{k(k-1)\cdots(k-r+3)}{(r-1)!}[(k-r+2)+(r-1)]$$

$$= \frac{(k+1)k(k-1)\cdots(k-r+3)}{(r-1)!}.^{*}$$

Thus the total right side is exactly that of Eq. (11–4). The conclusion, Part (c), should be clear, and the proof is complete.

---

* It is interesting to note here that we are adding $C(k, r-1)$ and $C(k, r-2)$, and by Problem 20, Article 10–3 this is the expected result, $C(k+1, r-1)$.

CHAPTER 12

EXPONENTIAL AND
LOGARITHMIC FUNCTIONS

We have considered in some detail certain simple algebraic functions. There are two other important functions, the exponential function and its inverse function, the logarithmic function, which should be considered in any algebra course. In this chapter we shall examine these two functions, their properties, and simple applications.

12–1 THE EXPONENTIAL FUNCTION a^x

Before we define an exponential function, we must define a^x, where a is any positive real number, and x is any real number. We are able to do this by using the Completeness Property (Article 4–3). We recall, for example, the set of rational approximations for $\sqrt{2}$. Since this set

$$A = \{1, 1.4, 1.41, 1.414\ldots\}$$

is bounded above, it has a least upper bound, which we call $\sqrt{2}$. If we wish to define $5^{\sqrt{2}}$, we consider the set $\{5^1, 5^{1.4}, 5^{1.41}, \ldots\}$ which is also bounded above. Its least upper bound is defined to be

$$5^{\sqrt{2}} = 9.738 \quad \text{(approximately)}$$

and is well defined since 5^r is well defined where r is rational.

Our general definition is similar. If $a \in R$, $a > 1$, and $x \in R$, let

$$S = \{a^r | r \le x, r \in F\}.$$

It should be clear that S is bounded above. For any $n \in I$ where $n > x$, $n > r$, so that $a^n > a^r$. (Problem 6, Article 4–1.) Since for any x there always exists such an integer n, a^n is an upper bound of S. Thus, S has a least upper bound by the Completeness Property, and we may define a^x under these conditions.

Definition 12–1. Consider $a, x \in R$, and $a > 0$.

1) If $a > 1$, a^x is the least upper bound of $\{a^r | r \le x, r \in F\}$.
2) If $a = 1$, $a^x = 1$.
3) If $a < 1$, $1/a > 1$. Then $a^x = 1/(1/a)^x$.

Since a^x has already been defined if $x \in F$ (Article 3–10), we now have a^x defined for all real x if $a > 0$. It is possible to show that these definitions of real exponents obey all the laws of exponents, although the proofs will not be given here.

With this understanding of the meaning of any real exponent, whether rational or irrational, let us consider the simplest exponential function f,

$$f: x \rightarrow a^x, \qquad a > 0, \qquad (12\text{–}1)$$

whose domain is R. Its defining equation is therefore $y = f(x) = a^x$.

Now let us examine the graphs of the two special cases of this type of function, $y = 2^x$ and $y = 3^x$. These are sketched by plotting points whose coordinates satisfy the equations (Fig. 12–1).

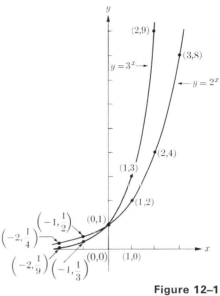

Figure 12–1

x	-2	-1	0	1	2	3
y	$\frac{1}{4}$	$\frac{1}{2}$	1	2	4	8

$$y = 2^x$$

x	-2	-1	0	1	2
y	$\frac{1}{9}$	$\frac{1}{3}$	1	3	9

$$y = 3^x$$

The following properties of the function whose defining equation is $y = a^x$ should be apparent from the graphs.

1. The function is positive (its graph lies above the x-axis) for all values of x.

2. If $a > 1$, the function is an increasing function. As x takes on larger and larger values, so does the function, and as x decreases algebraically, the function approaches, but never attains the value zero.

3. For all values of a, the function has the value 1 when $x = 0$.

4. There are no zeros of the function.

PROBLEMS

Sketch the graphs of the functions in 1 through 6.

  1. 4^x 2. 10^x 3. 2^{-x}
  4. $(\frac{1}{2})^x$ 5. 3^{-x} 6. $(\frac{1}{3})^x$

  7. For the function whose defining equation is $y = a^x$ state a property corresponding to Property 2 if $0 < a < 1$.

12–2 GEOMETRIC PROGRESSIONS

We recall (Article 6–2) that a sequence is the range, or functional values of a function, the domain of which is either all or a part of the set of positive integers. We are now able to define a geometric progression by using the exponential function a^x.

Definition 12–2. *A geometric progression* is a sequence in which each term after the first is obtained by multiplying the same fixed number, called the *common ratio*, by the preceding term.

Alternative Definition 12–2. A *geometric progression* is any sequence for which the defining function has an equation of the form ka^u, where u is a linear expression in x. (See Problem 28 of this article.)

Illustration 1. The sequence 2, 4, 8, . . . , 2^n is a geometric progression with the common ratio 2. The function defining this sequence is $f : x \rightarrow 2^x$.

Illustration 2. The sequence 3, 1, $\frac{1}{3}$, $\frac{1}{9}$, . . . is a geometric progression, with $\frac{1}{3}$ the common ratio. Its defining function is defined by $f(x) = 3^{2-x}$.

The general notation used for the geometric progression is similar to that of Article 6–2:

t_1, the first term, r, the common ratio,
n, the number of terms, t_n, the last or nth term.

Since each term is multiplied by the common ratio r to give its succeeding term, a geometric progression may be represented by

$$t_1, \quad t_1 r, \quad t_1 r^2, \quad t_1 r^3, \ldots, t_1 r^{n-1},$$

with the last value giving the expression for the nth term,

$$t_n = t_1 r^{n-1}. \tag{12–2}$$

Example 1. Find the 10th term of the geometric progression $-8, 4, -2, \ldots$

Solution. With $t_1 = -8$, $r = -\frac{1}{2}$, and $n = 10$, we have

$$t_{10} = (-8)(-\tfrac{1}{2})^9 = (-8)(-\tfrac{1}{512}) = \tfrac{1}{64}.$$

Example 2. If the 8th term of a geometric progression is 243 and the 5th term is 9, write the first three terms.

Solution. We have for $n = 8$,

$$t_8 = 243 = t_1 r^7,$$

and for $n = 5$,

$$t_5 = 9 = t_1 r^4.$$

If we divide the members of the first equation by those of the second, we get

$$r^3 = 27, \quad \text{or} \quad r = 3.$$

If we substitute this value in the second equation, we have

$$9 = t_1(3)^4, \quad \text{or} \quad 81t_1 = 9, \quad t_1 = \tfrac{1}{9}.$$

Therefore the first three terms of the required series are $\tfrac{1}{9}$, $\tfrac{1}{3}$, and 1.

The expression for the value of the sum of n terms of any geometric progression is easily obtained. Writing out the sum and multiplying this expression by r, we have

$$S_n = t_1 + t_1 r + t_1 r^2 + \cdots + t_1 r^{n-2} + t_1 r^{n-1},$$

and

$$r S_n = t_1 r + t_1 r^2 + \cdots + t_1 r^{n-1} + t_1 r^n.$$

Subtracting the members of the second equation from those of the first, we have

$$S_n - r S_n = t_1 - t_1 r^n, \quad \text{or} \quad (1 - r)S_n = (1 - r^n)t_1,$$

and solving for S_n,

$$S_n = t_1 \frac{1 - r^n}{1 - r} \quad (r \neq 1),$$

which proves the following theorem.

Theorem 12–1. The sum of n terms of any geometric progression is given by the expression

$$S_n = \frac{t_1(1 - r^n)}{1 - r} \quad (r \neq 1), \tag{12-3}$$

where t_1 is the first term, r the common ratio, and n the number of terms.*

Since the last or nth term $t_n = t_1 r^{n-1}$ or $r t_n = t_1 r^n$, we also have

$$S_n = \frac{t_1 - r t_n}{1 - r} \quad (r \neq 1). \tag{12-4}$$

We note that in Eqs. (12–3) and (12–4) $r \neq 1$. What can be said about any geometric progression when $r = 1$?

PROBLEMS

Write out the next three terms in each of the following geometric progressions, and find t_n and S_n.

1. 1, 4, 16, ... to 8 terms   2. 27, 9, 3, ... to 9 terms

3. $\tfrac{1}{125}$, $-\tfrac{1}{25}$, $\tfrac{1}{5}$, ... to 7 terms

4. $P(1 + r)$, $P(1 + r)^2$, $P(1 + r)^3$, ... to 10 terms

---

* This expression can also be proved by mathematical induction. (See Problem 16, Article 11–1.)

In Problems 5 through 11, three of the elements t_1, t_n, r, n, and S_n of the geometric progression are given. Find the missing elements in each case.

5. $t_1 = 2, r = 3, n = 6$ **6.** $t_1 = 2, n = 4, t_n = 16$

7. $t_1 = 1, n = 3, S_n = 13$ **8.** $r = -3, n = 5, t_n = 162$

9. $r = \frac{1}{3}, n = 5, S_n = \frac{4}{9}$ **10.** $t_1 = 3, r = \frac{2}{5}, S_n = \frac{609}{125}$

11. $t_1 = -2, r = 2, t_n = -64$

12. Find the value of k so that $2k + 2$, $5k - 11$, and $7k - 13$ will form a geometric progression.

13. What are the first three terms of the geometric progression whose third term is $\frac{25}{4}$ and whose 7th term is $\frac{4}{25}$?

14. The second term of a geometric progression is $\frac{5}{4}$ and its 4th term is $\frac{1}{5}$. Find its third term.

15. In the geometric progression $18, -12, 8 \ldots$, which term is $\frac{512}{729}$?

▶ **16.** The terms between any two terms of a geometric progression are called the *geometric means* between these two terms. Insert four geometric means between $\frac{25}{4}$ and $\frac{8}{125}$.

17. Insert three geometric means between $\frac{27}{8}$ and $\frac{2}{3}$.

▶ **18.** Insert one geometric mean between $\frac{7}{8}$ and $\frac{175}{32}$. A single number of this kind is called the *geometric mean of two numbers*.

19. What is the geometric mean of the two numbers a and b?

20. Find the geometric mean of
     a) 12 and $\frac{4}{3}$ b) 28 and 112

21. Prove that for the two unequal positive numbers a and b, the arithmetic mean is greater than the geometric mean.

22. The population of a certain town is 5000. If it increases 5% every year, what will the approximate population be at the end of 10 years?

23. A rubber ball is dropped from a height of 9 feet. If it rebounds one-third of the distance it has fallen after each fall, how far will it rebound the 6th time? Through what distance has it traveled when it strikes the ground the 7th time?

24. A man accepts a position at $3600 with the understanding that he will receive a 2% increase every year. What will his salary be after 10 years of service?

25. An automobile purchased for $3000 depreciates in value 12% every year. Find its value at the end of 5 years.

26. If a paper napkin 0.01 inch thick could be folded so that it was half as large but twice as thick, folded again in the same manner, and again until the process has been repeated 30 times, approximately how thick would the resulting piece of paper be?

27. If you had the choice of a salary of $1000 a day for a month of 31 days, or $1 for the first day's work, $2 for the second, $4 for the third, and each day thereafter for the rest of the month your salary would be doubled, which choice would result in the larger salary?

28. By using Eq. (12–2), prove that the two definitions of a geometric progression are equivalent.

12–3 GEOMETRIC PROGRESSIONS WITH INFINITELY MANY TERMS

In the discussion so far, we have considered only the sum of the terms of a finite sequence. If we consider the definition of the arithmetic progression, it should be clear that such a progression with an infinite number of terms has no finite sum. The same is true for a geometric progression with $|r|$ greater than 1. Each term being larger in size than the preceding one, no definite value representing such an infinite sum can exist. In fact, even if $r = 1$, each term is the same, so that no such infinite sum can exist.

If $|r| < 1$, we have a different situation. Consider the sum of the geometric progression

$$S_n = \frac{1}{2} + \frac{1}{4} + \frac{1}{8} + \cdots + \frac{1}{2^n},$$ (12–5)

where $r = \frac{1}{2}$.

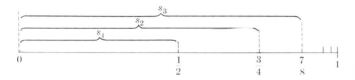

Figure 12–2

One interpretation of S_n may be seen in Fig. 12–2, which represents a line segment one unit in length. The brackets denote the sum of the terms, and the numbers below denote the sum of the progression at any stage. Each term that is added represents a length of half the total length remaining between the point representing the finite sum and the point 1. The more terms considered in Eq. (12–5), the closer we get to the point 1. In fact, we may get as close as we please to 1 by considering a sufficient number of terms, but no matter how many terms are considered, the sum will never exceed 1. Thus we say the limiting value of S_n is 1, and we write

$$S = \lim_{n \to \infty} S_n = 1.$$ (12–6)

This may be shown algebraically. Equation (12–3) may be written

$$S_n = \frac{t_1}{1 - r} - \frac{t_1 r^n}{1 - r}.$$ (12–7)

In the progression (12–5), $t_1 = r = \frac{1}{2}$, so that

$$S_n = \frac{\frac{1}{2}}{1 - \frac{1}{2}} - \frac{\frac{1}{2}(\frac{1}{2})^n}{1 - \frac{1}{2}}$$

$$= 1 - (\tfrac{1}{2})^n.$$

As n gets larger, $(\frac{1}{2})^n$ gets smaller, and in fact, $(\frac{1}{2})^n$ can be made as small in size as we please by choosing n sufficiently large. Thus, $\lim_{n \to \infty}(\frac{1}{2})^n = 0$, so that again we have

$$\lim_{n \to \infty} S_n = 1.$$

The same process holds for any geometric progression where $|r| < 1$. Using Eq. (12–7), we have

$$S_n = \frac{t_1}{1 - r} - \frac{t_1 r^n}{1 - r}.$$

If we let n increase without limit, since t_1 and r are fixed, and $|r| < 1$,

$$\lim_{n \to \infty} \frac{t_1 r^n}{1 - r} = 0.$$

*Theorem 12–2.** The "sum" S of a geometric progression with infinitely many terms exists if $|r| < 1$, and

$$S = \lim_{n \to \infty} S_n = \frac{t_1}{1 - r}. \tag{12–8}$$

Example 1. Find the sum of the infinite geometric progression $\frac{3}{2}$, 1, $\frac{2}{3}$, $\frac{4}{9}$, ...

Solution. With $t_1 = \frac{3}{2}$ and $r = \frac{2}{3}$, we find

$$S = \frac{a}{1 - r} = \frac{\frac{3}{2}}{1 - \frac{2}{3}} = \frac{\frac{3}{2}}{\frac{1}{3}} = 4\frac{1}{2}.$$

Example 2. Convert the repeating decimal 3.242424 ... into an equivalent common fraction.

Solution. We can represent the number 3.242424 ... as the number 3 plus a geometric progression with $t_1 = 0.24$ and $r = 0.01$, since

$$3.242424\ldots = 3 + (0.24 + 0.0024 + 0.000024 + \cdots).$$

The sum S, in the parentheses, may be given

$$S = \frac{t_1}{1 - r} = \frac{0.24}{1 - 0.01} = \frac{0.24}{0.99} = \frac{8}{33}.$$

Thus

$$3.242424\ldots = 3 + \tfrac{8}{33} = \tfrac{107}{33}.$$

This result may be checked by actually dividing 107 by 33.

We recall that any infinite repeating decimal can be converted into an equivalent common fraction. Moreover, any common fraction may be written as a periodic decimal. Recall Problems 4 and 5, Article 1–5.

PROBLEMS

Find the sum of each of the following infinite geometric progressions.

1. 1, $\frac{1}{3}$, $\frac{1}{9}$, ...
2. 128, 48, 18, ...
3. 16, -4, 1, ...
4. $\frac{4}{3}$, 1, $\frac{3}{4}$, ...
5. 2, $\sqrt{2}$, 1, ...
6. $\sqrt{2} + 1$, 1, $\sqrt{2} - 1$, ...

---

* Although we cannot add infinitely many terms, the limit $n \to \infty$ $S_n = S$ is called the "sum."

Convert each of the repeating decimals into equivalent common fractions.

7. 3.333 . . .　　　　　　　　**8.** 6.272727 . . .　　　　　　　**9.** 0.555 . . .

10. 8.690909 . . .　　　　　　**11.** 5.818181 . . .　　　　　　**12.** 0.142857142857 . . .

13. The sum of an infinite geometric progression is $\frac{7}{2}$ and the first term is 3. What is the common ratio?

14. The length of the side of a square is 4 inches. A second square is inscribed by connecting the midpoints of the sides of the first square, a third by connecting the midpoints of the sides of the second, and so on. Find the sum of the areas of the infinitely many squares thus formed, including the first.

15. Find the sum of the perimeters of all the squares described in Problem 14.

16. If the original figure in Problem 14 were an equilateral triangle, with sides 4 inches long, and new equilateral triangles were formed in the same way, what would the sum of their areas be, including the area of the original figure?

17. A ball is dropped from a height of 48 feet and rebounds two-thirds of the distance it falls. If it continues to fall and rebound in this way, how far will it travel before coming to rest?

18. The middle third of a line 1 foot long is erased. From each of the two remaining thirds, the middle thirds are erased. From each of the four remaining ninths, the middle thirds are erased. If this process is continued indefinitely, what will be the sum of the lengths of the remaining line segments?

12–4 THE LOGARITHMIC FUNCTION

Since for any positive number x and any positive number $a \neq 1$, there is one and only one real value of y which satisfies the equation $a^y = x$,* we can solve this equation for y, and have y equal to the power to which a must be raised in order to obtain the number x. We thus obtain the following definition.

> **Definition 12–3.** The exponent or power y to which the number a is raised to give the number x is called the *logarithm* of x to the base a, and is written

$$y = \log_a x, \qquad\qquad (12\text{–}9)$$

where $x > 0$, and $a > 0$, and $\neq 1$. This is the defining equation for the logarithmic function

$$\boxed{l : x \to \log_a x.} \qquad\qquad (12\text{–}10)$$

It should be clear that if $f : x \to a^x$, the function $l : x \to \log_a x$ is actually f^{-1}. As a result, if we keep in mind that the two expressions

$$x = a^y \qquad \text{and} \qquad y = \log_a x \qquad\qquad (12\text{–}11)$$

are equivalent, many of the logarithmic properties should be evident.

---

* The proof of this statement is beyond the scope of this book, but it should be evident from Fig. 12–2.

Illustration 1

$$\log_3 9 \;\; = 2 \;\; \leftrightarrow 3^2 \;\; = 9.*$$
$$\log_2 32 = 5 \;\; \leftrightarrow 2^5 \;\; = 32.$$
$$\log_6 1 \;\; = 0 \;\; \leftrightarrow 6^0 \;\; = 1.$$
$$\log_2 \tfrac{1}{16} = -4 \leftrightarrow 2^{-4} = \tfrac{1}{16}.$$
$$\log_8 4 \;\; = \tfrac{2}{3} \;\; \leftrightarrow 8^{2/3} = 4.$$

Let us sketch the graphs of two logarithmic functions whose defining equations are $y = \log_2 x$ and $y = \log_3 x$ and, with the help of these graphs (Fig. 12–3), consider some of the fundamental properties of the function $l: x \rightarrow \log_a x$.

x	$\frac{1}{4}$	$\frac{1}{2}$	1	2	4	8
y	-2	-1	0	1	2	3

$$y = \log_2 x \leftrightarrow 2^y = x$$

x	$\frac{1}{9}$	$\frac{1}{3}$	1	3	9
y	-2	-1	0	1	2

$$y = \log_3 x \leftrightarrow 3^y = x$$

1. The function is positive for all values of x greater than 1, but negative for all values of x less than 1. It is not defined for negative values of x.

2. The function is an increasing function.

3. The logarithm of any number with respect to itself as base is equal to 1. Graphically, all such curves pass through the point $(a, 1)$.

4. The function has $x = 1$ for its only zero.

There are several additional properties of logarithms which may be easily derived if we recall that a logarithm is an exponent. They will be stated and proved as theorems.

Theorem 12–3. The logarithm of the product of two quantities is equal to the logarithm of the first quantity plus the logarithm of the second,

$$\boxed{\log_a uv \equiv \log_a u + \log_a v.}$$ (12–12)

Figure 12–3

* The symbol $\leftrightarrow$ denotes "is the same as" or that the two expressions are equivalent.

Proof. Let u and v be any two positive quantities whose logarithms are x and y, respectively,

$$x = \log_a u \quad \text{and} \quad y = \log_a v,$$

or

$$a^x = u \quad \text{and} \quad a^y = v.$$

Multiplying the corresponding members of these equations, we have

$$uv = a^x a^y = a^{x+y},$$

which by the definition of a logarithm reduces to

$$\log_a uv = x + y = \log_a u + \log_a v.$$

Theorem 12–4. The logarithm of the quotient of two quantities is equal to the logarithm of the first quantity minus the logarithm of the second,

$$\log_a \frac{u}{v} \equiv \log_a u - \log_a v. \qquad (12\text{–}13)$$

Proof. With the same assumptions as in Theorem 12–3, we have

$$\frac{u}{v} = \frac{a^x}{a^y} = a^{x-y}.$$

Written in terms of logarithms, this becomes

$$\log_a \frac{u}{v} = x - y = \log_a u - \log_a v:$$

Theorem 12–5. The logarithm of a power of a quantity is equal to the power multiplied by the logarithm of the quantity, that is,

$$\log_a u^p \equiv p \log_a u. \qquad (12\text{–}14)$$

Proof. Let u be any positive quantity and its logarithm be x. Then $x = \log_a u$ or $a^x = u$. If we raise both members to the p power, we have

$$(a^x)^p = a^{xp} = u^p,$$

or, in terms of logarithms,

$$\log_a u^p = xp = p \log_a u.$$

Illustration 2. Theorem 12–3 implies that

$$\log_{10} (47)(93) = \log_{10} 47 + \log_{10} 93$$

or

$$\log_{10} 4700 = \log_{10} 47 \cdot 100 = \log_{10} 47 + \log_{10} 100.$$

Illustration 3. Theorem 12–4 implies that

$$\log_{10} \tfrac{82}{53} = \log_{10} 82 - \log_{10} 53.$$

Theorems 12–3 and 12–4 imply that

$$\log_{10} \frac{(48)(96)}{23} = \log_{10} 48 + \log_{10} 96 - \log_{10} 23.$$

Illustration 4. Theorem 12–5 is used for both integral powers and roots,

$$\log_{10} 28^5 = 5 \log_{10} 28,$$

$$\log_{10} \sqrt[3]{472} = \log_{10} (472)^{1/3} = \tfrac{1}{3} \log_{10} 472.$$

PROBLEMS

Express the following in logarithmic notation, using Eq. (12–11).

1. $3^3 = 27$ 2. $5^4 = 625$ 3. $4^0 = 1$

4. $10^3 = 1000$ 5. $8^{4/3} = 16$ 6. $2^{-6} = \frac{1}{64}$

7. $10^{-3} = 0.001$ 8. $b^z = w$ 9. $4^1 = 4$

Express in exponent notation using Eq. (12–11).

10. $\log_2 \frac{1}{8} = -3$ 11. $\log_{36} 6 = \frac{1}{2}$ 12. $\log_{10} 1 = 0$

Find by inspection the value of x, a, or u in the following expressions.

13. $x = \log_4 16$ 14. $x = \log_7 1$ 15. $x = \log_9 \frac{1}{9}$

16. $x = \log_{\sqrt{6}} 36$ 17. $\log_5 u = 2$ 18. $\log_a 16 = 4$

19. $x = \log_2 4^7$ 20. $\log_a 32 = -\frac{5}{7}$ 21. $\log_a \frac{2}{3} = -\frac{1}{3}$

Sketch the graphs of the following functions.

22. $y = \log_5 x$ 23. $y = \log_{1/2} x$

24. $y = \log_{10} x$ 25. $y = \log_{1/3} x$

Express as a single logarithm, using Theorems 12–3, 4, and 5.

26. $\log_a x + \log_a y - \log_a z$ 27. $\log_b (a + 2) - \log_b (a - 3)$

28. $4 \log_{10} x - 3 \log_{10} y$ 29. $\frac{1}{2} \log_a x - \frac{2}{3} \log_a y$

30. $\log_b 2x + 3 (\log_b x - \log_b y)$ 31. $-\log_a x + 6 \log_a (x - 1) + 3 \log_a x^2$

Write the logarithm of the given expression in terms of the logarithms of its factors.

32. $\log_{10} (895)(1.47)$ 33. $\log_{10} (60.3)^4$

34. $\log_{10} (68)^7 (\sqrt{147})$ 35. $\log_{10} \dfrac{(54.3)^3 (67)}{(93.9)(32.5)^2}$

12–5 COMMON LOGARITHMS

After the discussion in the previous article, it should be clear that any positive number other than 1 can be used as the base for a system of logarithms. For computational purposes, the most convenient system is that with 10 as its base. The first table of logarithms with 10 as the base was composed by Henry Briggs

(1560–1631). The advantages of this system will become apparent as we proceed. In writing

$$10^3 = 1000$$
$$10^2 = 100$$
$$10^1 = 10$$
$$10^0 = 1$$
$$10^{-1} = 0.1$$
$$10^{-2} = 0.01$$
$$10^{-3} = 0.001$$

and considering this list as extending upward and downward indefinitely, we have a method for representing certain numbers as powers of ten. Although these special numbers are the only ones which can be written as 10 with an integral exponent, all positive numbers can be represented approximately as 10 with some exponent. This exponent, we realize from our definition of a logarithm (Eq. 12–9), is the logarithm of the number to the base 10, and will be called the *common logarithm of a number*. Throughout the rest of this book, the base 10 will be assumed when no base is indicated. Thus, $\log 1000 = 3$, $\log 10 = 1$, or $\log 0.001 = -3$.

Not only do the powers of ten listed above have logarithms, but all positive numbers do. The values of the logarithms (to the base ten) of all positive numbers every hundredth of a unit between 1 and 10 have been approximated to four decimal places in Table II in the Appendix. For example, to find $\log 7.63$, we look down the first column N of the table for 7.6 and then move to the right of 7.6 to the number which appears in the column headed by 3. Finding 0.8825, we have $\log 7.63 = 0.8825$, which means, of course, $10^{0.8825} = 7.63$ (approximately).

Actually, by making use of the method of *linear interpolation*, similar to that used in Article 8–5, as well as Table II, we can find the logarithm of a number with four significant digits. If N lies between x and $x + 0.01$, then $N = x + 0.01r$, with r between 0 and 1, so that, assuming the graph of the logarithmic function is a straight line between x and $x + 0.01$,

$$\log N = \log x + r [\log (x + 0.01) - \log x]. \qquad (12\text{–}15)$$

Example 1. Find $\log 3.476$.

Solution. Since $3.47 < 3.476 < 3.48$, we have

$$\log 3.476 = \log 3.47 + 0.6 (\log 3.48 - \log 3.47)$$
$$= 0.5403 + 0.6(0.5416 - 0.5403)$$
$$= 0.5403 + 0.0008$$
$$= 0.5411.$$

This number can have only four significant figures, since the logarithms in the table are only four-figure approximations.

If the logarithm of a number is given to four decimal places, it is also possible to find the number by using Table II. If log N appears in the middle of the table, the process used to find N is reversed. If log N lies between log x and log $(x + 0.01)$, then $N = x + 0.01r$, with

$$r = \frac{\log N - \log x}{\log (x + 0.01) - \log x}, \tag{12–16}$$

rounded to the nearest tenth. (Why?)

Example 2. Find N if log $N = 0.7281$.

Solution. If we look in the middle of the table, we find

$$0.7275 < 0.7281 < 0.7284,$$

where

$$\log 5.35 = 0.7284,$$
$$\log 5.34 = 0.7275.$$

Therefore we have

$$r = \frac{0.7281 - 0.7275}{0.7284 - 0.7275} = 0.7 \qquad \text{(rounded off)},$$

and $N = 5.347$.

PROBLEMS

Using Table II, find the logarithm of each of the following numbers.

1. 2.57	**2.** 3.89	**3.** 6.92	**4.** 7.65
5. 4.71	**6.** 9.80	**7.** 6.875	**8.** 8.924
9. 3.276	**10.** 1.892	**11.** 7.689	**12.** 5.873

Using Table II, find N in each of the following if log N is equal to:

13. 0.3856	**14.** 0.8756	**15.** 0.6149	**16.** 0.6405
17. 0.9415	**18.** 0.7657	**19.** 0.2675	**20.** 0.5217
21. 0.9229	**22.** 0.7578	**23.** 0.5069	**24.** 0.6745

In general, the logarithm of N has two parts: a whole number, called the *characteristic*, and a positive decimal (a number n such that $0 \leq n < 1$), called the *mantissa*. If the decimal point in a number is just to the right of the first non-zero digit, the logarithm of that number has 0 for its characteristic. All the numbers between 1 and 10 in Table II are of this type. Such a number is said to have its *decimal point in standard position*.

If any number is multiplied by 10, the decimal point is moved one place to the right, or if divided by 10, one place to the left. But each time a number is multiplied by 10, since

$$\log 10N = \log N + \log 10$$
$$= \log N + 1,$$

the logarithm of the number is increased by one. Likewise, if a number is divided by 10, its logarithm is decreased by one, for

$$\log \frac{N}{10} = \log N - \log 10$$
$$= \log N - 1.$$

Thus the general rule for obtaining the characteristic can be stated as a theorem.

Theorem 12–6. The characteristic of the logarithm of a number is equal to the number of places the decimal point has been moved from standard position. The characteristic is positive if the point has been moved to the right, negative if to the left.

It is because of this property of our number system, and the corresponding ease of determining the characteristic, that logarithms to the base ten are used for computation.

The mantissa, that part of the logarithm which appears in the table, is not affected by the position of the decimal point in the number, but depends only on its succession of digits. Thus, because of the result of Example 1, log 347.6 = 2.5411, since its characteristic is 2, while

$$\log 0.003476 = -3 + 0.5411.$$

The characteristic -3 is usually written $7 - 10$ (it is common practice for computational purposes to write any negative characteristic as a positive integer minus a multiple of 10), so that

$$-3 + 0.5411 = 7.5411 - 10.$$

PROBLEMS

Give the characteristic and mantissa of each of the following logarithms.

1. $\log N = 1.3782$ **2.** $\log N = 3.4729$

3. $\log N = 0.5728 - 3$ **4.** $\log N = 9.6847$

5. $\log N = 5.8723$ **6.** $\log N = 6.7253 - 10$

7. $\log N = -3.7285$ **8.** $\log N = -0.6892$

Find the logarithms of each of the following numbers, using Table II.

9. 329   **10.** 0.00874

11. 4728   **12.** 32.46

13. 0.07284   **14.** 0.6877

Find N in each of the following, using Table II.

15. $\log N = 3.8228$ **16.** $\log N = 0.9643 - 2$

17. $\log N = 2.4268$ **18.** $\log N = 9.8818 - 10$

19. $\log N = 7.5627 - 10$ **20.** $\log N = -1.4892$

12–6 COMPUTATION BY THE USE OF LOGARITHMS

We are now prepared to show how any computation involving multiplication, division, raising to a power, or extracting roots is greatly simplified through the use of logarithms. The work should be outlined systematically before any actual computation is carried out. An orderly arrangement is most helpful, not only in simplifying the work but also in checking the result.

Example 1. Use logarithms to compute $(1280 \cdot 0.849)/62.8$.

Solution. By letting $N = (1280 \cdot 0.849)/62.8$, we have, using Theorems 12–3 and 12–4,

$$\log N = \log 1280 + \log 0.849 - \log 62.8.$$

The work should then be arranged as follows:

$$\begin{aligned}
\log 1280 &= 3.1072 \\
(+) \log 0.849 &= \underline{9.9289 - 10} \\
\log \text{numerator} &= 13.0361 - 10 \\
(-) \log 62.8 &= \underline{1.7980} \\
\log N &= 11.2381 - 10 \\
N &= 17.3.
\end{aligned}$$

N is given with three significant figures because the original numbers were of this type.

Example 2. Compute by using logarithms: $\sqrt{0.01278}/(0.4825)^3$.

Solution. We know

$$\log N = \tfrac{1}{2} \log 0.01278 - 3 \log 0.4825.$$

Arranging our work, we have

$$\begin{aligned}
\log 0.4825 &= 9.6834 - 10 & \log 0.01278 &= 18.1065 - 20 \\
3 \log 0.4825 &= 29.0502 - 30 & \tfrac{1}{2} \log 0.01278 &= 9.0532 - 10 \\
&= 9.0502 - 10 & (-) 3 \log 0.4825 &= \underline{9.0502 - 10} \\
& & \log N &= 0.0030 \\
& & N &= 1.007.
\end{aligned}$$

Example 3. Find the value of $x = 52.8 \log 6.79$.

Solution. It is important to note that this example asks for the product of the two factors 52.8 and log 6.79, *not* 52.8 and 6.79. Thus,

$$\log x = \log 52.8 + \log [\log 6.79].$$

$$\begin{aligned}
\log 52.8 &= 1.7226 \\
(+) \log [\log 6.79] = \log 0.832 &= \underline{9.9201 - 10} \\
\log x &= 1.6427 \\
x &= 43.9
\end{aligned}$$

PROBLEMS

Using logarithms, compute the following to the correct number of significant figures.

1. $(367)(87.2)$

2. $(47.2)(0.897)$

3. $\dfrac{32.7}{(0.892)^{1/2}}$

4. $\dfrac{(245)(8.62)}{(7.84)^2}$

5. $(32.79)(497.2)(9.738)$

6. $\sqrt{756.9}\,(4.796)$

*7. $(-0.8472)^4$

8. $(-3.472)^{-3}$

9. $\dfrac{(6.892)(-0.9245)^{2/3}}{2.475}$

10. $\left(-\dfrac{47.2}{6.783}\right)^3$

11. $\dfrac{\sqrt{738.2}\,(38.74)}{(0.9576)^2(8743)}$

12. $\left[\dfrac{\sqrt{8453}\,(0.002477)}{347.9}\right]^{1/2}$

13. $4.72 \log 63.9$

14. $\log\,(\log 82.4)$

15. $\dfrac{\log 48.5}{\log 67.2}$

16. $\dfrac{\log 0.8924}{\log 5.237}$

12–7 COMPOUND INTEREST AND ITS GENERALIZATION

The study of compound interest makes use of logarithmic computation, and it also logically introduces another important system of logarithms.

If an amount of money P is invested at an interest rate of r (expressed in decimals) per year, the amount of interest at the end of one year is Pr, so that the total amount is $P + Pr = P(1 + r)$. If this amount then draws interest for a second year, at the end of two years the total amount is

$$P(1 + r) + P(1 + r)r = P(1 + r)[1 + r] = P(1 + r)^2.$$

This represents the compound amount of money at the end of two years due to its investment at the interest rate r. If we continue this process, the amount P, invested for n years and compounded annually at the rate r, is given by

$$\boxed{A = P(1 + r)^n.} \qquad (12\text{–}17)$$

Example 1. Find the compound amount at the end of eight years on an original principal of \$500 at 6% compounded annually.

Solution. Using Eq. (12–17), we have $P = 500$, $r = 0.06$, and $n = 8$. Thus,

$$A = 500(1 + 0.06)^8 = 500(1.06)^8.$$

$$\log 1.06 = 0.0253 \qquad \qquad \log 500 = 2.6990$$

$$8 \log 1.06 = 0.2024 \qquad (+)\,8 \log 1.06 = 0.2024$$

$$\log A = 2.9014$$

$$A = \$796.80.$$

---

* Although the logarithm of a negative number is not defined, the calculation may be carried out by considering all factors positive and prefixing the correct sign to the result.

Since n represents the number of years and r the rate per year, we can consider the result due to amounts compounded annually, semiannually, quarterly, and so on, if we let s denote the number of conversion periods each year. Thus, in n years, with s conversion periods per year, the number of such periods is ns and the rate per period r/s, or

$$A = P\left(1 + \frac{r}{s}\right)^{ns}.$$

$$(12\text{–}18)$$

Example 2. If the \$500 in Example 1 were invested for eight years at 6% compounded quarterly, how large would the result be?

Solution. Since 6% compounded quarterly for eight years is $1\frac{1}{2}\%$ per period, with 32 periods, we have

$$A = 500(1.015)^{32},$$

which results in $A = \$804.20$.

Both this result and that in the first example are not very accurate, since four-place logarithm tables were used. For accurate results, since the exponent is large, either seven-place logarithmic or compound interest tables should be used.

One of the most important exponential functions is a direct result of a generalization of Eq. (12–18), which is sometimes called the *law of natural growth*. It has frequent applications in biology, chemistry, and economics, as well as in mathematics. Let us suppose that the number of conversion periods s increases indefinitely, so that the amount is compounded continuously. Letting $r/s = x$, and therefore $s/r = 1/x$, we have, from Eq. (12–18),

$$A = P\left[\left(1 + \frac{r}{s}\right)^{s/r}\right]^{rn} = P[(1 + x)^{1/x}]^{rn}.$$

$$(12\text{–}19)$$

With s increasing indefinitely, for a fixed r, $r/s = x$ decreases indefinitely through positive values and approaches zero. If Eq. (12–19) is expanded by the binomial theorem (see Problem 4, Article 10–5),

$$A = P\left[1^{1/x} + \frac{1}{x}\cdot 1^{(1/x)-1}\cdot x + \frac{\frac{1}{x}\left(\frac{1}{x}-1\right)}{2!}\cdot 1^{(1/x)-2}\cdot x^2\right.$$

$$\left. + \frac{\frac{1}{x}\left(\frac{1}{x}-1\right)\left(\frac{1}{x}-2\right)}{3!}\cdot 1^{(1/x)-3}\cdot x^3\cdots\right]^{rn}$$

$$= P\left[1^{1/x} + 1^{(1/x)-1} + \frac{1-x}{2!}\cdot 1^{(1/x)-2}\right.$$

$$\left. + \frac{(1-x)(1-2x)}{3!}\cdot 1^{(1/x)-3} + \cdots\right]^{rn},$$

and if we evaluate each term of this expression for x equals zero, we get

$$A = P\left(1 + 1 + \frac{1}{2} + \frac{1}{3!} + \cdots\right)^{rn}. \tag{12–20}$$

Although we have by no means shown that this infinite sum has a definite value,* it would seem probable that the expression within the brackets of Eq. (12–19) does have a definite value if x is allowed to approach zero. Such is the case. This constant value, denoted by e, is a nonterminating, nonrepeating decimal, and therefore irrational (Article 1–5). To six significant figures,

$$e = \lim_{x \to 0} (1 + x)^{1/x} = \left(1 + 1 + \frac{1}{2!} + \frac{1}{3!} + \cdots\right) = 2.71828. \tag{12–21}$$

We thus have the functional equation

$$\boxed{A = Pe^{rn},} \tag{12–22}$$

representing the amount of P compounded continuously for n years at a rate r.

Example 3. The population of a certain locality is 20,000 and is increasing continuously at a rate $r = 0.037$, according to the law of natural growth, Eq. (12–22). Find the approximate population after 25 years.

Solution. With the formula $A = Pe^{rn}$, we have $P = 20,000$, $r = 0.037$, and $n = 25$. Therefore, $A = 20,000e^{(0.037)(25)}$. Solving by logarithms, we have

$$\log A = \log 20,000 + (0.037)(25) \log e.$$
$$\log 20,000 = 4.3010$$
$$(+)\ (0.037)(25) \log e = 0.4017$$
$$\log A = 4.7027$$
$$A = 50,430 \text{ (approximate) population.}$$

PROBLEMS

1. Find the compound amount at the end of 10 years on an original principal of $200 at 4%
   a) compounded annually   b) compounded semiannually
   c) compounded quarterly   d) compounded continuously

2. Find the compound amount at the end of 20 years on an original principal of $3000 at 6%
   a) compounded annually   b) compounded monthly
   c) compounded continuously

---

* As in Article 10–5, any proof, in general, of the existence of a definite value for an infinite sum is beyond the scope of this book.

3. What time is required to double a certain amount

   a) compounded annually at 6%?   b) compounded continuously at 6%?

   Hint: Let $P = 1$ and $A = 2$.

In Problems 4 through 8, we shall assume the law of natural growth (Eq. 12–22).

4. The population of a certain town is 80,000 and has been increasing continuously for the past 20 years at the rate $r = 0.025$. What was the population 20 years ago?

5. There are originally 1000 bacteria in a culture, and 4 hours later there are 4000. Find the rate of increase per hour of the bacteria.

6. If the growth of a certain bacteria in a culture increases at the rate $r = 0.24$ per hour, how long will it take 50 bacteria to become 1,000,000?

7. In a certain chemical reaction, the original concentration of 0.03 is reduced to 0.01 in 4 minutes.

   a) What is the rate of decrease in the concentration per minute?

   b) What will the concentration be in 10 minutes?

8. If radium decomposes according to the relation $y = y_0 e^{-0.04t}$, where y_0 grams of radium reduce to y grams in t centuries, how long will it take one gram to reduce to one-half gram?

12–8 APPLICATIONS OF THE EXPONENTIAL FUNCTIONS

In the last article we saw one important application of the exponential function. Before examining other uses of this function, we shall discuss the method for finding the numerical value of a logarithm to any base and for changing from one base to another. Actually, the exponential function can be used to find the logarithm of a number to any base.

Example 1. Find the value of $\log_4 15$.

Solution. If $y = \log_4 15$, we have the equivalent equation

$$4^y = 15.$$

Any such equation may be solved by taking the common logarithm of each member and finding the required value of y. Thus,

$$\log 4^y = \log 15,$$
$$y \log 4 = \log 15.$$

Solving for y, we have

$$y = \frac{\log 15}{\log 4} = \frac{1.1761}{0.6021} = 1.953.$$

If the logarithm of a number to one base is known, it is often desirable to find the logarithm of this number to a different base. Let

$$y = \log_a N.$$

Writing this in the equivalent form

$$a^y = N,$$

and taking the logarithm to the base b of each member, we have

$$\log_b a^y = \log_b N,$$

or

$$y \log_b a = \log_b N.$$

Recalling that $y = \log_a N$, we have

$$\boxed{\log_a N \cdot \log_b a = \log_b N.} \tag{12–23}$$

Because of the importance of the case where one base is 10 and the other e, we note that in this case, with $a = e$ and $b = 10$, Eq. (12–23) reduces to

$$\log_{10} N = \log_e N \cdot \log_{10} e = 0.4343 \log_e N, \tag{12–24}$$

and

$$\log_e N = \frac{1}{\log_{10} e} \cdot \log_{10} N = 2.303 \log_{10} N. \tag{12–25}$$

These two expressions are used extensively in analytic work to change from the common logarithmic system to the logarithm system with base e, and vice versa.

Example 2. Find $\log_e 3.24$.

Solution 1. By Eq. (12–25),

$$\log_e 3.24 = 2.303 \log 3.24$$
$$= (2.303)(0.5105)$$
$$= 1.175.$$

Solution 2. This example may, of course, be solved as in Example 1. If we let

$$y = \log_e 3.24,$$
$$e^y = 3.24.$$

Taking the common logarithm of each member, we get

$$\log e^y = \log 3.24,$$

or

$$y \log e = \log 3.24.$$

Solving for y, we have

$$y = \frac{\log 3.24}{\log e} = \frac{0.5105}{0.4343} = 1.175.$$

The method used in solving Example 1 and in the second solution of Example 2 is similar to that used in solving many exponential as well as logarithmic equations.

Example 3. Solve $4^{x+3} = 7^{x-1}$ for x.

Solution. If we take the common logarithms of both members,

$$\log 4^{x+3} = \log 7^{x-1}.$$

By using Theorem 12–5, we have

$$(x + 3) \log 4 = (x - 1) \log 7.$$

Solving this linear equation for x, we get

$$x \log 4 + 3 \log 4 = x \log 7 - \log 7,$$

$$x (\log 4 - \log 7) = -\log 7 - 3 \log 4,$$

$$x = \frac{\log 7 + 3 \log 4}{\log 7 - \log 4}$$

$$= \frac{2.6514}{0.2430} = 10.92 \text{ (approximately)}.$$

Example 4. Solve $\log (x + 3) - \log x = 2$.

Solution. If we use Theorem 12–4,

$$\log (x + 3) - \log x = \log \frac{x + 3}{x} = 2,$$

so that

$$\frac{x + 3}{x} = 100, \qquad x + 3 = 100x,$$

$$99x = 3, \qquad \text{or} \qquad x = \tfrac{1}{33}.$$

PROBLEMS

Find the following logarithms.

1. $\log_2 14$	**2.** $\log_5 27$	**3.** $\log_7 128$	**4.** $\log_{27} 15$
5. $\log_e 7$	**6.** $\log_e 12$	**7.** $\log_e 1.79$	**8.** $\log_e 3.78$

Find the value of x in each of the following.

9. $\log_4 x = 23$ **10.** $\log_{12} x = 17$

11. $\log_e x = 3.28$ **12.** $\log_e x = 1.72$

13. $\log_e x = 0.8473$ **14.** $\log_c x = 2.547$

▶ **15.** Prove the relation $\log_b a = 1/(\log_a b)$.

Solve the following exponential equations for x.

16. $3^x = 27$ **17.** $2^x = 32$

18. $2^x = 27$ **19.** $3^x = 32$

20. $3^{x+1} = 4^{x-7}$ **21.** $5(6^x) = 21^{x-2}$

22. $17^{2x-3} = 25^{x-1}$ **23.** $2.78^x = 7.38^{3x-1}$

24. $e^x + e^{-x} = 2$ *Hint:* This is quadratic in e^x.

25. $e^x - e^{-x} = 2$

Solve the following logarithmic equations for x.

26. $\log x - 2 \log 4 = \log 32$ **27.** $\log (x + 2) - \log x = \log 12$

28. $\log (3x + 2) = \log (x - 4) + 1$ **29.** $\log (x + 1) - \log x = 2.4742$

CHAPTER 13

ALGEBRA OF ORDERED PAIRS

The possibility of extensions or generalizations of the real number system was mentioned in Article 1–5. One of these extensions is the algebra of all ordered pairs of real numbers. We shall briefly discuss this very useful generalization, and then we shall consider two of its most common interpretations in some detail.

13–1 ALGEBRA OF ORDERED PAIRS

With the set of all ordered pairs of real numbers (x, y) as elements, we can construct a generalized but somewhat restricted algebra. We shall do this by defining, for the elements in the set $P = \{(x, y)|x, y \in R\}$, an operation of addition as well as multiplication by a real number. We shall later define a more general type of multiplication, and in so doing, lift some of the restrictions. Before we do any of this, however, we must define what is meant by the equality of two elements. (Recall Problem 13, Article 1–3.)

Definition 13–1. Two ordered pairs (x_1, y_1) and (x_2, y_2) are said to be equal if and only if $x_1 = x_2$ and $y_1 = y_2$.

Thus, $(x + 2y, 2x - y) = (4, 3)$ if and only if $x + 2y = 4$ and $2x - y = 3$, or, specifically, $x = 2$ and $y = 1$.

We are now ready to define the operation of addition and also the multiplication by a real number (a *scalar*).

Definition 13–2. The sum of two ordered pairs (x_1, y_1) and (x_2, y_2) is the ordered pair $(x_1 + x_2, y_1 + y_2)$ and is written

$$(x_1, y_1) + (x_2, y_2) = (x_1 + x_2, y_1 + y_2). \tag{13-1}$$

For example, $(2, 1) + (3, 2) = (2 + 3, 1 + 2) = (5, 3)$.

It is clear because of the statement of this definition, that P is closed under the operation of addition. Also the operation is commutative and associative, since real numbers themselves enjoy these properties (see Problems 2 and 3). Since, by Eq. (13–1),

$$(x, y) + (0, 0) = (x, y) \tag{13-2}$$

for all (x, y), and $(0, 0)$ is an ordered pair, the identical element for addition exists, and is equal to $(0, 0)$.

Definition 13–3. The product of an ordered pair (x, y) by any scalar $c \in R$ is the ordered pair (cx, cy) and is written

$$c(x, y) = (cx, cy). \tag{13–3}$$

For example, $5(2, -4) = (10, -20)$.

A special case of Eq. (13–3) is an important one, namely, where $c = -1$. In fact, since for any ordered pair (x, y), the ordered pair $-1(x, y) = (-x, -y)$ has the property, by Definition 13–2, that

$$(x, y) + (-x, -y) = (0, 0), \tag{13–4}$$

there exists an inverse element for the operation of addition.

As in the case of real numbers, where the solution for x of the equation $a + x = b$, written $b - a$, is called the difference (recall Definition 2–1 and Problem 7, Article 2–4), the solution for (x, y) in the equation

$$(x_1, y_1) + (x, y) = (x_2, y_2) \tag{13–5}$$

is called the difference of the two ordered pairs (x_2, y_2) and (x_1, y_1). Since by Eq. (13–5)

$$x_1 + x = x_2, \qquad y_1 + y = y_2,$$

or

$$x = x_2 - x_1, \qquad y = y_2 - y_1,$$

the difference (x, y) is written as the ordered pair $(x_2 - x_1, y_2 - y_1)$ or

$$(x_2, y_2) - (x_1, y_1) = (x_2 - x_1, y_2 - y_1). \tag{13–6}$$

We have pointed out that this set of ordered pairs $P = \{(x, y) | x, y \in R\}$ observes certain algebraic laws. Specifically,

1) the set P is closed under addition,

2) the addition of ordered pairs in P is commutative,

3) the associative property for addition of ordered pairs in P holds,

4) there exists an identity for P, and

5) there exists an inverse for each ordered pair of P.

Any set whose elements satisfy these five laws is said to form a *commutative group* with respect to addition.

It is also possible to prove many other properties. We shall list four additional ones, the proofs of which are not difficult and appear as problems.

6) For any ordered pair (x, y) and any scalars c and d,

$$(cd)(x, y) = c(d(x, y)). \tag{13–7}$$

7) For any ordered pair (x, y) and any scalars c and d,

$$(c + d)(x, y) = c(x, y) + d(x, y). \tag{13–8}$$

8) For any two ordered pairs (x_1, y_1) and (x_2, y_2) and any scalar c,

$$c[(x_1, y_1) + (x_2, y_2)] = c(x_1, y_1) + c(x_2, y_2). \qquad (13\text{–}9)$$

9) For any ordered pair,

$$1(x, y) = (x, y). \qquad (13\text{–}10)$$

Any set of elements which satisfies, in addition to the first five, these four rules, is characterized in mathematics as an important algebraic system called a *linear space over the real numbers,* or sometimes, a *vector space.* The reason for this second name will become clear in the next section.

The question naturally arises of why we defined the second operation, multiplication of an ordered pair by a scalar, rather than by another ordered pair. We did so because we wished to introduce the algebraic system known as a linear space. We now will define the multiplication of two ordered pairs, a special case of which will, in fact, prove to be the scalar multiplication already defined in Definition 13–3 (see Problem 15). This definition of multiplication is not so obvious as that of addition.

> **Definition 13–4.** The product of two ordered pairs (x_1, y_1) and (x_2, y_2) is the ordered pair $(x_1x_2 - y_1y_2, x_1y_2 + x_2y_1)$, and is written

$$\boxed{(x_1, y_1) \cdot (x_2, y_2) = (x_1x_2 - y_1y_2, x_1y_2 + x_2y_1).} \qquad (13\text{–}11)$$

For example, $(2, 1) \cdot (3, 2) = (2 \cdot 3 - 1 \cdot 2, 2 \cdot 2 + 3 \cdot 1) = (4, 7)$.

Again, it is clear by definition, that P is closed under the operation of multiplication. Moreover, the operation of multiplication is commutative and associative. (See Problems 10 and 11.)

Since, by Eq. (13–11), $(x, y) \cdot (1, 0) = (x, y)$ for all (x, y), and $(1, 0)$ is an ordered pair, the identical element for multiplication exists, and is equal to $(1, 0)$. Also, since

$$\left(\frac{x}{x^2 + y^2}, \frac{-y}{x^2 + y^2} \right)$$

exists when $(x, y) \neq (0, 0)$ and

$$(x, y) \cdot \left(\frac{x}{x^2 + y^2}, \frac{-y}{x^2 + y^2} \right) = (1, 0)$$

for all $(x, y) \neq (0, 0)$, the inverse element for the operation of multiplication exists. It can also be demonstrated that the distributive law holds for the elements of P. (See Problem 14.)

In the case of real numbers, division is defined in terms of multiplication, and the definition for the quotient of two ordered pairs follows the same pattern. (Recall Definition 2–2 and Problem 11, Article 2–4.) Since the real number $x = a/b$ is defined by the equation $bx = a$, we define the quotient of two ordered pairs (x_1, y_1) and (x_2, y_2) as the ordered pair (x, y), which is the solution of the equation

$$(x_2, y_2) \cdot (x, y) = (x_1, y_1), \qquad (x_2, y_2) \neq (0, 0). \qquad (13\text{–}12)$$

Using Eq. (13–11), we get

$$(xx_2 - yy_2, xy_2 + x_2y) = (x_1, y_1),$$

and therefore

$$x_2x - y_2y = x_1, \qquad y_2x + x_2y = y_1.$$

Solving for x and y, we find the solution

$$x = \frac{x_1x_2 + y_1y_2}{x_2^2 + y_2^2}, \qquad y = \frac{x_2y_1 - x_1y_2}{x_2^2 + y_2^2}.$$

Thus the quotient of two ordered pairs may be written

$$\frac{(x_1, y_1)}{(x_2, y_2)} = \left(\frac{x_1x_2 + y_1y_2}{x_2^2 + y_2^2}, \frac{x_2y_1 - x_1y_2}{x_2^2 + y_2^2} \right). \qquad (13\text{–}13)$$

For example,

$$\frac{(4, 8)}{(3, 1)} = (2, 2).$$

PROBLEMS

1. Explain the statements in the text "$P = \{(x, y) | x, y \in R\}$ is closed under the operations of addition and multiplication."

2. Show that the addition defined for ordered pairs by Eq. (13–1) is commutative, that is,

$$(x_1, y_1) + (x_2, y_2) = (x_2, y_2) + (x_1, y_1).$$

3. Show that this addition is associative, that is

$$[(x_1 y_1) + (x_2, y_2)] + (x_3, y_3) = (x_1, y_1) + [(x_2, y_2) + (x_3, y_3)].$$

4. Show that $(x, y) + (0, 0) = (x, y)$ for all $(x, y) \in P$. What axiom of a field does this represent?

5. Show that $(x, y) + (-x, -y) = (0, 0)$ for all $(x, y) \in P$. What axiom of a field does this represent?

6. Explain why Eq. (13–7) holds.

7. Explain why Eq. (13–8) holds.

8. Show that Eq. (13–9) holds. What would this property be called?

9. Explain why Eq. (13–10) holds.

10. Show that the multiplication defined for ordered pairs by Eq. (13–11) is commutative, that is,

$$(x_1, y_1) \cdot (x_2, y_2) = (x_2, y_2) \cdot (x_1, y_1).$$

11. Show that this multiplication is associative, that is,

$$[(x_1, y_1) \cdot (x_2, y_2)] \cdot (x_3, y_3) = (x_1, y_1) \cdot [(x_2, y_2) \cdot (x_3, y_3)].$$

12. Show that $(x, y) \cdot (1, 0) = (x, y)$ for all $(x, y) \in P$. What axiom of a field does this represent?

13. Show that

$$(x, y) \cdot \left(\frac{x}{x^2 + y^2}, \frac{-y}{x^2 + y^2} \right) = (1, 0)$$

for all $(x, y) \in P$. What axiom of a field does this represent?

14. Show that the distributive axiom for the elements of P is satisfied.

15. Show that the multiplication of any ordered pair (x, y) by the ordered pair $(c, 0)$ is the same as multiplication by the scalar c, that is,

$$(x, y) \cdot (c, 0) = (cx, cy) = c(x, y).$$

16. Show that $(x, y) \cdot (0, 0) = (0, 0)$.

17. Show that $(x, y) = (y, x)$ if and only if $x = y$.

18. Show that $(0, 1)^2 = (0, 1) \cdot (0, 1) = (-1, 0)$.

Express each of the following as a single ordered pair.

19. $(0, 1)^4$ **20.** $(0, 1)^3$ **21.** $(0, 1)^8$ **22.** $(0, 1)^{100}$

Find the value of (x, y) in Problems 23 through 30.

23. $(x, y) = (2, 3) + (4, 5)$ **24.** $(x, y) = (-2, 1) + (3, -7)$

25. $(x, y) = (3, -1) - (4, -2)$ **26.** $(3, 1) = (x, y) + (5, -1)$

27. $(x, y) = (3, 1) \cdot (2, 3)$ **28.** $(x, y) = (-1, 2) \cdot (3, -5)$

29. $(x, y) = (2, -1)/(-1, 3)$ **30.** $(x, y) = (23, 11)/(5, -1)$

13–2 VECTORS

The notion of a vector in two dimensions* can be introduced in two ways. Before we define a vector, however, we will introduce the notation to be used. In this book we shall use boldface type such as **v**, **i**, or **v**$_1$, to identify a vector. Since the reader may have trouble in indicating such writing himself, it might be wise for him to indicate vectors by using small arrows over the letters. For example, the above vectors could be written $\overrightarrow{v}$, $\overrightarrow{i}$, or $\overrightarrow{v}_1$. We now make the following definitions.

Definition 13–5. A vector **v** is an ordered pair of real numbers (x, y).

The numbers x and y are called the *components* of **v**. We shall assume that these vectors (ordered pairs) obey the laws stated in Article 13–1 as Definitions 13–1, 13–2, and 13–3. As a result, these vectors obey any of the laws and have any of the properties which can be proved for this original, abstractly defined mathematical system. In this way a study of vectors may be developed without over-emphasizing the geometric interpretation. We shall also give a second

---

* In three dimensions, a definition similar to Definition 3–5 would involve an ordered triple (x, y, z). In fact, such a generalized definition can be given for any number of dimensions.

definition of a vector, that with a geometric representation, and learn how the two definitions may be considered as defining the same concept.

Definition 13–6. A vector **v** is a directed line segment of fixed length.

The directed line segment may be indicated by an arrow to show direction. It is customary to place the vector so that its initial end is "tied" or "bound" to the origin and its terminal end is located at the point (x, y) (see Fig. 13–1). Such a vector is called a *bound* vector and is in *standard position*, to distinguish it from a *free* vector, one which takes any position. We shall concern ourselves almost entirely with bound vectors.

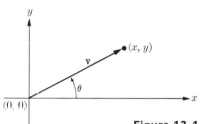

Figure 13–1

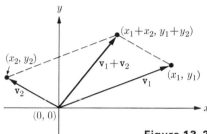

Figure 13–2

Let us make certain definitions for the algebraic concept of a vector as an ordered pair, and observe the geometric equivalence.

1a) If $v = (x, y)$, the *norm* of **v**, denoted by $|v|$, is defined by

$$|v| = \sqrt{x^2 + y^2}. \tag{13–14}$$

1g) The magnitude or length of the corresponding geometric vector or line segment between the points $(0, 0)$ and (x, y) is the distance given by Eq. (4–9) as $\sqrt{x^2 + y^2}$.

2a) The vector **0** is the zero vector $(0, 0)$. It has 0 for its norm and any convenient direction may be assigned to it.

2g) The corresponding geometric zero vector is a point, the origin.

3a) If $v = (x, y) \neq 0$, the *direction angle* of **v**, denoted by θ, is defined by

$$\cos \theta = \frac{x}{|v|}, \qquad \sin \theta = \frac{y}{|v|}, \qquad 0° \leq \theta < 360°.$$

3g) The angle that the geometric vector makes with the positive x-axis is considered to be the indication of the direction of the line segment, which can be expressed the same way, of course.

4a) In Definitions 13–1, 13–2, and 13–3, we stated certain algebraic properties for the set of vectors $V = \{v | v = (x, y) | x \text{ and } y \in R\}$.

4g) The sum (or *resultant*) of two geometric vectors, v_1 and v_2, is the geometric vector, $v_1 + v_2$, which emanates from the origin as do v_1 and v_2, and terminates at the opposite vertex of the parallelogram formed with its two sides coincident with v_1 and v_2 (see Fig. 13–2).

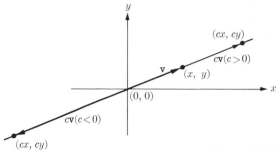

Figure 13–3

The product $c\mathbf{v}$ of a scalar and a geometric vector is a vector collinear with $\mathbf{v}$. Its magnitude is $|c|\,|\mathbf{v}|$, and its direction the same as that of $\mathbf{v}$, if $c > 0$, but opposite to that of $\mathbf{v}$, if $c < 0$. See Fig. 13–3.

Let us consider several examples.

Example 1. If $\mathbf{v}_1 = (2, -3)$, $c_1 = -2$, $\mathbf{v}_2 = (-1, 4)$, $c_2 = -3$, express each of the following vectors as an ordered pair and indicate your result graphically.

a) $c_1\mathbf{v}_1$ b) $c_2\mathbf{v}_2$ c) $c_1\mathbf{v}_1 + c_2\mathbf{v}_2$

Solution. a) $c_1\mathbf{v}_1 = -2(2, -3) = (-4, 6)$

b) $c_2\mathbf{v}_2 = -3(-1, 4) = (3, -12)$

c) $c_1\mathbf{v}_1 + c_2\mathbf{v}_2 = (-1, -6)$

The graphs are indicated in Fig. 13–4.

Example 2. If $\mathbf{v}_1 = (1, 1)$ and $\mathbf{v}_2 = (-2, 5)$, find the norm and the direction angle of

$$\mathbf{v}_1 - \mathbf{v}_2.$$

Solution. Since

$$\mathbf{v}_1 - \mathbf{v}_2 = (1, 1) - (-2, 5) = (3, -4),$$

we have

$$|\mathbf{v}_1 - \mathbf{v}_2| = \sqrt{(3)^2 + (-4)^2} = 5.$$

Also,

$$\cos\theta = \frac{3}{5} \quad \text{and} \quad \sin\theta = \frac{-4}{5},$$

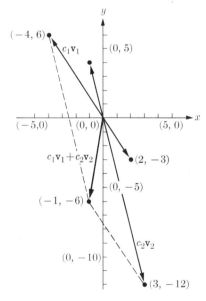

Figure 13–4

so that θ is in the fourth quadrant, and has the approximate value $\theta = 307°$.

It is important to emphasize that the definition and interpretation of vectors as ordered pairs is consistent with what we desire, if we assume the set of ordered pairs $P = \{(x, y)|x \text{ and } y \in R\}$ obeys the Definitions 13–1, 13–2, and 13–3.

PROBLEMS

Show graphically each of the vectors in Problems 1–6, and give their norms and direction angles (if trigonometric tables are available).

1. $v = (2, 3)$ 2. $v = (-3, 4)$ 3. $v = (1, -\sqrt{3})$

4. $u = (-2, -3)$ 5. $w = \left(\dfrac{-\sqrt{3}}{2}, \dfrac{1}{2}\right)$ 6. $v = (-4, 4)$

If $u = (-2, 3)$ and $v = (4, -1)$, find the norm and indicate the direction angle for each of the vectors given in Problems 7 and 8. If trigonometric tables are available, find θ (nearest degree).

7. a) $-u$ b) $2v$ c) $u + v$

8. a) $-v$ b) $u - 2v$ c) $-2u + 3v$

Find the vector expressed as an ordered pair, which has its norm and direction angle given in Problems 9–12.

9. $|v| = 1, \theta = 30°$ 10. $|v| = 4, \theta = 135°$

11. $|v| = 8, \theta - 270°$ 12. $|v| = 5, \theta - 120°$

If $u = (-2, 3)$, $v = (4, -1)$, $c = 2$, and $d = -3$, find the vector expressed as an ordered pair, indicated by each of the vectors in Problems 13–20, and show the result graphically.

13. $-cu$ 14. dv 15. $u - v$

16. $(c + d)u$ 17. $c(u + v)$ 18. $cu + dv$

19. $(c + d)(u - v)$ 20. $cd(du - cv)$

▶ 21. By definition, two vectors $v_1 = (x_1, y_1)$ and $v_2 = (x_2, y_2)$ are collinear if $v_1 = cv_2$ or $(x_1, y_1) = c(x_2, y_2)$. Show that $v_1 = (x_1, y_1)$ and $v_2 = (x_2, y_2)$ are collinear if and only if $x_1y_2 - x_2y_1 = 0$.

22. If $v_1 = (x_1, y_1)$ and $v_2 = (x_2, y_2)$ are not collinear, show that any vector $v_3 = (x_3, y_3)$ may be expressed as a linear combination of v_1 and v_2. *Hint:* It must be shown that there exist scalars c_1 and c_2 such that $v_3 = c_1v_1 + c_2v_2$, that is $(x_3, y_3) = c_1(x_1, y_1) + c_2(x_2, y_2)$. Use the results of Problem 21.

▶ 23. A special and yet most important application to the results stated in Problem 22 is represented by the situation where $v_1 = (1, 0)$ and $v_2 = (0, 1)$. If we let $i = (1, 0)$ and $j = (0, 1)$, show that any vector $v = (x, y)$ may be expressed $xi + yj$.

24. If we follow the idea stated in Problem 23, resolve (express) each of the following vectors into the sum of scalar multiples of i and j.
a) $(2, -3)$ b) $(-4, 3)$ c) $(5, 0)$
d) $(-2, 1)$ e) $(0, -2)$ f) $(0, 0)$

25. Find unit vectors in the same direction as each of the following vectors.
a) $(2, -3)$ b) $(-4, 3)$ c) $2(1, -3), -3(-2, 3)$
d) $5(-2, -3)$ e) $3i - 4j$ f) $-i - j$

▶ 26. Show that the two vectors $v_1 = x_1i + y_1j$ and $v_2 = x_2i + y_2j$ will be perpendicular if and only if $x_1x_2 + y_1y_2 = 0$.

By using the results obtained in Problem 26, tell which of the vectors in Problems 27 and 28 are perpendicular.

27. a) $v_1 = (2, 3)$ and $v_2 = (-2, \frac{4}{5})$

   b) $u_1 = (0, 2)$ and $u_2 = (-3, 0)$

28. a) $w_1 = 4i - \frac{2}{3}j$ and $w_2 = \frac{1}{8}i - \frac{3}{4}j$

   b) $z_1 = \dfrac{-\sqrt{3}}{2}i + \frac{1}{2}j$ and $z_2 = \dfrac{\sqrt{3}}{2}i + \frac{3}{2}j.$

29. a) Show that

$$v_1 = (-4, 3) \quad \text{and} \quad v_2 = (3, -4)$$

   are perpendicular vectors.

   b) Find scalars c_1 and c_2 so that $c_1 v_1$ and $c_2 v_2$ will be unit vectors.

   c) If $e_1 = c_1 v_1$ and $e_2 = c_2 v_2$ are used to express these two mutually perpendicular unit vectors, express $v = (5, -2)$ as a linear combination of e_1 and e_2.

30. Let (a, b) and (c, d) be fixed vectors. For any real scalar t such that $0 < t < 1$, let the vector $v = (x, y) = (1 - t)(a, b) + t(c, d)$. What can be said about the location of *point* (x, y) in relation to the *points* (a, b) and (c, d)?

13-3 COMPLEX NUMBERS

In Article 13-2, we discussed in some detail one of the interpretations of an algebra of ordered pairs, that of the notion of a set of vectors. That one, we emphasized, satisfied the properties listed in Definitions 13-1, 13-2, and 13-3. We now wish to consider an algebra of ordered pairs which, in addition to Definitions 13-1 and 13-2, satisfies the more general definition of multiplication given in Definition 13-4. This is the algebra of complex numbers. Here again we may make two definitions which are equivalent. The letter z is usually used to denote a complex number.

Definition 13-7. A complex number z is an ordered pair of real numbers (x, y).

The numbers x and y are called the *real part* and the *imaginary part* of the complex number. Let us repeat. We shall assume that these complex numbers (ordered pairs) obey the laws stated in Article 13-1 as Definitions 13-1, 13-2, and 13-4. An element of this set of complex numbers, denoted by C, where

$$C = \{z | z = (x, y), \ x \text{ and } y \in R\}, \tag{13-15}$$

may also be defined a second way.

Definition 13-8. A complex number z is any expression, written $x + yi$, where x and $y \in R$, and i has the property that $i^2 = -1$.

In either case, if $y = 0$, the complex number x or $(x, 0)$ is *real;* but if $y \neq 0$, the complex number is said to be *imaginary.* When $y \neq 0$ and $x = 0$, then yi or $(0, y)$ is a *pure imaginary number.*

With the numbers x and y obeying the ordinary laws for real numbers, and the new element i obeying the law

$$i^2 = -1,$$

the complex number $z = x + yi$ may be thought of as an abbreviation for the ordered pair (x, y). If the reader has encountered complex numbers previously, no doubt this is the notation that was used. To show that the two definitions are equivalent, we should verify that the complex numbers $x + yi$ satisfy the same laws as the ordered pairs $z = (x, y)$. This will be clear as we develop the set of complex numbers further, by using the notation $z = x + yi$. Specifically, in considering the sum of two complex numbers, we have

$$(x_1 + y_1i) + (x_2 + y_2i) = (x_1 + x_2) + (y_1 + y_2)i. \qquad (13\text{--}16)$$

The product of two complex numbers is given by

$$(x_1 + y_1i) \cdot (x_2 + y_2i) = x_1x_2 + x_1y_2i + x_2y_1i + y_1y_2i^2$$
$$= (x_1x_2 - y_1y_2) + (x_1y_2 + x_2y_1)i. \quad (13\text{--}17)$$

We see in this equation the reason for defining the product of two ordered pairs as in Eq. (13–11). The quotient of two complex numbers is given by

$$\frac{x_1 + y_1i}{x_2 + y_2i} = \frac{(x_1 + y_1i)(x_2 - y_2i)}{(x_2 + y_2i)(x_2 - y_2i)}$$

$$= \frac{x_1x_2 - x_1y_2i + x_2y_1i - y_1y_2i^2}{x_2^2 - x_2y_2i + x_2y_2i - y_2^2i^2}$$

$$= \frac{x_1x_2 + y_1y_2}{x_2^2 + y_2^2} + \frac{x_2y_1 - x_1y_2}{x_2^2 + y_2^2} i. \qquad (13\text{--}18)$$

Thus the complex numbers represented by the ordered pair (x, y) or the expression $x + yi$ may be regarded as equivalent.

Two complex numbers which differ only in the sign of their imaginary parts are called *conjugates* of each other. Thus $(3, 2)$ and $(3, -2)$, or $3 + 2i$ and $3 - 2i$ are conjugate complex numbers or, more generally, (x, y) and $(x, -y)$, that is, $x + yi$ and $x - yi$, are numbers of this type. (Note Problems 9 and 10.)

It is unfortunate that the word "imaginary" has been applied to the numbers $x + yi$ where $y \neq 0$. Although these numbers were originally introduced to solve quadratic equations, they have been extremely useful in physics and engineering, especially in the description of certain electrical phenomena. Used in these fields, the "imaginary" numbers have significance which is quite as real as that of the "real" numbers.

A few quadratic equations in Chapter 6 and other equations in Chapter 8 have imaginary numbers as solutions. These were given as square roots of negative numbers, with no additional explanation at that time. Graphically, we noticed that the functions involved had real zeros only where the corresponding curves crossed or touched the horizontal axis. We are now able to write such solutions in terms of the imaginary symbol i.

Example. Solve the equation $x^2 - 4x + 6 = 0$.

Solution. Using the quadratic formula Eq. (6–10), with $a = 1$, $b = -4$, and $c = 6$, we have

$$x = \frac{-(-4) \pm \sqrt{(-4)^2 - 4(1)(6)}}{2(1)}$$

$$= \frac{4 \pm \sqrt{16 - 24}}{2} = \frac{4 \pm \sqrt{-8}}{2}$$

$$= \frac{4 \pm 2\sqrt{-2}}{2} = 2 \pm \sqrt{2}\, i.$$

It is important to note that, although C is a field, it does not satisfy the Order Axioms given in Chapter 4, so that it is *not* an ordered field. (See Problem 18.)

PROBLEMS

In Problems 1 through 4, give the expression as a single complex number.

1. a) $(2 + 5i) + (4 - i)$ b) $(2 + 5i) - (4 - i)$

2. a) $(2 + 5i)(4 - i)$ b) $(2 + 5i)(4 + i)$

3. a) $\dfrac{2 + 5i}{4 - i}$ b) $\dfrac{2 + 5i}{4 + i}$

4. a) $i^3 = i \cdot i^2$ b) $i^4 = i^2 \cdot i^2$ c) i^5 d) $1/i$

5. Prove, for any positive integer n,

    a) $i^{4n} = 1$ b) $i^{4n+1} = i$ c) $i^{4n+2} = -1$

    d) $i^{4n+3} = -i$ e) $i^{n+4} = i^n$

6. State Problems 23, 27, and 29 of Article 13–1, interpreting the ordered pairs as complex numbers, and solve.

In Problems 7 through 10 use the ordinary properties of the real numbers and the fact that $i^2 = -1$ for one proof. Also, if possible, solve the problem using the algebra of ordered pairs, as defined for the set of complex numbers.

▶ **7.** If the complex number $x + yi = 0$, show algebraically that $x = 0$ and $y = 0$. *Hint:* Since $x = -yi$, $x^2 = -y^2$. What can be said about x and y?

8. If $x_1 + y_1i$ and $x_2 + y_2i$ are two complex numbers such that $x_1 + y_1i = x_2 + y_2i$, show by using algebra that $x_1 = x_2$ and $y_1 = y_2$. *Hint:* Transpose so that $x_1 - x_2 + (y_1 - y_2)i = 0$. Then use Problem 7.

9. Prove that the sum and product of two conjugate complex numbers are both real.

10. Prove that if the sum and product of two imaginary numbers are real, the numbers are conjugate complex numbers.

Solve the following equations, where some or all of the solutions may be imaginary.

11. $\dfrac{2x}{3} - 5i = 0$

12. $\dfrac{2x - 4i}{x + i} = 1$

13. $(2 + 5i)x + 2i = 0$

14. $\dfrac{ix}{2} = 3 - 4i$

15. $x^2 - (3 - i)x - 3i = 0$

16. $x^2 + ix - x - i = 0$

   Hint: Factor.

17. $ix^2 + 7x - 12i = 0$.

18. Show that the set of complex numbers C does not satisfy the four Order Axioms given in Chapter 4. *Hint:* Consider the complex numbers i and 0. If Axiom O1 is to be satisfied, either $i = 0$, $i > 0$, or $i < 0$.

   1) $i \neq 0$ since $i^2 = -1$, and $-1 \neq 0$.
   2) If $i > 0$, by Axiom O4 we may multiply both sides by i so that $i^2 > 0$ or $-1 > 0$. But this is impossible.
   3) If $i < 0$, what is the result?

Although C is not an ordered field (Problem 18, above) we can define the absolute value (or modulus) of a complex number and by this method prove certain interesting inequalities involving complex numbers.

Definition 13–9. If $z = x + yi$ is any complex number, where x and y are real, the *absolute value* of z, written $|z|$, is given by the expression

$$|z| = |x + yi| = \sqrt{x^2 + y^2}. \tag{13–19}$$

This definition is not surprising as we recall the norm of a vector or the length of a line segment.

It should be clear that this definition of absolute value is consistent with the definition given by Eq. (4–1), when the complex number z is real, that is, $y = 0$. We recall that

$$|x| = x \qquad \text{if } x \geq 0$$
$$|x| = -x \qquad \text{if } x < 0,$$

where x is real. If the complex number $z = x + yi$ is real $(y = 0)$, we have by Definition 13–9, $z = \sqrt{x^2}$. But $\sqrt{x^2} = |x|$ by Definition 4–4, so that the two definitions are consistent.

In the following problems, let us denote any complex number $x + yi = (x, y)$ by z, and its conjugate $x - yi = (x, -y)$ by $\bar{z}$.

PROBLEMS

1. The complex number $z = 0$ if and only if $|z| = 0$. Recall Problem 7 in the first list of problems in this article.

2. Show that $|z| = |\bar{z}|$.

3. Show that the conjugate of the conjugate of a complex number is the number itself, that is, $\bar{\bar{z}} = z$.

4. Show that $z \cdot \bar{z} = |z|^2$.

5. Show that the sum of the conjugate of two complex numbers is the conjugate of their sum, that is, $\bar{z}_1 + \bar{z}_2 = \overline{z_1 + z_2}$.

6. Show that the product of the conjugate of two complex numbers is the conjugate of their product, that is, $\bar{z}_1 \cdot \bar{z}_2 = \overline{z_1 \cdot z_2}$.

7. For any complex number $z = x + iy$, show that $x \leq |z|$ and $y \leq |z|$.

8. For any complex number $z = x + iy$, show that $z + \bar{z} = 2x$.

9. Show that for any two complex numbers, the absolute value of the product is the product of the absolute values, that is, $|z_1 \cdot z_2| = |z_1| \cdot |z_2|$.   *Hint:* By using Problem 4, we have $|z_1 \cdot z_2|^2 = (z_1 \cdot z_2)(\overline{z_1 \cdot z_2})$.   But $\overline{z_1 \cdot z_2} = \bar{z}_1 \cdot \bar{z}_2$ by Problem 6, so that $|z_1 \cdot z_2|^2 = z_1 \cdot \bar{z}_1 \cdot z_2 \cdot \bar{z}_2 = |z_1|^2 \cdot |z_2|^2$.

10. It is possible to show that for any two complex numbers, the absolute value of their sum is less than or equal to the sum of their absolute values, that is, $|z_1 + z_2| \leq |z_1| + |z_2|$.   Give the reasons for each step in the following proof.

$$|z_1 + z_2|^2 = (z_1 + z_2)(\overline{z_1 + z_2}) = (z_1 + z_2)(\bar{z}_1 + \bar{z}_2)$$
$$= z_1\bar{z}_1 + z_2\bar{z}_1 + z_1\bar{z}_2 + z_2\bar{z}_2.$$

Now $z_1\bar{z}_2$ and $z_2\bar{z}_1$ are conjugates, so that

$$z_1\bar{z}_2 + z_2\bar{z}_1 = 2 \text{ (real part of } z_1\bar{z}_2)$$
$$\leq 2|z_1 \cdot \bar{z}_2|$$
$$= 2|z_1| \cdot |\bar{z}_2|$$
$$= 2|z_1| \cdot |z_2|.$$

Therefore, we have

$$|z_1 + z_2|^2 \leq z_1\bar{z}_1 + 2|z_1| \cdot |z_2| + z_2\bar{z}_2$$
$$= |z_1|^2 + 2|z_1| \cdot |z_2| + |z_2|^2 = (|z_1| + |z_2|)^2,$$

so that $|z_1 + z_2| \leq |z_1| + |z_2|$.

13–4 COMPLEX ROOTS OF AN EQUATION

In an example of the preceding article the roots of the equation were the two conjugate imaginary numbers $2 + \sqrt{2}\,i$ and $2 - \sqrt{2}\,i$.   In any polynomial equation with real coefficients, such roots always occur in pairs.   This result may be stated as a fundamental theorem.

Theorem 13–1. If the complex number $a + bi$, $b \neq 0$, is a root of the polynomial equation

$$f(x) = a_0 x^n + a_1 x^{n-1} + a_2 x^{n-2} + \cdots + a_{n-1}x + a_n = 0, \quad (13\text{–}20)$$

where $a_0 \neq 0$, n is a positive integer, and a_i are real constants, then its conjugate $a - bi$ is also a root.

Proof. Since $a + bi$ is a root of $f(x) = 0$, $a + bi$ is a factor of $f(x)$.   Let us divide $f(x)$ by the product $[x - (a + bi)][x - (a - bi)] \equiv x^2 - 2ax + a^2 + b^2$

until the remainder is of degree less than $x^2 - 2ax + a^2 + b^2$. The remainder will therefore be of the first degree at most. Symbolically, this can be expressed

$$\frac{f(x)}{x^2 - 2ax + a^2 + b^2} \equiv q(x) + \frac{Rx + S}{x^2 - 2ax + a^2 + b^2}, \qquad (13\text{–}21)$$

or

$$f(x) \equiv [x^2 - 2ax + a^2 + b^2]q(x) + Rx + S,$$

where R and S are real constants. Since this equality is true for all x, it is true for $x = a + bi$. Thus,

$$f(a + bi) = 0 \cdot q(a + bi) + R(a + bi) + S = 0.$$

Consequently, by the property stated in Problem 7 in the first list of problems in Article 13–2,

$$Ra + S = 0 \quad \text{and} \quad Rbi = 0.$$

Since $b \neq 0$, $R = 0$, and therefore $S = 0$, which shows that the division in Eq. (13–21) is exact. Hence $a - bi$ is also a factor of $f(x)$; that is, $a - bi$ is a root of $f(x) = 0$.

As a result of the theorem, we note several properties of the roots of Eq. (13–20). (1) The imaginary roots of such an equation occur in pairs. (2) Any such equation has an even number of imaginary roots. (3) If the degree of such an equation is odd, the equation has at least one real root.

PROBLEMS

Find the third-degree equation with integral coefficients having the given numbers as roots.

1. $3, 2 - i$ 2. $-4, 6i$

3. $\frac{1}{2}, -5 + i$ 4. $\frac{3}{2}, i - 4$

5. $-\frac{1}{3}, 3 + \sqrt{2}\,i$ 6. $\frac{2}{3}, (-3 + \sqrt{5}\,i)/2$

Solve the following equations given the one root in parentheses. *Hint:* Use division.

7. $x^3 - 4x^2 + 9x - 36 = 0$, $(3i)$

8. $2x^3 + 9x^2 + 14x + 5 = 0$, $(-2 + i)$

9. $x^3 - 8x^2 + 23x - 22 = 0$, $(3 - \sqrt{2}\,i)$

10. $2x^3 - 8x^2 + 11x - 5 = 0$, $\frac{1}{2}(3 + i)$

13–5 GRAPHICAL REPRESENTATION OF COMPLEX NUMBERS*

The interpretation of the ordered pair (x, y) as the complex number $x + yi$ lends itself to a simple graphical representation of the complex numbers. Since (x, y) may be plotted as a point in the rectangular coordinate system, every complex number $x + yi$ may be associated with some point in the plane, and every point in the plane with some complex number. This plane is called the *complex plane*,

---

* Articles 13–5 and 13–6 assume a knowledge of trigonometry, and may be omitted.

and the figure on which the complex numbers are plotted is called the *Argand diagram*.* As a result, one can represent the complex numbers or their sums and differences graphically, just as in the case of vectors. In fact, the representations will be identical. The real numbers lie on the *x*-axis, the pure imaginaries on the *y*-axis, and a number such as $5 - 2i$ is represented by the point $(5, -2)$.

Example 1. If $z_1 = -2 + 3i$ and $z_2 = 5 - i$, find $z_1 + z_2$, and show graphically z_1, z_2, and $z_1 + z_2$.

Solution. 1) $(-2 + 3i) + (5 - i) = (-2 + 5) + (3 - 1)i$

$$= 3 + 2i.$$

2) $(-2, 3) + (5, -1) = (3, 2).$

For the graph, see Fig. 13–5.

Any point $P(x, y)$ in the plane, other than $(0, 0)$, lies on some circle with center at $(0, 0)$ and radius r, where $r = \sqrt{x^2 + y^2}$. Let θ be the angle in standard position having OP as its terminal side (see Fig. 13–6), so that

$$x = r \cos \theta, \qquad y = r \sin \theta. \tag{13–22}$$

Thus the complex number, $x + yi$, may be written in trigonometric form,

$$x + yi = r (\cos \theta + i \sin \theta). \tag{13–23}†$$

Since $\sin \theta$ and $\cos \theta$ are both periodic with period $2\pi = 360°$, for $r > 0$ and any integer k,

$$r[\cos (\theta + k\, 360°) + i \sin (\theta + k\, 360°)]$$

is also a trigonometric form for $x + yi$. We note that r must be greater than zero. The value

$$r = \sqrt{x^2 + y^2} \tag{13–24}$$

we recall is called the *absolute value* or *modulus* of $x + yi$. The angle θ is called the *amplitude* or *argument* of $x + yi$.

Example 2. Express the complex number $-2 - 2i$ in trigonometric form.

Solution. By locating the point $(-2, -2)$ which corresponds to $-2 - 2i$ (see Fig. 13–7), we have

$$r = \sqrt{(-2)^2 + (-2)^2} = 2\sqrt{2}$$

---

* The system of representing complex numbers graphically was discovered independently by Wessel (Norwegian), Argand (French), and Gauss (German), about 1800.
† The form $r(\cos \theta + i \sin \theta)$ is sometimes abbreviated r cis θ.

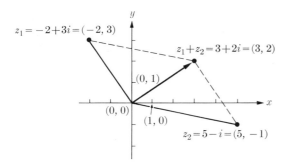

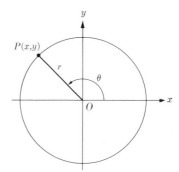

Figure 13–5   **Figure 13–6**

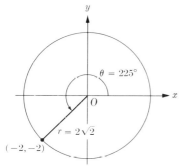

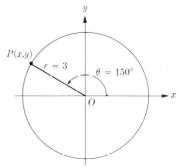

Figure 13–7   **Figure 13–8**

and $\tan \theta = 1$, with θ terminating in the third quadrant. Thus,

$$\theta = 225°, \quad \text{and} \quad -2 - 2i = 2\sqrt{2}(\cos 225° + i \sin 225°).$$

Example 3. Express the complex number $3(\cos 150° + i \sin 150°)$ in the form $x + yi$.

Solution. On the terminal side of the angle of 150°, in standard position, locate the point P three units from the origin, as in Fig. 13–8. Since $P(x, y)$ represents the complex number, we have

$$x = 3 \cos 150° = \frac{-3\sqrt{3}}{2} \quad \text{and} \quad y = 3 \sin 150° = \frac{3}{2}.$$

Hence,

$$3(\cos 150° + i \sin 150°) = -\frac{3\sqrt{3}}{2} + \frac{3}{2} i.$$

One of the advantages of the trigonometric form for complex numbers is its usefulness in obtaining products. By letting $r_1(\cos \theta_1 + i \sin \theta_1)$ and $r_2(\cos \theta_2 + i \sin \theta_2)$ be two complex numbers, we have the following theorem.

Theorem 13–2. The modulus of the product of two complex numbers is the product of the moduli, and the amplitude is the sum of the amplitudes.

Proof

$r_1(\cos \theta_1 + i \sin \theta_1) \cdot r_2 (\cos \theta_2 + i \sin \theta_2)$

$\quad = r_1 r_2 (\cos \theta_1 \cos \theta_2 + i \cos \theta_1 \sin \theta_2 + i \sin \theta_1 \cos \theta_2 + i^2 \sin \theta_1 \sin \theta_2)$

$\quad = r_1 r_2 [(\cos \theta_1 \cos \theta_2 - \sin \theta_1 \sin \theta_2) + i(\sin \theta_1 \cos \theta_2 + \cos \theta_1 \sin \theta_2)]$

$\quad = r_1 r_2 [\cos (\theta_1 + \theta_2) + i \sin (\theta_1 + \theta_2)].$ \hfill (13–25)

Example 4. Find the complex number w which is the product of the two complex numbers $z = x + yi = (x, y)$ and $i = (0, 1)$. Using vectors, show that w is a vector perpendicular to z, but with the same magnitude.

Solution. The first part of this example can be carried out by three methods.

a) With the use of algebra only, we have

$$w = i(x + iy) = ix + i^2 y = -y + ix.$$

b) By Definition 13–4, $w = (0, 1) \cdot (x, y) = (0x - 1y, 0y + x1) = (-y, x).$

c) If we put each of the numbers in complex form, we get

$$i = \cos 90° + i \sin 90° \quad \text{and} \quad x + iy = r(\cos \theta + i \sin \theta).$$

We may now make use of Theorem 13–2 and find

$$w = r \cos \big((\theta + 90°) + i \sin (\theta + 90°)\big)$$
$$= r(-\sin \theta + i \cos \theta)$$
$$= -y + ix.$$

In order to show that w is perpendicular to z and has the same magnitude, we need merely to observe the first expression for w in (c). In fact, this indicates that multiplication by i is analogous to 90° counterclockwise rotation of a complex number about the origin.

PROBLEMS

1. Locate the point representing graphically each of the following complex numbers. Give the trigonometric form for each, using the least positive or zero value of its amplitude.

   a) 2 \hspace{3cm} b) -2 \hspace{3cm} c) $3i$

   d) $-i$ \hspace{2.7cm} e) $2 - 2i$ \hspace{2.5cm} f) $-2 + 2i$

   g) $-\dfrac{1}{2} + \dfrac{\sqrt{3}}{2} i$ \hspace{2cm} h) $-\dfrac{1}{2} - \dfrac{\sqrt{3}}{2} i$

2. Express each of the following in the form $x + yi$.

   a) $3(\cos 0° + i \sin 0°)$ \hspace{2.5cm} b) $2(\cos 90° + i \sin 90°)$

   c) $\cos 180° + i \sin 180°$ \hspace{2.3cm} d) $2(\cos 225° + i \sin 225°)$

   e) $2(\cos 270° + i \sin 270°)$ \hspace{2cm} f) $8(\cos 135° + i \sin 135°)$

   g) $4(\cos 300° + i \sin 300°)$ \hspace{2cm} h) $6(\cos 150° + i \sin 150°)$

3. Perform the indicated multiplications, expressing the final result in the form $x + yi$. Check your result by expressing each of the given numbers in the form $x + yi$ and then performing the multiplication algebraically.

a) $3(\cos 60° + i \sin 60°) \cdot 2(\cos 30° + i \sin 30°)$

b) $4(\cos 120° + i \sin 120°) \cdot 2(\cos 90° + i \sin 90°)$

c) $3(\cos 135° + i \sin 135°) \cdot 4[\cos (-45°) + i \sin (-45°)]$

d) $[2(\cos 120° + i \sin 120°)]^3$

▶ 4. Prove that the quotient of the two complex numbers $r_1(\cos \theta_1 + i \sin \theta_1)$ and $r_2(\cos \theta_2 + i \sin \theta_2)$ is given by

$$\frac{r_1}{r_2} [\cos (\theta_1 - \theta_2) + i \sin (\theta_1 - \theta_2)]. \qquad (13\text{–}26)$$

5. Use Eq. (13–26) to perform the following divisions. Check as in Problem 3.

a) $4(\cos 60° + i \sin 60°) \div 2(\cos 30° + i \sin 30°)$

b) $6(\cos 0° + i \sin 0°) \div 3(\cos 240° + i \sin 240°)$

6. Prove that the reciprocal of $r (\cos \theta + i \sin \theta)$ is

$$\frac{1}{r} (\cos \theta - i \sin \theta).$$

7. Prove that $[r(\cos \theta + i \sin \theta)]^2 = r^2(\cos 2\theta + i \sin 2\theta)$.

As we have noted, the graphical representation is the same whether it be of a geometric vector or a complex number. This is also true for sums and differences.

8. a) Explain why the last statement in the solution of Example 4, multiplication of $z = (x, y)$ by i, is also equivalent to counterclockwise rotation of the corresponding vector $\mathbf{v} = (x, y)$ through an angle of 90°.

b) If the vector represented by the ordered pair (x, y) is rotated counterclockwise through an angle α, give its ordered pair representation when $\alpha = 90°$, 180°, $-90°$. Indicate each of these graphically.

▶ 9. a) Show that the product of two complex numbers $z_1 = x_1 + y_1 i$ and $z_2 = x_2 + y_2 i$ can be written as the sum of the two complex numbers

$$x_2(x_1 + y_1 i)$$

and

$$y_2(-y_1 + x_1 i).$$

b) Writing the result of (a) in terms of ordered pairs, $x_2(x_1, y_1) + y_2(-y_1, x_1)$, consider this expression as the sum (or resultant) of two vectors. Give a geometric interpretation for the product of two complex numbers in terms of their corresponding vectors. A graph appears in Fig. 13–9.

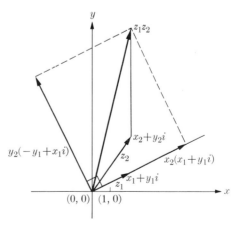

Figure 13–9

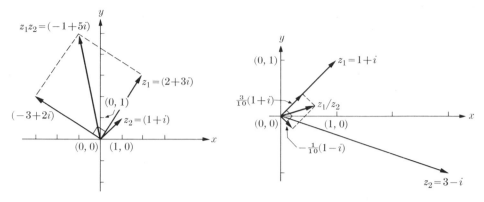

Figure 13–10   Figure 13–11

10. Express the following complex number products as the sum of two complex numbers, as indicated in Problem 9. Show the results graphically. Figure 13–10 shows part (a).

a) $z_1z_2 = (2 + 3i)(1 + i)$ b) $z_1z_2 = (-2 + i)(3 - 2i)$

c) $z_1z_2 = (2, 3)(1, 4)$

▶ **11.** a) Show that the quotient of two complex numbers $z_1 = x_1 + y_1i$ and $z_2 = x_2 + y_2i$ can be written as the sum of two complex numbers:

$$\frac{z_1}{z_2} = \frac{x_1 + y_1i}{x_2 + y_2i} = \frac{x_2}{x_2^2 + y_2^2}(x_1 + y_1i) + \frac{y_2}{x_2^2 + y_2^2}(y_1 - x_1i).$$

b) Give a geometric interpretation for the quotient of two complex numbers in terms of their corresponding vectors. See Fig. 13–11.

12. Express the following complex number quotients as the sum of two complex numbers, as indicated in Problem 11. Show the results graphically. Figure 13–11 shows part (a).

a) $\dfrac{z_1}{z_2} = \dfrac{1 + i}{3 - i}$ b) $\dfrac{z_1}{z_2} = \dfrac{(-1, 4)}{(2, -3)}$

c) $\dfrac{z_1}{z_2} = \dfrac{(-2, 1)}{(3, -2)}$

13–6 POWERS AND ROOTS OF COMPLEX NUMBERS

In Article 13–5, we obtained an expression for the product of two complex numbers in trigonometric form. By using Eq. (13–25), we immediately have

$$[r(\cos \theta + i \sin \theta)]^2 = r^2(\cos 2\theta + i \sin 2\theta),$$

and then,

$$[r(\cos \theta + i \sin \theta)]^3 = r^3(\cos 3\theta + i \sin 3\theta).$$

In fact, we can prove by mathematical induction a general theorem known as De Moivre's Theorem, discovered by Abraham De Moivre (1667–1754).

Theorem 13–3. If n is any positive integer,

$$[r(\cos \theta + i \sin \theta)]^n = r^n(\cos n\theta + i \sin n\theta). \qquad (13\text{–}27)$$

This theorem holds for rational, irrational, and even complex values of the exponent, but we shall make use of it only with integral values.

Proof. Part (a). Verification. This has been done at the beginning of this article.
     Part (b). Assuming

$$[r(\cos \theta + i \sin \theta)]^k = r^k(\cos k\theta + i \sin k\theta), \qquad (13\text{–}28)$$

we must show

$$[r(\cos \theta + i \sin \theta)]^{k+1} = r^{k+1}[\cos(k + 1)\theta + i \sin (k + 1)\theta]. \quad (13\text{–}29)$$

Multiplying each member of Eq. (13–28) by $r(\cos \theta + i \sin \theta)$, we have

$$[r(\cos \theta + i \sin \theta)]^{k+1} = r^k(\cos k\theta + i \sin k\theta)r(\cos \theta + i \sin \theta),$$

and by Eq. (13–25),

$$[r(\cos \theta + i \sin \theta)]^{k+1} = r^{k+1}[\cos (k\theta + \theta) + i \sin (k\theta + \theta)]$$
$$= r^{k+1}[\cos (k + 1)\theta + i \sin (k + 1)\theta],$$

which is exactly Eq. (13–29).
     Part (c) follows immediately.

Example 1. Show that $z^3 = 1$ if $z = -\frac{1}{2} + (\sqrt{3}/2)i$.

Solution. Putting z in trigonometric form, we have

$$z = \cos 120° + i \sin 120°.$$

Thus,

$$z^3 = (\cos 120° + i \sin 120°)^3$$
$$= \cos 3(120°) + i \sin 3(120°)$$
$$= \cos 360° + i \sin 360° = 1.$$

A more important use of Eq. (13–27) is made in finding the roots of complex numbers. In our discussion we should recall that for r positive the notation $\sqrt[n]{r}$ represents the principal nth root of r, that is, the only nth root of r which is positive and real.

Example 2. Find the three cube roots of $-2 - 2\sqrt{3}\, i$.

Solution. We wish to find values of r and θ such that

$$[r(\cos \theta + i \sin \theta)]^3 = -2 - 2\sqrt{3}\, i.$$

If we use Theorem 13–3, and express $-2 - 2\sqrt{3}\, i$ in trigonometric form, this becomes

$$r^3(\cos 3\theta + i \sin 3\theta) = 4(\cos 240° + i \sin 240°).$$

When two complex numbers are equal, their moduli are equal and their amplitudes are either equal or differ by integral multiples of 360°. Thus,

$$r^3 = 4 \qquad \text{and} \qquad 3\theta = 240° + k\,360°,$$

or

$$r = \sqrt[3]{4} \qquad \text{and} \qquad \theta = 80° + k\,120°,$$

where k is any positive or negative integer, or zero. Hence,

$$r(\cos\theta + i\sin\theta)$$

will be

$$\sqrt[3]{4}(\cos\ 80° + i\sin\ 80°), \qquad \text{for} \quad k = 0,$$

$$\sqrt[3]{4}(\cos 200° + i\sin 200°), \qquad \text{for} \quad k = 1,$$

$$\sqrt[3]{4}(\cos 320° + i\sin 320°), \qquad \text{for} \quad k = 2.$$

These three values are all distinct, and they represent the three different cube roots of $-2 - 2\sqrt{3}\,i$. For any other integral value of k, the expression will reduce to one of these three values, so that these three numbers are the only cube roots. A complex number has three and only three cube roots, four and only four fourth roots, and in general, n and only n nth roots. Should it be required to reduce our answers to the form $x + yi$, we can use tables to find $\sqrt[3]{4}$ and the values of the functions of 80°, 200°, and 320°.

The general theorem concerning such roots should now be apparent.

Theorem 13–4. For any complex number $r(\cos\theta + i\sin\theta)$ and any positive integer n,

$$\sqrt[n]{r}(\cos\theta_k + i\sin\theta_k), \qquad\qquad (13\text{–}30)$$

where

$$\theta_k = \frac{\theta + k360°}{n}, \qquad k = 0, 1, 2, \ldots (n-1),$$

represents the n distinct nth roots of $r(\cos\theta + i\sin\theta)$.

Proof. To show that Eq. (13–30) is an nth root of $r\,(\cos\theta + i\sin\theta)$ for each k, we merely use Eq. (13–27) to raise it to the nth power:

$$[\sqrt[n]{r}(\cos\theta_k + i\sin\theta_k)]^n = r(\cos n\theta_k + i\sin n\theta_k)$$

$$= r[\cos(\theta + k\,360°) + i\sin(\theta + k\,360°)]$$

$$= r(\cos\theta + i\sin\theta).$$

Also, we must note that the n complex numbers given by Eq. (13–30) for the n different values of k are distinct, since no two of their amplitudes differ by a multiple of 360°.

The use of Eq. (13–30) will enable us to find the n nth roots of any complex number directly by substitution.

PROBLEMS

Write each of the expressions in Problems 1 through 7 in the form $x + yi$.

1. $[2(\cos 15° + i \sin 15°)]^6$ **2.** $[3(\cos 120° + i \sin 120°)]^5$

3. $[2(\cos 315° + i \sin 315°)]^3$ **4.** $(\cos 36° + i \sin 36°)^{10}$

5. $\left(-\dfrac{\sqrt{3}}{2} + \dfrac{i}{2}\right)^5$ **6.** $(1 - i)^8$ **7.** $\left(\dfrac{1}{\sqrt{2}} + \dfrac{i}{\sqrt{2}}\right)^{200}$

Find and represent graphically the required roots in Problems 8 through 15.

8. The square roots of $4 + 4\sqrt{3}\,i$ **9.** The square roots of $-16i$

10. The cube roots of 1   **11.** The cube roots of -8

12. The fourth roots of $4 - 4\sqrt{3}\,i$

13. The fourth roots of $16 (\cos 120° + i \sin 120°)$

14. The cube roots of $8 (\cos 300° + i \sin 300°)$

15. The tenth roots of 1

Solve the equations in Problems 16 through 19, expressing the roots in the form $x + yi$, and represent them graphically.

16. $z^6 = 64$ **17.** $z^4 = 1$ **18.** $z^3 + i = 0$ **19.** $z^5 + 32 = 0$

REVIEW PROBLEMS

1. Prove that the following is valid for all positive integral values of n:

$$1 \cdot 3 + 2 \cdot 4 + 3 \cdot 5 + \cdots + n(n + 2) = \frac{n(n + 1)(2n + 7)}{6}.$$

2. Prove by mathematical induction that

$$\frac{10^n}{3} + \frac{5}{3} + 4^{n+2}$$

is divisible by 3.

3. A vacuum pump removes one-fifth of the air in a container with each stroke. What part of the air has been removed after 6 strokes? How many strokes are required to remove 80% of the air?

4. Which of the following are true?

a) $\dfrac{\log a}{\log b} = \log a - \log b$ b) $\dfrac{\log a}{\log b} = \log \left(\dfrac{a}{b}\right)$

c) $\dfrac{\log a}{b} = \log \dfrac{a}{b}$ d) $\dfrac{\log a}{b} = \log (a^{1/b})$

e) $\dfrac{\log a}{b} = (\log a)^{1/b}$

5. Prove that for all integers $n > 3$,

$$(n + 1)^n < n^{n+1}.$$

6. Solve Problem 18, Article 12–3, if middle tenths are erased rather than middle thirds.

7. Sketch a graph of the function

$$E = \left\{ (x, y) \,\middle|\, y = \frac{2^x + 2^{-x}}{2} \right\}.$$

Hint: Consider the equations $y = 2^x/2$ and $y = 2^{-x}/2$.

8. Determine whether

$$\log \left(\frac{x + \sqrt{x^2 - 4}}{2} \right)$$

is identical to

a) $\log \left(\dfrac{x}{2} \right) + \log \dfrac{\sqrt{x^2 - 4}}{2}$ b) $\log \dfrac{x + \frac{1}{2}(x^2 + 4)}{2}$

c) $\log (x + \sqrt{x^2 - 4}) - \log 2$ d) $\frac{1}{2} \log x + \frac{1}{4} \log (x^2 - 4)$

9. Determine whether

$$\log \sqrt{\frac{1 + x}{1 - x}}$$

is identical to

a) $\log \sqrt{1 + x} - \log \sqrt{1 - x}$ b) $\log (1 + \sqrt{x}) - \log (1 - \sqrt{x})$

c) $\log \sqrt{x} - \log (-\sqrt{x})$ d) $\frac{1}{2} \log \dfrac{1 + x}{1 - x}$

e) $\frac{1}{2} \log (1 + x) - \frac{1}{2} \log (1 - x)$

10. Find the amount on deposit at the end of 12 years on an original principal of $6000 at 6%

a) compounded annually   b) compounded quarterly

c) compounded monthly   d) compounded daily

11. Consider the matrix

$$J = \begin{bmatrix} 0 & 1 \\ -1 & 0 \end{bmatrix}.$$

Determine $J^2 (=J \times J)$, J^3, J^4, and J^5, and express in terms of I, the identity matrix, and J. Do these seem to parallel any multiplications involving complex numbers? (See Problem 4, Article 13–3.)

12. Find real values of x and y such that

$$(x - 3yi)(i + 4) = 10 - 23i.$$

Hint: Recall Problem 7, Article 13–3.

13. Find a fifth degree equation with integral coefficients having the numbers 4, $2 - i$, and $3 + 2i$ as roots.

14. Let p_1 (an ordered pair) $= (3, -2)$, and $p_2 = (1, 4)$. Find an ordered pair equal to

a) $p_1 + p_2$ b) $p_1 - p_2$ c) $p_1 p_2$ d) p_1/p_2

15. Express the complex number $(1 - i)^4(2 + 2i)^3$ in the form $x + iy$.

16. Sketch the graph of

a) $\left\{(x, y)|y = \log \dfrac{4}{x^2}, \ 1 \le x \le 3\right\}$

b) $\{(x, y)|y = \log \sqrt{1 - x^2}, \ -\tfrac{1}{2} \le x \le \tfrac{1}{2}\}$

17. For what values of x is $\dfrac{\log 5x}{\log 3x}$

    a) positive?   b) negative?   c) zero?

18. If

$$z_1 = 6(\cos 135° + i \sin 135°)$$

and

$$z_2 = 12(\cos 15° + i \sin 15°),$$

express z_1/z_2 in the form $x + iy$.

TABLES

Table I Powers and roots

No.	Sq.	Sq. Root	Cube	Cube Root	No.	Sq.	Sq. Root	Cube	Cube Root
1	1	1.000	1	1.000	51	2,601	7.141	132,651	3.708
2	4	1.414	8	1.260	52	2,704	7.211	140,608	3.733
3	9	1.732	27	1.442	53	2,809	7.280	148,877	3.756
4	16	2.000	64	1.587	54	2,916	7.348	157,464	3.780
5	25	2.236	125	1.710	55	3,025	7.416	166,375	3.803
6	36	2.449	216	1.817	56	3,136	7.483	175,616	3.826
7	49	2.646	343	1.913	57	3,249	7.550	185,193	3.849
8	64	2.828	512	2.000	58	3,364	7.616	195,112	3.871
9	81	3.000	729	2.080	59	3,481	7.681	205,379	3.893
10	100	3.162	1,000	2.154	60	3,600	7.746	216,000	3.915
11	121	3.317	1,331	2.224	61	3,721	7.810	226,981	3.936
12	144	3.464	1,728	2.289	62	3,844	7.874	238,328	3.958
13	169	3.606	2,197	2.351	63	3,969	7.937	250,047	3.979
14	196	3.742	2,744	2.410	64	4,096	8.000	262,144	4.000
15	225	3.873	3,375	2.466	65	4,225	8.062	274,625	4.021
16	256	4.000	4,096	2.520	66	4,356	8.124	287,496	4.041
17	289	4.123	4,913	2.571	67	4,489	8.185	300,763	4.062
18	324	4.243	5,832	2.621	68	4,624	8.246	314,432	4.082
19	361	4.359	6,859	2.668	69	4,761	8.307	328,509	4.102
20	400	4.472	8,000	2.714	70	4,900	8.367	343,000	4.121
21	441	4.583	9,261	2.759	71	5,041	8.426	357,911	4.141
22	484	4.690	10,648	2.802	72	5,184	8.485	373,248	4.160
23	529	4.796	12,167	2.844	73	5,329	8.544	389,017	4.179
24	576	4.899	13,824	2.884	74	5,476	8.602	405,224	4.198
25	625	5.000	15,625	2.924	75	5,625	8.660	421,875	4.217
26	676	5.099	17,576	2.962	76	5,776	8.718	438,976	4.236
27	729	5.196	19,683	3.000	77	5,929	8.775	456,533	4.254
28	784	5.292	21,952	3.037	78	6,084	8.832	474,552	4.273
29	841	5.385	24,389	3.072	79	6,241	8.888	493,039	4.291
30	900	5.477	27,000	3.107	80	6,400	8.944	512,000	4.309
31	961	5.568	29,791	3.141	81	6,561	9.000	531,441	4.327
32	1,024	5.657	32,768	3.175	82	6,724	9.055	551,368	4.344
33	1,089	5.745	35,937	3.208	83	6,889	9.110	571,787	4.362
34	1,156	5.831	39,304	3.240	84	7,056	9.165	592,704	4.380
35	1,225	5.916	42,875	3.271	85	7,225	9.220	614,125	4.397
36	1,296	6.000	46,656	3.302	86	7,396	9.274	636,056	4.414
37	1,369	6.083	50,653	3.332	87	7,569	9.327	658,503	4.431
38	1,444	6.164	54,872	3.362	88	7,744	9.381	681,472	4.448
39	1,521	6.245	59,319	3.391	89	7,921	9.434	704,969	4.465
40	1,600	6.325	64,000	3.420	90	8,100	9.487	729,000	4.481
41	1,681	6.403	68,921	3.448	91	8,281	9.539	753,571	4.498
42	1,764	6.481	74,088	3.476	92	8,464	9.592	778,688	4.514
43	1,849	6.557	79,507	3.503	93	8,649	9.644	804,357	4.531
44	1,936	6.633	85,184	3.530	94	8,836	9.695	830,584	4.547
45	2,025	6.708	91,125	3.557	95	9,025	9.747	857,375	4.563
46	2,116	6.782	97,336	3.583	96	9,216	9.798	884,736	4.579
47	2,209	6.856	103,823	3.609	97	9,409	9.849	912,673	4.595
48	2,304	6.928	110,592	3.634	98	9,604	9.899	941,192	4.610
49	2,401	7.000	117,649	3.659	99	9,801	9.950	970,299	4.626
50	2,500	7.071	125,000	3.684	100	10,000	10.000	1,000,000	4.642

Table II Logarithms of numbers

N	0	1	2	3	4	5	6	7	8	9
1.0	.0000	.0043	.0086	.0128	.0170	.0212	.0253	.0294	.0334	.0374
1.1	.0414	.0453	.0492	.0531	.0569	.0607	.0645	.0682	.0719	.0755
1.2	.0792	.0828	.0864	.0899	.0934	.0969	.1004	.1038	.1072	.1106
1.3	.1139	.1173	.1206	.1239	.1271	.1303	.1335	.1367	.1399	.1430
1.4	.1461	.1492	.1523	.1553	.1584	.1614	.1644	.1673	.1703	.1732
1.5	.1761	.1790	.1818	.1847	.1875	.1903	.1931	.1959	.1987	.2014
1.6	.2041	.2068	.2095	.2122	.2148	.2175	.2201	.2227	.2253	.2279
1.7	.2304	.2330	.2355	.2380	.2405	.2430	.2455	.2480	.2504	.2529
1.8	.2553	.2577	.2601	.2625	.2648	.2672	.2695	.2718	.2742	.2765
1.9	.2788	.2810	.2833	.2856	.2878	.2900	.2923	.2945	.2967	.2989
2.0	.3010	.3032	.3054	.3075	.3096	.3118	.3139	.3160	.3181	.3201
2.1	.3222	.3243	.3263	.3284	.3304	.3324	.3345	.3365	.3385	.3404
2.2	.3424	.3444	.3464	.3483	.3502	.3522	.3541	.3560	.3579	.3598
2.3	.3617	.3636	.3655	.3674	.3692	.3711	.3729	.3747	.3766	.3784
2.4	.3802	.3820	.3838	.3856	.3874	.3892	.3909	.3927	.3945	.3962
2.5	.3979	.3997	.4014	.4031	.4048	.4065	.4082	.4099	.4116	.4133
2.6	.4150	.4166	.4183	.4200	.4216	.4232	.4249	.4265	.4281	.4298
2.7	.4314	.4330	.4346	.4362	.4378	.4393	.4409	.4425	.4440	.4456
2.8	.4472	.4487	.4502	.4518	.4533	.4548	.4564	.4579	.4594	.4609
2.9	.4624	.4639	.4654	.4669	.4683	.4698	.4713	.4728	.4742	.4757
3.0	.4771	.4786	.4800	.4814	.4829	.4843	.4857	.4871	.4886	.4900
3.1	.4914	.4928	.4942	.4955	.4969	.4983	.4997	.5011	.5024	.5038
3.2	.5051	.5065	.5079	.5092	.5105	.5119	.5132	.5145	.5159	.5172
3.3	.5185	.5198	.5211	.5224	.5237	.5250	.5263	.5276	.5289	.5302
3.4	.5315	.5328	.5340	.5353	.5366	.5378	.5391	.5403	.5416	.5428
3.5	.5441	.5453	.5465	.5478	.5490	.5502	.5514	.5527	.5539	.5551
3.6	.5563	.5575	.5587	.5599	.5611	.5623	.5635	.5647	.5658	.5670
3.7	.5682	.5694	.5705	.5717	.5729	.5740	.5752	.5763	.5775	.5786
3.8	.5798	.5809	.5821	.5832	.5843	.5855	.5866	.5877	.5888	.5899
3.9	.5911	.5922	.5933	.5944	.5955	.5966	.5977	.5988	.5999	.6010
4.0	.6021	.6031	.6042	.6053	.6064	.6075	.6085	.6096	.6107	.6117
4.1	.6128	.6138	.6149	.6160	.6170	.6180	.6191	.6201	.6212	.6222
4.2	.6232	.6243	.6253	.6263	.6274	.6284	.6294	.6304	.6314	.6325
4.3	.6335	.6345	.6355	.6365	.6375	.6385	.6395	.6405	.6415	.6425
4.4	.6435	.6444	.6454	.6464	.6474	.6484	.6493	.6503	.6513	.6522
4.5	.6532	.6542	.6551	.6561	.6571	.6580	.6590	.6599	.6609	.6618
4.6	.6628	.6637	.6646	.6656	.6665	.6675	.6684	.6693	.6702	.6712
4.7	.6721	.6730	.6739	.6749	.6758	.6767	.6776	.6785	.6794	.6803
4.8	.6812	.6821	.6830	.6839	.6848	.6857	.6866	.6875	.6884	.6893
4.9	.6902	.6911	.6920	.6928	.6937	.6946	.6955	.6964	.6972	.6981
5.0	.6990	.6998	.7007	.7016	.7024	.7033	.7042	.7050	.7059	.7067
5.1	.7076	.7084	.7093	.7101	.7110	.7118	.7126	.7135	.7143	.7152
5.2	.7160	.7168	.7177	.7185	.7193	.7202	.7210	.7218	.7226	.7235
5.3	.7243	.7251	.7259	.7267	.7275	.7284	.7292	.7300	.7308	.7316
5.4	.7324	.7332	.7340	.7348	.7356	.7364	.7372	.7380	.7388	.7396
N	0	1	2	3	4	5	6	7	8	9

N	0	1	2	3	4	5	6	7	8	9
5.5	.7404	.7412	.7419	.7427	.7435	.7443	.7451	.7459	.7466	.7474
5.6	.7482	.7490	.7497	.7505	.7513	.7520	.7528	.7536	.7543	.7551
5.7	.7559	.7566	.7574	.7582	.7589	.7597	.7604	.7612	.7619	.7627
5.8	.7634	.7642	.7649	.7657	.7664	.7672	.7679	.7686	.7694	.7701
5.9	.7709	.7716	.7723	.7731	.7738	.7745	.7752	.7760	.7767	.7774
6.0	.7782	.7789	.7796	.7803	.7810	.7818	.7825	.7832	.7839	.7846
6.1	.7853	.7860	.7868	.7875	.7882	.7889	.7896	.7903	.7910	.7917
6.2	.7924	.7931	.7938	.7945	.7952	.7959	.7966	.7973	.7980	.7987
6.3	.7993	.8000	.8007	.8014	.8021	.8028	.8035	.8041	.8048	.8055
6.4	.8062	.8069	.8075	.8082	.8089	.8096	.8102	.8109	.8116	.8122
6.5	.8129	.8136	.8142	.8149	.8156	.8162	.8169	.8176	.8182	.8189
6.6	.8195	.8202	.8209	.8215	.8222	.8228	.8235	.8241	.8248	.8254
6.7	.8261	.8267	.8274	.8280	.8287	.8293	.8299	.8306	.8312	.8319
6.8	.8325	.8331	.8338	.8344	.8351	.8357	.8363	.8370	.8376	.8382
6.9	.8388	.8395	.8401	.8407	.8414	.8420	.8426	.8432	.8439	.8445
7.0	.8451	.8457	.8463	.8470	.8476	.8482	.8488	.8494	.8500	.8506
7.1	.8513	.8519	.8525	.8531	.8537	.8543	.8549	.8555	.8561	.8567
7.2	.8573	.8579	.8585	.8591	.8597	.8603	.8609	.8615	.8621	.8627
7.3	.8633	.8639	.8645	.8651	.8657	.8663	.8669	.8675	.8681	.8686
7.4	.8692	.8698	.8704	.8710	.8716	.8722	.8727	.8733	.8739	.8745
7.5	.8751	.8756	.8762	.8768	.8774	.8779	.8785	.8791	.8797	.8802
7.6	.8808	.8814	.8820	.8825	.8831	.8837	.8842	.8848	.8854	.8859
7.7	.8865	.8871	.8876	.8882	.8887	.8893	.8899	.8904	.8910	.8915
7.8	.8921	.8927	.8932	.8938	.8943	.8949	.8954	.8960	.8965	.8971
7.9	.8976	.8982	.8987	.8993	.8998	.9004	.9009	.9015	.9020	.9025
8.0	.9031	.9036	.9042	.9047	.9053	.9058	.9063	.9069	.9074	.9079
8.1	.9085	.9090	.9096	.9101	.9106	.9112	.9117	.9122	.9128	.9133
8.2	.9138	.9143	.9149	.9154	.9159	.9165	.9170	.9175	.9180	.9186
8.3	.9191	.9196	.9201	.9206	.9212	.9217	.9222	.9227	.9232	.9238
8.4	.9243	.9248	.9253	.9258	.9263	.9269	.9274	.9279	.9284	.9289
8.5	.9294	.9299	.9304	.9309	.9315	.9320	.9325	.9330	.9335	.9340
8.6	.9345	.9350	.9355	.9360	.9365	.9370	.9375	.9380	.9385	.9390
8.7	.9395	.9400	.9405	.9410	.9415	.9420	.9425	.9430	.9435	.9440
8.8	.9445	.9450	.9455	.9460	.9465	.9469	.9474	.9479	.9484	.9489
8.9	.9494	.9499	.9504	.9509	.9513	.9518	.9523	.9528	.9533	.9538
9.0	.9542	.9547	.9552	.9557	.9562	.9566	.9571	.9576	.9581	.9586
9.1	.9590	.9595	.9600	.9605	.9609	.9614	.9619	.9624	.9628	.9633
9.2	.9638	.9643	.9647	.9652	.9657	.9661	.9666	.9671	.9675	.9680
9.3	.9685	.9689	.9694	.9699	.9703	.9708	.9713	.9717	.9722	.9727
9.4	.9731	.9736	.9741	.9745	.9750	.9754	.9759	.9763	.9768	.9773
9.5	.9777	.9782	.9786	.9791	.9795	.9800	.9805	.9809	.9814	.9818
9.6	.9823	.9827	.9832	.9836	.9841	.9845	.9850	.9854	.9859	.9863
9.7	.9868	.9872	.9877	.9881	.9886	.9890	.9894	.9899	.9903	.9908
9.8	.9912	.9917	.9921	.9926	.9930	.9934	.9939	.9943	.9948	.9952
9.9	.9956	.9961	.9965	.9969	.9974	.9978	.9983	.9987	.9991	.9996
N	0	1	2	3	4	5	6	7	8	9

ANSWERS TO SELECTED
ODD-NUMBERED PROBLEMS

ANSWERS TO SELECTED
ODD-NUMBERED PROBLEMS

Article 1–1

3. $\{1, \frac{1}{2}, \frac{1}{3}, \frac{1}{4}, \frac{1}{5}, \frac{1}{6}, \frac{1}{7}, \frac{1}{8}, \frac{1}{9}\}$, $\{1/x | x$ is a counting number and less than $10\}$

5. $\{6, 12, 18, 24, 30, 36, 42, 48\}$, $\{x | x$ is a multiple of 6 and less than $50\}$

7. $\{x^2 | x$ is a counting number and less than $6\}$

9. $\{3x - 2 | x$ is a counting number and less than $6\}$

17. a) Equivalent, equal   b) Equivalent, not equal

     c) Equivalent, equal   d) Not same size

     e) Equivalent, equal   f) Not same size

19. (a), (b), (c), (d), and (e) are equivalent   (a), (b), (c), and (d) are equal

Article 1–2

5. a) Not true   b) Not true   c) True

     d) Not true   e) True   f) Not true

     g) True   h) True   i) Not true

7. $Y = \{1, 2\}$ or $\{1, 3\}$ or $\{1\}$

9. a) $\{a, b, c, d\}$

     b) $\{a, b, c\}$, $\{a, b, d\}$, $\{a, c, d\}$, $\{b, c, d\}$

     c) $\{a, b\}$, $\{a, c\}$, $\{a, d\}$, $\{b, c\}$, $\{b, d\}$, $\{c, d\}$

     d) $\{a\}$, $\{b\}$, $\{c\}$, $\{d\}$

     e) $\emptyset$

11. a) True   b) Not true   c) True

     d) Not true   e) True   f) Not true

     g) Not true   h) True   i) Not true

     j) Not true

13. a) Yes   b) Yes   c) Not necessarily

     d) Yes   e) Yes   f) Yes

Article 1–3

1. a) $\{0, 1, 2, 3, 4, 5\}$ b) $\{2, 3, 4, 5, 6, 7\}$ c) $\{6, 7\}$

     d) U e) $\emptyset$ f) $\{4, 5\}$

     g) A h) $\emptyset$ i) U

     j) D k) $\{0, 1, 6, 7, 8, 9\}$ l) $\{0, 1, 2, 3, 8, 9\}$

     m) $\{6, 7, 8, 9\}$ n) U o) $\emptyset$

3. a) $X \cup U = U$

9. a) A and B disjoint, or A or $B = \emptyset$

13. a) (a, b),   b) (a, c), (b, c)

15. Infinite

Article 1–4(1)

1. a) Yes   b) No

3. a) Closed under multiplication   b) Not closed under either

 c) Closed under multiplication

5. a) No   b) Yes

Article 1–4(2)

1. 1, 2, 3, 4, 6, 12 are factors of 12; 1, 2, 3, 4, 5, 6, 8, 10, 12, 15, 20, 24, 30, 40, 60, 120 are factors of 120

3. a) I b) $\emptyset$

5. The set consisting of integral multiples of $2 \cdot 3 \cdot 5 = 30$

7. a) No   b) No

9. a) 41, 43, 47, 53, 61   b) 113, 131, 151

 c) Yes   d) 41^2, no

15. $4 = 2^2, 6 = 2 \cdot 3, 8 = 2^3, 9 = 2^2, 10 = 2 \cdot 5, 12 = 2^2 \cdot 3, 14 = 2 \cdot 7, 15 = 3 \cdot 5,$
$16 = 2^4, 18 = 2 \cdot 3^2, 20 = 2^2 \cdot 5, 21 = 3 \cdot 7, 22 = 2 \cdot 11, 24 = 2^3 \cdot 3$

Article 1–5

1. a) $\frac{3}{5}$ b) $\frac{31}{7}$ c) $-\frac{1473}{100}$ d) $\frac{0}{1}$

3. a) $0.6666\ldots$ b) $0.571428571428\ldots$

 c) 0.03125 d) $0.0588235294117647\ldots$

5. b) $\frac{69}{11}$ c) $\frac{64}{11}$ d) $\frac{5}{9}$ e) $\frac{1}{7}$

9. a) $\{5\}$ b) $\{\sqrt[3]{-1}, 5\}$

 c) $\{0.001, \sqrt[3]{-1}, 3.14159, 2.3737\ldots, 5, 3\frac{2}{3}\}$ d) $\{\sqrt{3}\}$

Article 2–2(1)

1. The union of two sets is a set; the intersection of two sets is a set.

5. Yes, no   **7.** No

Article 2–2(2)

1. $A5$ **3.** $A5$ **5.** $A5$ **7.** $A5$

9. $A3$ and $A6$ **11.** $A6$ **13.** $A6$ **15.** $A5$

17. $A3, A1, A6$ **19.** $A1, A5, A3, A6$

23. $a + 0 = a$ (Axiom 5), $a \cdot 1 = a$ (Axiom 5)

Article 3–1

1. $3a + b - 1, a + 5b - 7$ **3.** $6x + 6y - z, 2x + 3z$

5. $-8x - 11y, 12x - y$ **7.** $-2x - 4y$

9. $-6x - 9y - 4$

11. $16x - 3y - 9$

13. $13x - 10y$

15. $a^2 - (b^2 - 2bc + c^2)$

17. $4x^2 - (4y^2 + 4y + 1)$

19. $(c - a)x, \; -(a - c)x$

21. $(a + b)x, \; -(-a - b)x$

23. 7

25. 17   **27.** 5

29. 35   **31.** 2

33. -4 **35.** a^2

37. $-a^3$ **39.** $2(a^3 - a)$

Article 3–2

1. a^9 **3.** $3x^{12}$

5. y^{24} **7.** a^{20}

9. $125c^7$ **11.** $32a^{15}$

13. $a^{(r+s)t}$ **15.** $2^n x^{n^2}$

17. $2x^2 + x - 15$

19. $16x^2 - 4y^2$

21. $r^3 - r^2s - rs^2 + s^3$

23. $x^3 + y^3$

25. $x^2 + 4y^2 - 4xy + 6x - 12y + 9$

27. $a^3 + 3a^2b + 3ab^2 + b^3$

29. $a^6 - 3a^4b + 3a^2b^2 - b^3$

31. $2x^4 - 3x^3 - 10x^2 + 6x + 8$

33. $x^3 - 2x^2 - 5x + 6$

35. $x^6 - 8y^6$

37. $a^{2n+1} - a^{2n} - 7a^{n+1} + 7a^n + 10a - 10$

39. $x^{4n} - 2x^{2n}y^{2n} + y^{4n}$

41. $x^4 - 4x^3y + 6x^2y^2 - 4xy^3 + y^4$

43. $a^4 + 4a^3 + 6a^2 + 4a + 1$

45. $x^4 - 8x^3 + 24x^2 - 32x + 16$

Article 3–3(1)

1. $3y^2 - 2x^2$

3. $2x^2/y - 3x^3$

5. $3x - 4y + 6x^2y^2$

7. $x^2 - 7x + 10 \equiv (x - 2)(x - 5)$

9. $3x^2 - 13x + 4 \equiv (3x - 1)(x - 4)$

11. $2x^3 - 7x^2 + 11x - 4 \equiv (x^2 - 3x + 4)(2x - 1)$

13. $x^2y - 6x^3 - 12xy^2 - 6y^3 \equiv (-3x^2 - 4xy - 12y^2)(2x - 3y) - 42y^3$

15. $4x^3 + 5 + 4x^2 - 13x \equiv (2x^2 - 3x + 1)(2x + 5)$

17. $5x^3 - 2x^2 + 3x - 4 \equiv (5x + 8)(x^2 - 2x + 1) + (14x - 12)$

19. $x^6 - y^6 \equiv (x^5 + x^4y + x^3y^2 + x^2y^3 + xy^4 + y^5)(x - y)$

Article 3–3(2)

1. $Q = 3x + 7, \; R = 17$

3. $Q = x^2 - 4x + 8, \; R = -7$

5. a) $Q = x^3 - 3x - 10, \; R = -28$

   b) $Q = x^3 - 3x^2 - 4, \; R = -4$

7. a) $Q = 3x^3 + 6x^2 + 12x + 17, \; R = 14$

   b) $Q = 3x^3 - 6x^2 + 12x - 31, \; R = 42$

9. $x^3 - 2x^2 + 3x - 4 \equiv (x^2 + x + 6)(x - 3) + 14$

11. $x^4 - 5x^3 + x^2 - 6 \equiv (x^3 - 4x^2 - 3x - 3)(x - 1) - 9$

13. 14

15. -9

Article 3–4

1. $6ax - 8ay$
3. $-21x^3y - 28xy^2$
5. $4x^2 - 9y^2$
7. $x^4 - 16y^4$
9. $4x^2 + 28xy + 49y^2$
11. $x^2 - 7x + 10$
13. $x^2y^4 - 2xy^2z^2w + z^4w^2$
15. $28x^2 - 9xy - 9y^2$
17. $4x^2 + 12xy + 9y^2 - 9$
19. $x^2 + 4y^2 + z^2 - 4xy - 2xz + 4yz$
21. $x^3 + 8$
23. $x^2 + 6xy + 9y^2 - 4z^2 + 16zw - 16w^2$
25. $a^2 + b^2 + c^2 + d^2 - 2ab + 2ac - 2ad - 2bc + 2bd - 2cd$
27. $4(x + 2y)^2 + 2(x + 2y) - 12$
29. $8x^3 + 36x^2y + 54xy^2 + 27y^3$

Article 3–5(1)

1. $4(x - 5)$
3. $3y(y - 3)$
5. $xyz^2(yz - 3x + 5y^2)$
7. $(2x + 5)(3y - 4x)$
9. $2z(x + 3y)(z - 3x)$
11. $(3 - a)(3 + a)$
13. $(15a^4 - 8b)(15a^4 + 8b)$
15. $x(xy^2 - 5d^3)(xy^2 + 5d^3)$
17. $(x + 2y - z)(x + 2y + z)$
19. $(a + b + c + d)(a + b - c - d)$
21. $[9(4x - 3y) + 5(3z + w)][9(4x - 3y) - 5(3z + w)]$
23. $(x - 4)^2$
25. $(3xy + 11)^2$
27. $5(z - 3w)^2$
29. $(7 - x)^2$
31. $(a - 2)(a^2 + 2a + 4)$
33. $(2x^{2n} + 3y^m)(4x^{4n} - 6x^{2n}y^m + 9y^{2m})$
35. $(x - 5y)(19x^2 - 10xy + 7y^2)$
37. $(x - 4)(x - 3)$
39. $(ab - 5)(ab + 4)$
41. $(7x - 2)(5x - 2)$
43. $(3a - 4)(2a + 5)$
45. $(x + y - 5)(x + y - 2)$
47. $(4x + 2y - 5)(2x + y + 2)$
49. $2(2a + 2b + c + d)(3a + 3b - 5c - 5d)$

Article 3–5(2)

1. $(a + b)(x - y)$
3. $(x - 2)(x^2 + 4)$
5. $(a - 3)(2 - b^2)$
7. $(x - 1 + y)(x - 1 - y)$
9. $(2x + y - 2)(2x - y + 2)$
11. $(x + y + z - w)(x + y - z + w)$
13. $(x + 2y - 3)(x + 2y + 2)$
15. $(x^2 - xy - 3y^2)(x^2 + xy - 3y^2)$
17. $(a^2 - 2ab + 3b^2)(a^2 + 2ab + 3b^2)$
19. $(b^2 + 2bc + 5c^2)(b^2 - 2bc + 5c^2)$
21. $(x - 2y)(3a + 4b + c)$
23. $(z^3 - 2)(z + 4)$
25. $(a^4 + b^4)(a^2 + b^2)(a + b)(a - b)$
27. $(x - z)(x + 2y + z)$
29. $3(z - x)(x + 2y + z)$

Article 3–6

1. $\dfrac{4}{9}$
3. $\dfrac{a^2x^2}{y^2}$
5. $\dfrac{a}{x + y}$

7. $\dfrac{x+1}{x}$

9. $\dfrac{x+4}{x-4}$

11. $\dfrac{y+2}{y+5}$

13. $\dfrac{3a+1}{2a-1}$

15. $\dfrac{2(3-x)}{x+5}$

17. $\dfrac{x+6}{x^2+6x+36}$

19. $\dfrac{x^2+2xy+y^2}{x^2+y^2}$

21. $\dfrac{1}{3-a}$

23. $x-4$

Article 3–7

1. $\dfrac{6}{5}$

3. $\dfrac{(3x-4y)(3x+4y)}{12xy}$

5. $\dfrac{23-2x}{18}$

7. $\dfrac{2x^2-y^2}{x-y}$

9. $\dfrac{x-y}{5x-3}$

11. $\dfrac{5yz-4xz+3xy}{xyz}$

13. $\dfrac{5(1-x)}{3(x-4)}$

15. $\dfrac{2x^2-9x-9}{(2x-3)(x-5)(x-6)}$

17. $\dfrac{4a^2+9a+29}{a^3-27}$

19. $-\dfrac{5}{(x+2)(x+3)}$

21. $\dfrac{8y^4-28y^3+21y^2+27y-35}{(2y-3)^2(y+1)}$

23. $\dfrac{xz-x^2+xy-y^2+yz-z^2}{(x-y)(y-z)(z-x)}$

Article 3–8(1)

1. $\frac{20}{21}$

3. $\frac{1}{6}$

5. $\frac{3}{10}$

7. $\dfrac{15x}{4y}$

9. $\dfrac{40x^3}{81}$

11. $\dfrac{x}{x^2+xy+y^2}$

13. $\dfrac{1}{x+3}$

15. $\dfrac{x+1}{(x+4)(x+5)}$

17. $\dfrac{x+2}{6(x-2)}$

19. y

21. 1

23. $-\dfrac{2+3x}{x^2(x+1)}$

Article 3–8(2)

1. $-\dfrac{57}{5}$

3. $\dfrac{x}{z}$

5. $\dfrac{2y+5x}{2y-5x}$

7. $x-1$

9. $(3x+2y)(y-2x)$

11. $\dfrac{x^2+xy+y^2}{x^2+2xy+y^2-x}$

Article 3–9

1. 8

3. $\dfrac{3y^4}{x^2}$

5. $\dfrac{2x^5}{3y^5}$

7. $\dfrac{cd(a+b)}{ab}$

9. $\dfrac{(a+b)^2}{ab}$

11. $x^{nm}y^{2m}$

Article 3–10

1. 5

3. $\frac{4}{7}$

5. $\frac{16}{9}$

7. $\frac{1}{64}$

9. 81

11. $\sqrt[20]{x}$

13. $\sqrt[20]{x}$

15. $\sqrt[20]{x}$

17. $\dfrac{1}{64xy^5}$

19. $\dfrac{5x^2}{3y}$

21. $a + 2\sqrt{ab} + b$

23. $x + y$

25. $x^2 + \dfrac{2x}{y} + \dfrac{1}{y^2}$

27. $\dfrac{a^{7/2} + 2\sqrt{a} - a}{a^2}$

29. $|x - 1| + |x + 1|$

Article 3–11

1. $2\sqrt{2}$

3. $\frac{5}{2}$

5. $-5\sqrt[3]{5}$

7. $3xy^2\sqrt{3xy}$

9. $3zx^2y\sqrt[3]{3zy^2}$

11. $5\sqrt{35}/21$

13. $b\sqrt{a^2 + c^2}$

15. $\sqrt{3xy}/y^2$

17. $\sqrt[3]{12}/4$

19. $3x\sqrt[3]{4xy}/2y$

21. $\dfrac{(x + 3)\sqrt{x}}{x}$

23. $xy\sqrt[4]{27x^3y^2}/9$

25. $\sqrt{5}$

27. $\sqrt[3]{45x}/3x$

29. $x\sqrt{13xz}/y$

Article 3–12

1. $4\sqrt{3}$

3. $11\sqrt{2}$

5. $-2\sqrt{2}$

7. $14\sqrt{3}$

9. $10\sqrt{2}$

11. $\left(a + 3b + \dfrac{1}{ab}\right)\sqrt[3]{ab}$

13. $-\sqrt{x + y}$

15. $(ac^2 + b^3c + a^4b^2)\sqrt{abc}$

17. $32\sqrt{3}/3$

19. 5, 2

Article 3–13

1. $\sqrt{65}$

3. $2\sqrt[3]{13}$

5. $(x - y)\sqrt{x + y}$

7. $(x + y)\sqrt{x^2 - xy + y^2}$

9. $2\sqrt[3]{3}$

11. $2(\sqrt{3} + \sqrt{7})$

13. -2

15. $-13 - \sqrt{15}$

17. $(3 - \sqrt{5})/2$

19. $\frac{8}{3}$

21. $\sqrt[3]{9}/3$

23. $\sqrt[4]{3a^2b^2}/b$

25. $\sqrt{15}/10$

27. $\sqrt[3]{4}$

29. $\dfrac{x^2\sqrt{1 - x^2}}{1 - x^2}$

31. $(5\sqrt{7} + 5\sqrt{3})/4$

33. $\dfrac{x^2 - x\sqrt{y}}{x^2 - y}$

35. $-(57 + 13\sqrt{21})/12$

37. $\dfrac{x^2(\sqrt{x^2 - 1} + \sqrt{x + 3})}{x^2 - x - 4}$

39. $\dfrac{2x^2 - 2x\sqrt{x^2 - 9} - 9}{9}$

41. $\dfrac{x^2 + x + 2\sqrt{x}\sqrt{x^2 - 1} - 1}{1 + x - x^2}$

43. $2(4 + 2\sqrt[3]{3} + \sqrt[3]{9})/5$

45. $(2\sqrt{3} + 3\sqrt{2} - \sqrt{30})/12$

47. 3.134

49. 1.094

REVIEW PROBLEMS
Chapters 1–3

1. (c)   **3.** (c)   **5.** (e)

7. No   **9.** Yes   **11.** Yes

13. Yes   **15.** $\dfrac{(2 - x^2)\sqrt{1 - x^2}}{(1 - x^2)^2}$ **17.** No

19. $3/2 - 5\sqrt{2}$ **21.** $\dfrac{4\sqrt{2}}{\sqrt{32 - x^2}}$ **25.** 1

Article 4–2

1. $-6.5,\ -5,\ -1,\ 0,\ 0.333,\ \frac{1}{3},\ \sqrt{4},\ 2.3,\ 2^3$

5. $(0),\ (-1),\ (1),\ \left(\dfrac{\sqrt{2} + \sqrt{3}}{2}\right),\ \left(\dfrac{x_1 + x_2}{2}\right)$

7. a) ± 2 b) $\pm\sqrt{5}$ c) ± 3
    d) $\pm\frac{1}{4}$ e) $7,\ -3$ f) 4
    g) $9,\ -3$ h) $6,\ -4$ i) $6,\ -2$
    j) None   k) None   l) $8,\ 2$

15. a) True   b) True

17. Two

Article 4–3

1. a) lub $-$ 3, no glb   b) No lub, no glb
    c) lub 0, glb $-$ 3   d) lub 1, glb 0

Article 4–4

3. a) $(3, 2)$ b) $(-4, 6)$ c) $(5, 0)$
5. II, IV, III, I, II, IV
7. a) $(8, 4),\ (4, -4),\ (-4, 4)$ b) $(-1, 6),\ (3, -2),\ (-3, -4)$
11. a) $(-1, \frac{7}{2})$ b) $(\frac{11}{2}, -\frac{9}{2})$ c) $(-1, 0)$

Article 4–5(1)

1. a) $\sqrt{34}$ b) $\sqrt{106}$ c) $3\sqrt{2}/4$
9. Yes; no   **11.** $h = 6$
13. $(1, 0),\ (0, -1),\ (1/\sqrt{2},\ 1/\sqrt{2}),\ (-\frac{1}{2},\ \sqrt{3}/2)$

Article 4–5(2)

1. a) $(x - 3)^2 + (y - 1)^2 = 25$ b) $(x - 4)^2 + (y + 2)^2 = 9$
    c) $(x + 1)^2 + (y - 3)^2 = 9$ d) $(x - 2)^2 + (y + 4)^2 = 25$
3. $x^2 + y^2 = r^2$
5. a) All points in the plane
    b) All points on or between circles with centers at $(2, -7)$ and radii 1 and 3

Article 5–1(1)

1. a) Domain, all real numbers; range, all real numbers
   b) Domain, all non-negative real numbers; range, all non-negative real numbers
   c) Domain, all real numbers; range, all non-negative real numbers
   d) Domain, all real numbers between 2 and -2 inclusive; range, all real numbers between 0 and 2 inclusive
   e) Domain, all real numbers greater than or equal to 1 or less than or equal to -1; range, all nonnegative real numbers
   f) Domain, all real numbers except 1; range, all real numbers except -1
   g) Domain, all real numbers except 1 and -1; range, all real numbers except those equal to or between -1 and 0
   h) Domain, all real numbers; range, all real numbers greater than or equal to -2

3. a) Domain 1, 2, 3; range 2, 3, 4
   b) Domain 1, 2; range 2, 3, 4
   c) Domain R; range R
   d) Domain R; range R
   e) Domain, all real numbers less than or equal to 1; range R
   f) Domain R; range, all real numbers less than or equal to 1
   g) Domain, all real numbers between -1 and 5 inclusive; range, all real numbers between 0 and 6 inclusive
   h) Domain R; range R
   i) Domain, R except 7; range, R except 3
   j) Domain, all real numbers between -1 and 1 inclusive; range, all real numbers between -1 and 1 inclusive

5. a) Domain, R; range, all nonnegative real numbers; function
   b) Domain, R; range, all real numbers greater than or equal to $-\frac{5}{4}$; function
   c) Domain, all positive real numbers; range, R; relation

7. $0, 0, -2, 10$

9. $1, 2, 32, \frac{1}{32}$

11. $0, 1, 2, -2$

13. $6, -3, 4$

15. $A = \pi x^2, x \rightarrow \pi x^2$

17. $0, 12, 16, 12, 0$

21. a) $-1/ax$ b) $x + a$ c) $\dfrac{1}{\sqrt{x} + \sqrt{a}}$

Article 5–1(2)

1. $f + g : 5x - 1$
   $fg : 6x^2 - 5x - 6$
   $f/g : (2x - 3)/(3x + 2), x \neq -\frac{2}{3}$
   $f \circ g : 6x + 1$
   $g \circ f : 6x - 7$

3. $f + g : -3x^2 - x + 4$

$fg : 9x^3 - 18x^2 + 8x$

$f/g : (4 - 3x)/(2x - 3x^2)$ $x \neq 0, \frac{2}{3}$

$f \circ g : 9x^2 - 6x + 4$

$g \circ f : -27x^2 + 66x - 40$

5. $f + g : x^3 + \sqrt{x}$ $\quad x > 0$

$fg : x^3 \sqrt{x}$ $\qquad\quad x > 0$

$f/g : 1/x^{5/2}$ $\qquad x \neq 0$

$f \circ g : x \sqrt{x}$ $\qquad\quad x > 0$

$g \circ f : |x| \sqrt{x}$ $\qquad x > 0$

7. $f(x) = 1 - x^2$ $\hspace{3cm}$ **9.** $g(x) = x^2 + 1$

11. $(f \circ g) \circ h : x^2$

$f \circ (g \circ h) : x^2$

Yes

Article 5–2

1. $-\frac{5}{2}$ $\hspace{3cm}$ **3.** 0 $\hspace{3cm}$ **5.** 2, 5

7. 1 $\hspace{3.5cm}$ **9.** 1 $\hspace{3.3cm}$ **11.** $0, \pm 1$

Article 6–1

1. -2 $\hspace{2.9cm}$ **3.** $\frac{5}{6}$ $\hspace{3cm}$ **5.** -3

7. -7 $\hspace{2.9cm}$ **9.** $\frac{11}{9}$ $\hspace{2.8cm}$ **11.** -5

13. $-\frac{16}{9}$ $\hspace{2.5cm}$ **15.** $-\frac{1}{4}$ $\hspace{2.6cm}$ **17.** $\frac{1}{3}$

19. $-\frac{17}{14}$

21. $\dfrac{c}{a - b}$ $\hspace{2cm}$ **23.** $2A/h$ $\hspace{2.3cm}$ **25.** $\dfrac{l - a}{n - 1}$

27. $\dfrac{Sr + a - S}{r}$ $\hspace{1.3cm}$ **29.** $\dfrac{2S - an}{n}$ $\hspace{1.8cm}$ **31.** $\dfrac{aK_1}{K_2 - K_1}$

41. 18 years $\hspace{1.8cm}$ **43.** \$45,000 $\hspace{1.7cm}$ **45.** $1\frac{5}{7}$ hr

Article 6–2

1. 10, 13, 16; $t_9 = 25$, $S_9 = 117$ $\hspace{1cm}$ **3.** 1, -2, -5; $t_{15} = -32$, $S_{15} = -165$

5. $t_{12} = 46$, $S_{12} = 288$ $\hspace{2.5cm}$ **7.** $d = \frac{48}{91}$, $t_{14} = \frac{34}{7}$

9. $t_1 = -\frac{31}{28}$, $t_{14} = \frac{151}{28}$ $\hspace{2.3cm}$ **11.** $n = 7$, $S_7 = 147$

13. 8, 9, 10 $\hspace{4cm}$ **15.** 187,026

17. 2, 5, 8, 11 $\hspace{3.3cm}$ **19.** $-\frac{25}{2}$, -7, $-\frac{3}{2}$

21. a) -4; b) $\frac{17}{15}$ $\hspace{2.8cm}$ **25.** 27 numbers; $S = 2835$

27. 1092 times $\hspace{3cm}$ **29.** 1610 ft

31. \$5075

Article 6–3

1. Minimum -4, when $x = -3$

3. Minimum $-\frac{121}{8}$, when $x = -\frac{5}{4}$

5. Minimum $-\frac{169}{24}$, when $x = \frac{17}{12}$

7. Minimum 2, when $x = -3$

9. 8, 8

11. 40 ft, 40 ft

Article 6–4(1)

1. -1, -5

3. $\frac{3}{2}$, 4

5. $\frac{1}{3}$, $\frac{5}{2}$

7. None

9. $\pm\frac{4}{3}$

11. $\pm a/2$

13. $\frac{10}{3}$, $-\frac{5}{2}$

15. 4, $-\frac{3}{2}$

17. $-\frac{5}{3}$, 2

19. -1, $\frac{2}{3}$

21. $-a \pm b$

23. $r/2$, $-s$

25. $-\frac{1}{2}$, $-\frac{14}{3}$

Article 6–4(2)

1. $\frac{3}{2}$, -4

3. $\dfrac{-1 \pm \sqrt{5}}{2}$

5. 1, 2

7. a, b

9. 1, $\dfrac{c-a}{a-b}$

11. $\frac{2}{3}$, -1

13. 1, $-5/4$

15. $(1 \pm \sqrt{5})/4$

17. $\dfrac{v_0 \pm \sqrt{v_0^2 - 2gs}}{g}$

19. -3

21. $\frac{3}{5}$ or $\frac{5}{3}$

23. 1

25. $\dfrac{-27 + \sqrt{909}}{2}$ yd

Article 6–5(1)

1. $x > 9$

3. $x < 7$

5. $x > 9$ or $x < -11$

7. $-\frac{1}{2} < x < \frac{1}{3}$

9. $x > -1 + \sqrt{13}$ or $x < -1 - \sqrt{13}$

11. No real values

13. $x > 5$ or $x < 0$

15. $3 < x < 5$

17. $-\frac{1}{2} \leq x \leq \frac{7}{2}$

19. $x \leq -26$ or $x \geq -22$

Article 6–6

1. The sums of the zeros are -6, -1, $-\frac{5}{2}$, $\frac{11}{2}$, $\frac{17}{6}$, $\frac{5}{2}$, -6, and $\frac{5}{3}$
   The products of the zeros are 5, -6, -6, $\frac{15}{2}$, $\frac{5}{6}$, -4, 11, $\frac{4}{3}$

3. $x^2 + x - 20 = 0$

5. $12x^2 + x - 6 = 0$

7. $x^2 - 4x + 1 = 0$

9. $8x^2 + 12x + 1 = 0$

11. $5x^2 - 8x - 4 = 0$

13. $2x^2 + 5x - 3 = 0$

15. $36x^2 + 24x - 5 = 0$

17. $6x^2 - 5x - 1 = 0$

19. $k = -1$

21. $k = 1$

23. $k = \frac{49}{12}$

25. $k = -5$

27. $k = 0$

29. All values of k

31. $-8 < k < 8$ **33.** $k = \frac{27}{4}$ **35.** $k > \frac{3}{2}$ or $k < -1$

Article 6–7

1. $\pm 2, \pm\sqrt{7}$

5. Real roots: $-2, 1$

9. $5, 2, \dfrac{7 \pm \sqrt{53}}{2}$

13. $-\dfrac{23}{9}$

3. $\pm\frac{1}{3}, \pm\frac{1}{2}$

7. $-64, 8$

11. $0, 0$

15. $5, -5/2, \dfrac{5 \pm \sqrt{57}}{4}$

Article 6–8

1. $\frac{11}{2}$ **3.** $7, 1$ **5.** -2 **7,** 16

9. -5 **11.** $3, \frac{107}{25}$ **13.** 6

Article 6–9

1. $z = \dfrac{kx}{y}$ **3.** $z = 6xy$ **5.** $C = kd$

7. $A = kx^2$ **9.** $y = 2x/3$ **11.** 90

13. 576π in^2 **15.** 72 ergs   **17.** 2 ft

19. Multiplied by 16

Article 6–10

1. $x = 2, y = -1$ **3.** $x = 3, y = 5$

5. $x = \frac{2}{3}, y = \frac{3}{2}$ **7.** $x = \frac{1}{2}, y = 1$

9. $x = 2\sqrt{3}/3, y = \sqrt{3}/3$ **11.** $x = 5, y = -2$

13. $x = \dfrac{a^3 + a^2b + 3ab^2 + b^3}{a^2 + b^2}$ **15.** $x = \dfrac{a}{k_2 - k_1}$

$y = \dfrac{a^3 - a^2b + ab^2 + b^3}{a^2 + b^2}$ $y = \dfrac{ak_1}{k_2 - k_1}$

17. $x' = bx + ay$ **29.** $\frac{27}{36}$

$y' = by - ax$

31. 150 mi/hr, 10 mi/hr   **33.** 12 hr, 15 hr

35. $(-1, 2), (2, 5), (3, -1)$

37. $(\frac{18}{7}, \frac{8}{7}), (\frac{30}{7}, \frac{4}{7}), (\frac{23}{7}, -\frac{10}{7}), (\frac{11}{7}, -\frac{6}{7})$

39. a) $y = -\dfrac{x}{3} + \dfrac{11}{3}$ b) $y = -\dfrac{3}{10}x + \dfrac{4}{5}$

Article 6–11

1. $x = 1, y = 2, z = 3$ **3.** $x = 3, y = -1, z = 4$

5. $x = \frac{1}{3}, y = -\frac{2}{5}, z = \frac{1}{2}$ **7.** $x = 5, y = 6, z = 7$

9. $x = 3, y = 4, z = 6$ **11.** $\{(-1, 2, 3)\}$

13. 10 nickels, 10 dimes, 5 quarters

15. $x^2 + y^2 - x - 7y + 6 = 0$ **17.** $x = y + 2z - 1$

Article 6–12

1. $x = 0, 2$ $y = 0, 16$ 3. No real values

5. $x = \dfrac{3 \pm \sqrt{7}}{2}, \ y = \dfrac{5 \mp \sqrt{7}}{2}$ 7. $\{(2, 1), \ (-8/5), \ -1/5)\}$

9. $\left\{ \left(\dfrac{-2 + 2\sqrt{5}}{3}, \ 1 + \sqrt{5} \right), \ \left(\dfrac{-2 - 2\sqrt{5}}{3}, \ 1 - \sqrt{5} \right) \right\}$

11. $b = \pm a\sqrt{1 + m^2}$ 13. 23, 32

15. 7, 4

REVIEW PROBLEMS

Chapters 4–6

1. a) Positive if $x < 0$ 3. a) Positive if $x < 3$
    b) Negative if $x > 0$ b) Negative if $3 < x < 9/2$
    c) Zero if $x = 0$ c) Zero if $x = 3$

5. a) Positive if $x > 2$ or $x < 0$ 7. No real values
    b) Negative if $0 < x < 2, \ x \neq 1$
    c) Zero if $x = 0$

9. $w = \dfrac{y^{1/3}}{3x^{4/3}}(1 + x^2 y^{2/3})$ 11. $\{(2, 1), \ (-2, 1)\}$ 13. (b)

25. The intersection of the graphs of f and g.

Article 7–1

1. $a = 2, \ b = -1, \ c = 3$ 3. $a = -1, \ b = 0, \ c = 0, \ d = 2$

5. $\begin{bmatrix} 1 & 2 & 3 \\ 2 & 0 & 3 \end{bmatrix}$ 7. $\begin{bmatrix} 3 & -4 & 3 \\ -2 & 2 & 1 \end{bmatrix}$

9. $\begin{bmatrix} -4 & 7 & -3 \\ 4 & -3 & 0 \end{bmatrix}$ 11. $\begin{bmatrix} 2 + 3x & -1 + 3y & x + 6 \\ 3 & y - 3 & 11 \end{bmatrix}$

23. $\begin{bmatrix} -4 & 11 \\ 4 & -2 \end{bmatrix}$ 25. $\begin{bmatrix} 1 & 5 \\ -2 & -1 \end{bmatrix}$

27. No. Matrices must have same number of rows and columns.

Article 7–2

1. $\begin{bmatrix} 5 & 3 \\ 6 & 4 \end{bmatrix}$ 3. $\begin{bmatrix} 4 & 5 \\ 5 & 9 \end{bmatrix}$

5. $\begin{bmatrix} 2 & 10 & 12 \\ -10 & -2 & 2 \\ -3 & 2 & 3 \end{bmatrix}$ 7. $[7]$

9. $\begin{bmatrix} -4 & 2 \\ 4 & 2 \end{bmatrix}$ **11.** $\begin{bmatrix} 2 & 4 \\ -2 & 1 \end{bmatrix}$ **13.** $\begin{bmatrix} 6 & 4 \\ 2 & -7 \end{bmatrix}$ **15.** $\begin{bmatrix} -2 \\ 3 \end{bmatrix}$

17. $\begin{bmatrix} \frac{2}{3} \\ \frac{3}{2} \end{bmatrix}$ **19.** Yes   **21.** Yes

Article 7–3

1. $\begin{bmatrix} 5 & -3 \\ -8 & 5 \end{bmatrix}$ **3.** Does not exist   **5.** $\begin{bmatrix} \frac{1}{8} & \frac{3}{16} \\ \frac{1}{8} & -\frac{5}{16} \end{bmatrix}$ **7.** $\begin{bmatrix} 2 & -1 \\ -5 & 3 \end{bmatrix}$

13. $\begin{bmatrix} \frac{2}{3} \\ \frac{3}{2} \end{bmatrix}$ **15.** Three rows and three columns

Article 7–4(1)

1. -2 **3.** 3 **5.** 1 **11.** $x = 1$

15. Real; equal; imaginary

Article 7–4(2)

1. 5 **3.** 0

15. $\dfrac{4x + 3y - 17}{2}$ **17.** $9x - 5y - 2 = 0$ **19.** $x = -1, y = 4$

Article 7–5

1. Rows and columns are interchanged

3. Two columns are identical   **5.** 1008

9. $x = a, b$ **11.** $x = 3, 1$

Article 7–6

1. -110 **3.** -484 **5.** 0

Article 7–7

9. $x = -4, y = -3, z = 2, w = 1$

11. $x = 1, y = 2, z = -1, w = 3$

15. $f(x) = 2x^2 - 5x + 4$

Article 8–1(1)

1. $R = 17$ **3.** $R = -7$ **5.** a) -6,   b) 57

7. Yes   **9.** No   **11.** Yes

15. -23 **17.** -52

Article 8–1(2)

1. 2, one; 3, two; -4, three   **3.** -7, single; $\frac{3}{2}$, three

5. $-\frac{5}{3}$, single; 3, four   **7.** Upper bound 3, lower bound -4

9. Upper bound 3, lower bound -2 **11.** Upper bound 3, lower bound -3

13. Upper bound 2, lower bound -1 **15.** Upper bound 2, lower bound -3

Article 8–2

5. 2, double; single between 1 and 2; single between -5 and -6

7. Single at -3; double between 0 and 1

9. Single between -2 and -3

11. Single between -1 and 0; single between 0 and 1; single between 3 and 4

13. Single between -3 and -2

15. Single between -1 and 0 and between 0 and 1

Article 8–4

1. -2, 3, $\frac{1}{2}$

3. 1, 3, 5, 7

5. 1, 2, 3, -5

7. $-\dfrac{3}{2}$, $-\dfrac{3}{2}$, $\dfrac{1 \pm \sqrt{5}}{2}$

9. 1, 1, 1, 1

11. $\frac{1}{2}$, $\frac{1}{2}$, $\frac{1}{2}$, $\pm\sqrt{-1}$

13. $\frac{3}{2}$, -1, $\dfrac{-1 \pm \sqrt{-3}}{2}$

15. 2, 3, 4, 5

17. 1, 1, -2, 5

Article 8–5

1. 0.75   **3.** 0.45   **5.** 1.36, 1.69

7. -0.62, 1.62   **9.** 1.817   **11.** 1.189

13. Three   **15.** Roots of $x^3 - x^2 - 12x - 18 = 0$

Article 9–1

1. $y = 5x - 6$, domain R; inverse $y = (x + 6)/5$, domain R

3. $y = x^2 - 4x$, domain $x > 2$; inverse $y = 2 + \sqrt{x + 4}$, domain $x > -4$, domain $x < 2$; inverse $y = 2 - \sqrt{x + 4}$, domain $x > -4$

5. $y = (x^2 - 1)/x^2$, domain $x > 0$; inverse $y = 1/\sqrt{1 - x}$, domain $x < 1$, domain $x < 0$; inverse $y = 1/(-\sqrt{1 - x})$, domain $x < 1$

7. Depends on whether n is even or odd

9. $y = \sqrt{x^2 - 4}$, domain $x > 2$; inverse $y = \sqrt{x^2 + 4}$, domain $x > 0$, domain $x < -2$; inverse $y = -\sqrt{x^2 + 4}$, domain $x > 0$

11. $y = x/(x^2 - 1)$, domain $x > 0$ and $x \neq 1$; inverse $y = (1 + \sqrt{1 + 4x^2})/2x$, domain $x < 0$ and $x \neq -1$; inverse $y = (1 - \sqrt{1 + 4x^2})/2x$

REVIEW PROBLEMS
Chapters 7–9

1. $\{(0, 2), (0, -2)\}$ **3.** (a)

5. Not unique, one possibility: $A = 1$, $B = 27$, $C = 3$.

7. $x^4 - 3x^3 - 16x^2 - 19x + 85$ **9.** $\sqrt{2}$, $\sqrt{2\sqrt{2}}$, $\sqrt{2\sqrt{2\sqrt{2}}}$; 2

11. a) $y = 2x + 4$, function

b) $y = \dfrac{1 \pm \sqrt{1 + 36x^2}}{2x}$, relation

13. a) $y = x^2 + 5$, function

b) $y = \pm\sqrt{x^2}$, $x > 0$, relation

19. $1 - \dfrac{10}{x} + \dfrac{45}{x^2} - \dfrac{120}{x^3} + \dfrac{210}{x^4}$

Article 10–1

1. 4	**3.** 120	**5.** 240
7. 1920	**9.** 60	**11.** a) 56, b) 64

Article 10-2

1. 504	**3.** 585	**5** a) 5040, b) 144
7. 5040	**9.** 103,680	**11.** 1440
13. 468,000	**15.** 3780	**17.** 360
19. $n = 8$		

Article 10–3

1. a) 35,   b) 45,   c) 210   **3.** 12,650

5. 84,456   **7.** 18,375

9. 560   **11.** $384C(36, 6)$

13. a) 36,   b) 84   **15.** 126

17. a) 28,   b) 56,   c) 247   **19.** $n = 7$

Article 10–4

1. $a^7 + 7a^6b + 21a^5b^2 + 35a^4b^3 + 35a^3b^4 + 21a^2b^5 + 7ab^6 + b^7$

3. $32x^5 + 80x^4y^2 + 80x^3y^4 + 40x^2y^6 + 10xy^8 + y^{10}$

5. $625x^4 - 500x^3y^2 + 150x^2y^4 - 20xy^6 + y^8$

7. $x^2 + 6x^{5/3}y^{1/3} + 15x^{4/3}y^{2/3} + 20xy + 15x^{2/3}y^{4/3} + 6x^{1/3}y^{5/3} + y^2$

9. $x^2 - \dfrac{15x^{8/5}}{y^2} + \dfrac{90x^{6/5}}{y^4} - \dfrac{270x^{4/5}}{y^6} + \dfrac{405x^{2/5}}{y^8} - \dfrac{243}{y^{10}}$

11. $\dfrac{x^{24}}{4096} + \dfrac{3x^{22}}{256y^2} + \dfrac{33x^{20}}{128y^4} + \dfrac{55x^{18}}{16y^6} + \cdots$

13. $x^{11/3} - \dfrac{11x^{10/3}}{y^{1/3}} + \dfrac{55x^3}{y^{2/3}} - \dfrac{165x^{8/3}}{y} + \cdots$

15. $1 + kx + \dfrac{k(k - 1)}{2}x^2 + \dfrac{k(k - 1)(k - 2)}{3!}x^3 + \cdots$

17. $59{,}136x^6y^6$ **19.** $\dfrac{35y^8}{8}$

21. $-414{,}720x^7$ **23.** $(7/2)x^5$

Article 10–5

1. $1 - x + x^2 - x^3 + \cdots$ **3.** $1 + \dfrac{x}{2} + \dfrac{3x^2}{8} + \dfrac{5x^3}{16} + \cdots$

5. 0.9803   **7.** 1.005   **9.** 5.745   **11.** 4.932

13. $\dfrac{23}{4}, \dfrac{65}{32}, \dfrac{74}{15}$

Article 12–2

1. 64, 256, 1024; $t_n = 16{,}384$, $S_8 = 21{,}845$

3. -1, 5, -25; $t_n = 125$, $S_7 = 13{,}021/125$

5. $t_n = 486$, $S_6 = 728$

7. $r = 3$, or -4; $t_n = 9$, or 16   **9.** $t_1 = \frac{36}{121}$; $t_n = \frac{4}{1089}$

11. $n = 6$; $S = -126$ **13.** $t_1 = \frac{625}{16}$, $\frac{125}{8}$, $\frac{25}{4}$

15. $n = 9$ **17.** $\pm\frac{9}{4}$, $\frac{3}{2}$, ± 1

19. $\pm\sqrt{ab}$ **23.** $\frac{1}{81}$ ft; $26\frac{79}{81}$ ft

25. $1583   **27.** Second

Article 12–3

1. $\frac{3}{2}$ **3.** $\frac{64}{5}$ **5.** $4 + 2\sqrt{2}$

7. $\frac{10}{3}$ **9.** $\frac{5}{9}$ **11.** $\frac{64}{11}$

13. $r = \frac{1}{7}$ **15.** $16[2 + \sqrt{2}]$ **17.** 240 ft

Article 12–4

1. $\log_3 27 = 3$ **3.** $\log_4 1 = 0$ **5.** $\log_8 16 = \frac{4}{3}$

7. $\log_{10} 0.001 = -3$ **9.** $\log_4 4 = 1$ **11.** $36^{1/2} = 6$

13. $x = 2$ **15.** $x = -1$ **17.** $u = 25$

19. $x = 14$ **21.** $a = \frac{27}{8}$ **27.** $\log_b \dfrac{a + 2}{a - 3}$

29. $\log_a \dfrac{\sqrt{x}}{\sqrt[3]{y^2}}$ **31.** $\log_a x^5(x - 1)^6$ **33.** $4 \log_{10} 60.3$

35. $3 \log_{10} 54.3 + \log_{10} 67 - \log_{10} 93.9 - 2 \log 32.5$

Article 12–5(1)

1. 0.4099   **3.** 0.8401   **5.** 0.6730   **7.** 0.8373

9. 0.5153   **11.** 0.8858   **13.** 2.43   **15.** 4.12

17. 8.74   **19.** 1.851   **21.** 8.374   **23.** 3.213

Article 12–5(2)

1. Characteristic, 1; mantissa, 0.3782

3. Characteristic, -3; mantissa, 0.5728

5. Characteristic, 5; mantissa, 0.8723

7. Characteristic, -4; mantissa, 0.2715

9. 2.5172   **11.** 3.6747   **13.** $8.8623 - 10$

15. 6650   **17.** 267.2   **19.** 0.003653

Article 12–6

1. 32000   **3.** 34.6   **5.** 158,800   **7.** 0.5152

9. 2.642   **11.** 0.1313   **13.** 8.52   **15.** 0.923

Article 12–7

(All problems worked with four-place tables in back of book.)

1. a) \$295.80   b) \$297.10

c) \$297.10 [larger than (b) if more accurate tables were used]

d) \$298.30

3. a) 11.9 yr   **5.** $r = 0.3467$ **7.** a) -0.2746

b) 11.55 yr   b) 0.002

Article 12–8

1. 3.808   **3.** 2.493   **5.** 1.947

7. 0.5824   **9.** 7.052×10^{13} **11.** 26.6

13. 2.33   **17.** 5   **19.** 3.155

21. 6.14   **23.** 0.402   **25.** $\log_e (1 \pm \sqrt{2})$

27. $\frac{2}{11}$ **29.** $\frac{1}{297}$

Article 13–1

19. $(1, 0)$ **21.** $(1, 0)$ **23.** $(6, 8)$

25. $(-1, 1)$ **27.** $(3, 11)$ **29.** $(-\frac{1}{2}, -\frac{1}{2})$

Article 13–2

7. a) $\sqrt{13}, 124°$ b) $2\sqrt{17}, 346°$ c) $2\sqrt{2}, 45°$

9. $\left(\dfrac{\sqrt{3}}{2}, \dfrac{1}{2}\right)$ **11.** $(0, -8)$ **13.** $(-4, 6)$

15. $(-6, 4)$ **17.** $4, 4$ **19.** $(6, -4)$

25. a) $\left(\dfrac{2}{\sqrt{13}}, \dfrac{-3}{\sqrt{13}}\right)$ b) $(-\frac{4}{5}, \frac{3}{5})$ c) $\left(\dfrac{8}{17}, \dfrac{-15}{17}\right)$

27. a) No   b) Yes

29. b) $c_1 = c_2 = \frac{1}{5}$ c) $\mathbf{v} = -10\mathbf{e}_1 - 5\mathbf{e}_2$

Article 13–3

1. a) $6 + 4i$ b) $-2 + 6i$ **3.** a) $\frac{3}{17} + \frac{22}{17}i$ b) $\frac{13}{17} + \frac{18}{17}i$

11. $-15i/2$ **13.** $-(4i + 10)/29$

15. $3, -i$ **17.** $3i, 4i$

Article 13–4

1. $x^3 - 7x^2 + 17x - 15 = 0$ **3.** $2x^3 + 19x^2 + 42x - 26 = 0$

5. $3x^3 - 17x^2 + 27x + 11 = 0$ **7.** $4, \pm 3i$

9. $2, 3 \pm \sqrt{2}\,i$

Article 13–5

1. a) $2(\cos 0° + i \sin 0°)$ b) $2(\cos 180° + i \sin 180°)$

c) $3(\cos 90° + i \sin 90°)$ d) $\cos 270° + i \sin 270°$

e) $2\sqrt{2}\,(\cos 315° + i\sin 315°)$ f) $2\sqrt{2}\,(\cos 135° + i\sin 135°)$

g) $\cos 120° + i\sin 120°$ h) $\cos 240° + i\sin 240°$

3. a) $6i$ b) $-4\sqrt{3} - 4i$ **5.** a) $\sqrt{3} + i$

c) $12i$ d) 8 b) $-1 + \sqrt{3}\,i$

Article 13–6

1. $64i$ **3.** $-4\sqrt{2} - 4\sqrt{2}\,i$

5. $\dfrac{\sqrt{3}}{2} + \dfrac{i}{2}$ **7.** 1

9. $-2\sqrt{2} + 2\sqrt{2}\,i,\ 2\sqrt{2} - 2\sqrt{2}\,i$

11. $1 + \sqrt{3}\,i,\ -2,\ 1 - \sqrt{3}\,i$

13. $\sqrt{3} + i,\ -1 + \sqrt{3}\,i,\ -\sqrt{3} - i,\ 1 - \sqrt{3}\,i$

15. $(\cos 36° + i\sin 36°),\ (\cos 72° + i\sin 72°),\ \ldots$

17. $1,\ i,\ -1,\ -i$

19. $\dfrac{\sqrt{5}+1}{2} + \sqrt{\dfrac{5-\sqrt{5}}{2}}\,i,\quad \dfrac{1-\sqrt{5}}{2} + \sqrt{\dfrac{5+\sqrt{5}}{2}}\,i,\quad -2,$

$\dfrac{1-\sqrt{5}}{2} - \sqrt{\dfrac{5+\sqrt{5}}{2}}\,i,\quad \dfrac{\sqrt{5}+1}{2} - \sqrt{\dfrac{5-\sqrt{5}}{2}}\,i$

REVIEW PROBLEMS
Chapters 10–13

3. $1 - \dfrac{4^6}{5^6},\ n = 7$ **9.** (a)(b)

11. Yes, similar to i

13. $x^5 - 14x^4 + 80x^3 - 250x^2 + 393x - 260 = 0$

15. $64 - 64i$

17. a) $x < \tfrac{1}{5}$ or $x > \tfrac{1}{3}$ b) $\tfrac{1}{5} < x < \tfrac{1}{3}$ c) $x = \tfrac{1}{5}$

INDEX

INDEX

ABCDE6987